Jones & Bartlett
Student Edi...

Quantum
Mechanics

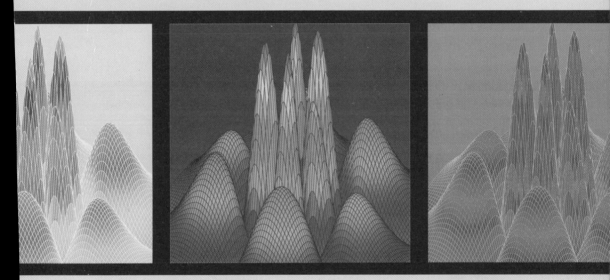

Bruce Cameron Reed

JONES & BARTLETT
LEARNING

World Headquarters
Jones and Bartlett Learning
5 Wall Street
Burlington, MA 01803
978-443-5000
info@jblearning.com
www.jblearning.com

First Indian Edition 2010
Reprinted 2015

Jones and Bartlett India Pvt. Ltd.
B-1, 4262/3, Ansari Road, Daryaganj
New Delhi – 110 002
Tel. 011–4361 3900
info@jbpubindia.net
www.jblearning.com

ISBN : 978-93-80108-24-7

Printed and bound in India by Raj Press, R-3, Inderpuri, New Delhi - 110 012.

For Laurie

The Author

Cameron Reed earned his PhD at the University of Waterloo (Canada) and is currently a Professor of Physics at Alma College in Alma, Michigan. He teaches a spectrum of physics classes from freshman-level algebra-based mechanics to senior-level quantum physics. He is the author of approximately 90 published papers; his research interests include galactic structure, pedagogical contributions in quantum and nuclear physics, and the physics and history of the development of nuclear weapons during the Manhattan Project. He lives in Michigan with his wife Laurie (an astronomer) and their cats Leo and Stella.

Preface

This text is directed at the needs of physics and chemistry students in smaller colleges and universities who are encountering their first serious course in quantum mechanics (QM), typically at about the junior level. The curricula of such institutions often leaves room for only one semester of QM as opposed to the two or more that are common at larger schools, so such students face the task of trying to absorb in a short time both the underlying physics and mathematical formalism of quantum theory. My goal is to give students a sense of "where it all leads" before they encounter that full mathematical formalism in, say, a senior-level or first graduate course by providing a treatment of the basic theories and results of wave mechanics that falls intermediate between sophomore-level "modern physics" texts and those typical of more advanced treatments.

Background preparation assumed here includes advanced calculus (partial differentiation and multiple integration); some exposure to basic concepts of differential equations (particularly the series solution method); vector calculus in Cartesian, spherical, and cylindrical coordinates; and the standard menu of physics courses: mechanics, electricity and magnetism, and modern physics. Some previous exposure to the historical context from which quantum mechanics developed is helpful but not strictly necessary as these matters are reviewed briefly in Chapter 1.

I am firmly of the belief that it is only by working through the derivations of a number of classical problems and by doing numerous homework exercises can students come to develop a feeling for the conceptual content of quantum mechanics and the necessary analytic skills involved in actually applying it. Present-day physics represents the cumulative knowledge of a chain of reasoning and experiment that stretches back over centuries, and it is important for students to have a sense of how we came to be where we are. Consequently, this book emphasizes the development of exact or approximate analytic solutions to Schrödinger's equation (SE), that is, solutions that can be expressed in algebraic form. To this end, the layout of this book follows a fairly conventional ordering. Chapter 1 reviews some of the developments of early twentieth-century physics that indicated the need for a radical rethinking of fundamental physical laws on the atomic scale: Planck's quantum hypothesis, the Rutherford–Bohr atomic model, and de Broglie's matter-wave concept. Chapter 2 develops the SE, the fundamental "law" of quantum mechanics. Chapter 3 explores applications of the SE to one-dimensional problems (potential wells and barriers), working up to a treatment of alpha-decay as a barrier-penetration phenomenon. Chapter 4 forms a sort of intermission to introduce some of the mathematical formalisms of QM such as operators, expectation values, the uncertainty principle, Ehrenfest's theorem, the orthogonality theorem, the superposition principle, the virial theorem, and Dirac notation. Chapter 5 is devoted to an analysis of the important harmonic-oscillator potential. Extension of the SE to three dimensions appears in Chapter 6, along with a treatment of separation of variables and angular momentum operators for central potentials. These developments set the stage for a fairly rigorous analysis of the Coulomb potential in Chapter 7. Chapter 8 deals with some more advanced aspects of angular momentum, and can be considered optional. Chapter 9 explores techniques for obtaining approximate analytic solutions of the SE in situations where full analytic solutions are too difficult or impossible to achieve: the WKB method, perturbation theory, and the variational method. In view of the central role of computers in almost all contemporary research, Chapter 10 explores a simple algorithm for numerically integrating the SE with a Microsoft Excel spreadsheet. This chapter comes with an important caveat, however: no physicist, either beginning student or seasoned researcher, should ever let playing with a computer become a substitute for first exploring a problem conceptually and analytically. The emphasis in this book is on the time-independent SE, but a taste of some results of considering time-dependence are taken up briefly in Chapter 11. A few particularly lengthy mathematical derivations of limited physical content are gathered together in Appendix A. Answers to a number of the end-of-chapter problems appear in Appendix B. Appendices C and D list a number of useful integrals, mathematical identities, and physical constants.

In each chapter I try to get directly to the essential physics and illustrate it with examples that contain actual numbers and which can serve as vehicles to introduce powerful ancillary techniques such as dimensional analysis and numerical integration. Each chapter contains a number of problems; it would not be unreasonable for students to do most of them throughout the course of a semester.

To students I offer three main pieces of advice: First, quantum mechanics is unique among the subdisciplines of physics in that so many of its essential concepts seem contrary to experience and intuition. There is no one formula or description through which you can comprehend it quickly. It will take time and thought: mull things over in your own mind, discuss them with your classmates and professors, and, when you come to understand something, *write it down in your own words*. In this spirit I have tried to keep the tone of this work informal while preserving a sensible level of mathematical and physical rigor.

Second, a number of problems appear at the end of each chapter. Only by doing them for yourself can you become familiar with the tools of the trade. Problems are classified as elementary (E), intermediate (I), or advanced (A), although these classifications are somewhat arbitrary. For handy reference, brief summaries of important concepts and formulae appear before each problem set.

Third, there are likely many QM texts in your school's library. Consult them. What may seem opaque as expressed by one author may be clearer in the words of another. One source I have found particularly valuable over the years is *Introduction to Quantum Mechanics with Applications to Chemistry* by Linus Pauling and E. B. Wilson (New York: Dover Publications, 1985). Originally published in 1935 when quantum physics was still relatively new, this venerable work contains detailed analyses of many classic problems. Another work I find appealing for its lucid explanations is *An Introduction to Quantum Physics* by A. P. French and E. F. Taylor (New York: W. W. Norton, 1978; recently reprinted by CRC Press, Boca Raton, FL). Any serious student of physics should also always have at hand a good reference to the many special functions that crop up in mathematical physics; Hans Weber and George Arfken's *Essential Mathematical Methods for Physicists* (Amsterdam: Elsevier, 2004) can be strongly recommended and is referenced frequently in the present work. Also, a good reference for techniques of numerical analysis is indispensable: a standard work in this area is *Numerical Recipes: The Art of Scientific Computing* by William H. Press, Brian P. Flannery, Saul A. Tuekolsky, and William T. Vetterling (Cambridge, UK: Cambridge University Press, 1986). This work, too, is occasionally referenced throughout the present text.

Quantum mechanics and its applications are a vibrant, central part of much present-day research. To give students a flavor of the nature and diversity of current work, references to semi-popular articles appearing in *Physics Today*, a monthly publication of the American Institute of Physics, appear occasionally throughout the text. These articles are sometimes brief "update" pieces and sometimes feature-length works, but all should be largely accessible to undergraduates and contain references to the original research literature. Students are strongly encouraged to explore them.

Finally, a word on the numbering of equations and footnotes. Equations are numbered sequentially beginning with (1) within each section. Equation (3.9.8), for example, designates Equation (8) in Section 3.9. Some sections in Chapters 6 and 7 have subsections. Endnotes are designated with square brackets, beginning anew with [1] in each chapter.

Acknowledgments

My interest in quantum mechanics was stimulated in my own student days by a number of excellent teachers at both the University of Waterloo and Queen's University, and has only grown over the intervening years. A number of special friends from those years, especially Peter Burns, Michael DeRobertis, Bob Hayward, Lisa Jylänne, Patricia Kinnee, Lorne Nelson, John Palimaka, Dave Schwarz, John Schreiner, and George Wagner encouraged me in my academic career and I am grateful to have this opportunity to acknowledge them. Alma-area friends Karen Ball, Richard Bowker, Eugene Deci, Patrick Furlong, John Gibson, Gilles Labrie, Paul Splitstone, and Ute Stargardt provided tremendous moral support; I am particularly grateful to Dr. Deci for covering some classes for me during a period of personal difficulty.

This work developed out of notes from QM courses I have taught at Saint Mary's University in Canada and at Alma College, and I am thankful to the many students over the years who pointed out numerous confusing or erroneous statements: their diligence has made this work infinitely better than it would otherwise have been. The following individuals gave generously of their time and expertise in reviewing various chapters of this work prior to publication and I am grateful for their valuable insights and suggestions:

Xi Chen, Central College
James Clemens, Miami University
Joseph Ganem, Loyola College
Noah Graham, Middlebury College
Rick McDaniel, Henderson State University
Soma Mukherjee, University of Texas, Brownsville
David Olsgaard, Simpson College
Vasilis Pagonis, McDaniel College
Harvey Picker, Trinity College
Darrell Schroeter, Occidental College
Blair Tuttle, Pennsylvania State University, Erie
Ann Wright, Hendrix College

Any errors that do remain I claim exclusive ownership of. The very professional staff at Jones and Bartlett, especially Amy Rose, Cathy Sether, and Molly Steinbach are to be credited for turning my manuscript into a polished reality.

Most of all I thank my wife Laurie, whose encouragement, wisdom, patience, sense of humor, and love know no bounds. It is to her that this work is dedicated.

Brief Contents

Preface   v

Chapter 1   Foundations   1

Chapter 2   Schrödinger's Equation   35

Chapter 3   Solutions of Schrödinger's Equation in One Dimension   59

         Part I: Potential Wells   60

         Part II: Potential Barriers and Scattering   88

Chapter 4   Operators, Expectation Values, and the Uncertainty Principle   113

Chapter 5   The Harmonic Oscillator   159

Chapter 6   Schrödinger's Equation in Three Dimensions and an Introduction to the Quantum Theory of Angular Momentum   191

Chapter 7   Central Potentials   231

Chapter 8   Further Developments with Angular Momentum and Multiparticle Systems   275

Chapter 9   Approximation Methods   299

Chapter 10   Numerical Solution of Schrödinger's Equation   351

Chapter 11   A Sampling of Results from Time-Dependent Quantum Mechanics: Transition Rates and Probabilities   369

Appendix A   Miscellaneous Derivations   379

Appendix B   Answers to Selected Problems   393

Appendix C   Integrals and Trigonometric Identities   401

Appendix D   Physical Constants   405

Notes and References   407

Index   411

Contents

Preface   v

Chapter 1   **Foundations**   1
1.1   Faraday, Thomson, and Electrons   2
1.2   Spectra, Radiation, and Planck   4
1.3   The Rutherford–Bohr Atom   14
1.4   de Broglie Matter-Waves   23
Summary   28
Problems   29

Chapter 2   **Schrödinger's Equation**   35
2.1   The Classical Wave Equation   36
2.2   The Time-Independent Schrödinger Equation   41
2.3   The Time-Dependent Schrödinger Equation   45
2.4   Interpretation of ψ: Probabilities and Boundary
        Conditions   49
Summary   56
Problems   56

Chapter 3   **Solutions of Schrödinger's Equation in One Dimension**   59
Part I: Potential Wells   60
3.1   Concept of a Potential Well   60
3.2   The Infinite Potential Well   62
3.3   The Finite Potential Well   70
3.4   Finite Rectangular Well—Even Solutions   79
3.5   Number of Bound States in a Finite Potential Well   81
3.6   Sketching Wavefunctions   85

Part II: Potential Barriers and Scattering   88
3.7   Potential Barriers   88
3.8   Penetration of Arbitrarily Shaped Barriers   94

3.9   Alpha-Decay as a Barrier Penetration Effect   97
3.10   Scattering by One-Dimensional Potential Wells   103
Summary   106
Problems   108

Chapter 4   Operators, Expectation Values, and the Uncertainty Principle   113
4.1   Properties of Operators   114
4.2   Expectation Values   118
4.3   The Uncertainty Principle   126
4.4   Commutators and Uncertainty Relations   131
4.5   Ehrenfest's Theorem   134
4.6   The Orthogonality Theorem   137
4.7   The Superposition Theorem   139
4.8   Constructing a Time-Dependent Wave Packet   141
4.9   The Virial Theorem   146
Summary   153
Problems   154

Chapter 5   The Harmonic Oscillator   159
5.1   A Lesson in Dimensional Analysis   160
5.2   The Asymptotic Solution   164
5.3   The Series Solution   165
5.4   Hermite Polynomials and Harmonic Oscillator
Wavefunctions   172
5.5   Comparing the Classical and Quantum Simple Harmonic
Oscillators   176
5.6   Raising and Lowering Operators (Optional)   179
Summary   186
Problems   187

**Chapter 6   Schrödinger's Equation in Three Dimensions and an Introduction
to the Quantum Theory of Angular Momentum   191**
6.1   Separation of Variables: Cartesian Coordinates   192
6.2   Spherical Coordinates   201
6.3   Angular Momentum Operators   203
6.4   Separation of Variables in Spherical Coordinates: Central
Potentials   209
6.5   Angular Wavefunctions and Spherical Harmonics   211
6.5.1   Solution of the Φ Equation   212

6.5.2   Solution of the Θ Equation   215

6.5.3   Spherical Harmonics   220

Summary   225

Problems   227

Chapter 7   Central Potentials   231

7.1   Introduction   231

7.2   The Infinite Spherical Well   234

7.3   The Finite Spherical Well   236

7.4   The Coulomb Potential   240

7.5   Hydrogen Atom Probability Distributions   253

7.5.1   The $(1, 0, 0)$ State of Hydrogen   254

7.5.2   The $(2, 0, 0)$ and Other States of Hydrogen   257

7.6   The Effective Potential   264

7.7   Some Philosophical Remarks   266

Summary   267

Problems   268

Chapter 8   Further Developments with Angular Momentum and Multiparticle Systems   275

8.1   Angular Momentum Raising and Lowering Operators   275

Section 8.1 Problems   282

8.2   The Stern–Gerlach Experiment: Evidence for Quantized Angular Momentum and Electron Spin   282

Section 8.2 Problems   287

8.3   Diatomic Molecules and Angular Momentum   287

Section 8.3 Problems   291

8.4   Identical Particles, Indistinguishability, and the Pauli Exclusion Principle   291

Section 8.4 Problems   297

Chapter 9   Approximation Methods   299

9.1   The WKB Method   299

9.2   The Superposition Theorem Revisited   305

9.3   Perturbation Theory   309

9.4   The Variational Method   327

9.5   Improving the Variational Method (Optional)   336

Summary   340

Problems   343

Chapter 10   Numerical Solution of Schrödinger's Equation   351
    10.1   Atomic Units   352
    10.2   A Straightforward Numerical Integration Method   353
    Problems   365

**Chapter 11   A Sampling of Results from Time-Dependent Quantum
Mechanics: Transition Rates and Probabilities   369**
    11.1   Transition Frequencies   369
    11.2   Transition Rules   373
    11.3   The Sudden Approximation   374
    Summary   376
    Problems   376

Appendix A   Miscellaneous Derivations   379
    A.1   Heisenberg's Uncertainty Principle   379
    A.2   Explicit Series Form for Associated Legendre Functions   384
    A.3   Proof that $Y_{\ell,-m} = (-1)^m Y^*_{\ell,m}$ 386
    A.4   Radial Nodes in Hydrogen Wavefunctions   391

Appendix B   Answers to Selected Problems   393

Appendix C   Integrals and Trigonometric Identities   401

Appendix D   Physical Constants   405

Notes and References   407

Index   411

1 Foundations

The tremendous success of Newton's laws of mechanics on scales from footballs to clusters of galaxies is nothing less than staggering. These laws also possess a strong intuitive appeal: the relative ease with which even beginning students can assimilate and apply them is due in no small part to the fact that one can often literally see what the mathematics is describing. Arcing footballs, spinning and colliding billiard balls, rolling tires, flowing water, oscillating pendula, and to some extent even orbiting satellites, are the stuff of everyday life and common experience: it's easy to formulate a picture in the mind's eye around which an analysis can be developed. Conversely, quantum mechanics deals with the nature of matter at the atomic level, far removed from the domain of practical experience. Although it now constitutes the foundation of our understanding of everything from the structure of atoms and molecules to the life cycles of stars, it is also often counterintuitive. Its formulation, use, and interpretation are so vastly different from Newtonian mechanics that questions regarding familiar concepts such as position and velocity largely lose their meaning.

The counterintuitiveness of quantum mechanics renders it practically impossible to develop the subject with the smoothness and logical flow of Newtonian mechanics. To a great extent one must simply plunge in and trust that the customs of quantum culture will become familiar as one's experience with it grows. Quantum mechanics is not, however, without its points of contact to classical physics, and these can be exploited to ease the transition to a quantum mode of thinking. The danger in this is that familiar ideas and unquestioned assumptions can be difficult to release; there is an art to sensing how far analogies can be extended. Scientific theories, however revolutionary, do not arise in isolation, and classical mechanics formed the background against which the architects of quantum mechanics constructed their edifice. Qualitatively, quantum mechanics can be viewed as a theory that correctly describes the behavior of microscopic material particles but incorporates the predictions of Newtonian mechanics on macroscopic scales.

The purpose of this chapter is to review some of the facts that led physicists in the early part of the twentieth century to the realization that Newtonian mechanics is invalid in the realm of atomic-scale phenomena. You may have encountered some of the following material in an earlier course: the experiments of Michael Faraday and

J.J. Thomson (Section 1.1), the nature of atomic spectra (Section 1.2), the Rutherford-Bohr model of the atom (Section 1.3), and wave-particle duality (Section 1.4). The intention here is not in-depth explanation, but rather the context of early twentieth-century physics and the discrepancies between experiment and theory that forced the development of a whole new area of physics.

■ 1.1 Faraday, Thomson, and Electrons

The roots of modern scientific speculation on atomic structure trace their origins to the early nineteenth century. From the chemical experiments of Antoine Lavoisier and John Dalton, the concept of an atom as the smallest unit representative of a given element was firmly established by about 1810. Michael Faraday's electrolysis experiments of the early 1830s suggested that electrical current involved the transport of "ions," which were what we now recognize as individual atoms or molecules bearing net positive or negative electrical charges. Faraday thus perceived that nature **quantizes** certain quantities: ions could apparently not possess any arbitrary amount of electrical charge, but rather only integral multiples of a fundamental unit of charge. In 1881 Irish physicist George Stoney [1] first estimated the fundamental unit of negative charge to be about -10^{-20} Coulomb. In 1891, he coined the term "electron" to describe the carriers of the fundamental unit of negative charge.

Knowledge of Avogadro's number, N_A, along with knowledge of the density and atomic weight of an element, makes it possible to estimate the effective sizes of atoms constituting that element. If one imagines a substance to be composed of tightly packed spherical atoms of radius R, the distance between atomic centers will be $2R$. Each atom will effectively occupy a volume of space equivalent to a cube of side length $2R$, namely $8R^3$. If the atomic weight of the substance is A grams per mole, the mass of an individual atom will be A/N_A and the density will be $\rho = A/8N_AR^3$, which we can turn into an expression for the atomic radius:

$$R = \left(\frac{A}{8N_A\rho}\right)^{1/3}.$$

(1)

By applying Equation (1) to light and heavy elements, we can get an idea of the range of atomic sizes. At one extreme is lithium, the lightest naturally solid element. With $A = 7$ gram/mole (1.1×10^{-26} kg/atom) and $\rho = 0.534$ gram/cm^3, we find $R \sim 1.40 \times 10^{-10}$ meter, or 1.40 Å (1 Ångstrom = 10^{-10} meter). At the other end of the periodic table is uranium, the heaviest naturally occurring element, with $A = 238$ gram/mole (4×10^{-25} kg/atom) and $\rho \sim 18.95$ gram/cm^3, which give $R \sim 1.38$ Å. Despite a factor of 80 difference in mass, uranium and lithium atoms effectively act as if they are about the same size! This is a simplistic analysis, but it does demonstrate the chemical wisdom that essentially all atoms act as if they are on the order of 1 Å in radius. The Ångstrom is a convenient unit of length for atomic-scale problems and will be used extensively throughout this text.

In 1897, J. J. Thomson [2] undertook his famous cathode-ray deflection experiments ("cathode ray" was an early term for electron), from which he determined the charge-to-mass ratio (e/m) of the electron. In modern units he arrived at a value of about -2×10^{11} Coulombs/kg; in combination with Stoney's charge estimate of $\sim -10^{-20}$ Coulomb, it became clear at once that the mass of the electron must be on the order of 10^{-31} kg, some four orders of magnitude smaller than atomic masses. Moreover, Thomson found the same result for a variety of different cathode materials, demonstrating that electrons are universal constituents of all atoms.

At the time of Thomson's e/m experiments, Robert Millikan's oil drop experiments to precisely determine the value of e lay well in the future (1909). However, let us break with historical sequence to make a point about the size of the electron itself. We begin with the modern values for the mass and charge of the electron:

$$m_e = 9.10954 \times 10^{-31} \text{ kg,}$$

and

$$e = -1.60219 \times 10^{-19} \text{ C.}$$

Now, a common demonstration in elementary texts on electricity and magnetism is the derivation of an expression for the self-potential-energy V of a solid sphere of radius r bearing an electrical charge e distributed uniformly throughout. The result is

$$V = \frac{3e^2}{20\pi \epsilon_o r}. \tag{2}$$

If we assume that this self-energy is equivalent to the sphere's Einsteinian rest energy $E = mc^2$ (another break from historical sequence: Einstein did not develop his special theory of relativity until 1905), we can solve for the radius of the sphere:

$$r = \frac{3e^2}{20\pi \epsilon_o mc^2}. \tag{3}$$

For an electron the numbers give

$$r_e = \frac{3(-1.602 \times 10^{-19} C)^2}{20\pi(8.85 \times 10^{-12} C^2/Nm^2)(9.11 \times 10^{-31} kg)(2.998 \times 10^8 m/s)^2}$$

$$= 1.69 \times 10^{-15} \, \text{m} \sim 10^{-5} \text{ atomic radii.}$$

Electrons are minute in comparison to their host atoms; essentially, they are point masses. Actually, the current experimental evidence is that electrons are in fact point masses, and that protons have radii of about 0.8×10^{-15} m.[1] The preceding analysis predicts a radius of $\sim 10^{-18}$ m for the proton; we can interpret the discrepancy as indicating that the origin of mass cannot purely be energy. (This is not to imply that $E = mc^2$ is somehow in error, only that this approach cannot be an adequate model for the origin of mass. Modern versions of quantum field theory hold that mass is built up of particles known as quarks and gluons and fields that connect them.[2])

Considerations along these lines stimulated development of models of atoms wherein pointlike, negatively charged electrons were held in stable configurations by their mutual repulsion within a larger positively charged cloud; Thomson himself was one of the prime movers in this effort. (Atomic model-building had a venerable history well before Thomson; an engaging account is given by Pais [3].) However, these efforts met with little success, for they failed to explain atomic and molecular spectra. In addition, Thomson's 1898 atomic model proved of no value in explaining the continuous spectrum of blackbody radiation. These phenomena played pivotal roles in the development of quantum mechanics.

■ 1.2 Spectra, Radiation, and Planck

In 1814, German scientist Joseph Fraunhofer passed sunlight through a prism and examined the resulting continuous spectrum of colors with a magnifying glass. To his surprise, he observed hundreds of dark lines crossing the spectrum at specific wavelengths. Later, in the 1850s, Gustav Kirchhoff observed the same effect on passing light from artificial sources through samples of gas. Work along these lines culminated in Kirchhoff's three law of spectroscopy:

1. Light from a hot solid object, on passing through a prism, yields a continuous spectrum with no lines.

---

[1]*Physics Today* 1995; 48(11):9.

[2]*Physics Today* 1999; 52(11):11 and 2000; 53(1):13.

2. The same light, when passed through a cool gas, yields the same continuous spectrum but with certain wavelengths of light removed, a so-called absorption spectrum.

3. If the light emitted by a hot gas alone is viewed through a prism, one observes a series of bright lines at certain wavelengths superimposed on an otherwise black background, a so-called emission spectrum.

The key observation was that if the same gas is used in (2) and (3), the absorption and emission lines appear at the same wavelengths in both cases. These phenomena are illustrated schematically in Figure 1.1.

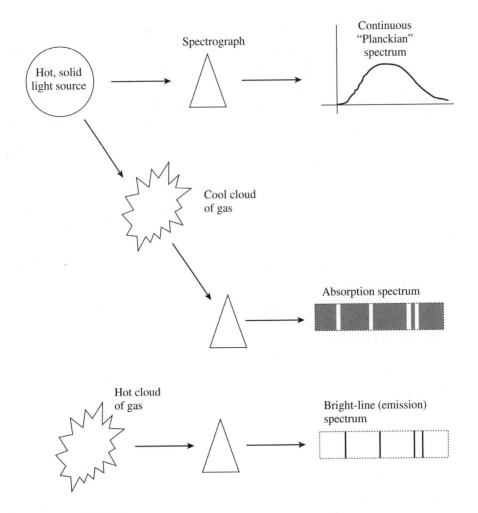

| FIGURE 1.1 Kirchhoff's Laws.

It soon became clear that every chemical element or compound produces a characteristic pattern of spectral lines; spectroscopy serves as a diagnostic test for the presence or absence of an element or compound in a given sample. Spectra of a few substances are shown in Figure 1.2 (reproduced from [4]). Hydrogen displays the simplest pattern of any element: a series of lines separated by ever-decreasing gaps until a "continuum" of emission is reached at a wavelength of about 3646 Å. Molecular spectra are characterized by overlapping patterns of lines, but regularities are still apparent.

Explaining line spectra posed a tremendous challenge to builders of atomic models. Because Maxwell's equations revealed that an accelerating electrical charge radiates energy in the form of light, it was logical to suggest that spectral lines arise from the motion of Thomson's "corpuscular" electrons in the vicinity of whatever constitutes the massive, positively charged part of the atom. Thomson proposed an atomic model consisting of pointlike electrons embedded within a much larger spherical cloud of positive charge, the so-called "raisin bread" or "plum pudding" model. In such an arrangement the electrons will oscillate back and forth through the cloud in simple harmonic motion as would a billiard ball dropped into a frictionless hole bored through the Earth. Although these oscillations lead to frequencies on the order of that of visible light, Thomson's model suffers from two serious difficulties. The first is that only one frequency results from an atom of a given size. How are we to account for whole series of spectral lines? The second difficulty is even more catastrophic. As the electron radiates away energy the amplitude of its motion should steadily decrease until it comes to rest in the center of the atom. In short, matter should collapse!

How, then, to explain discrete-line spectra at all? Thomson worked with immense dedication over many years on a variety of models of this general sort, but with no real success. Understanding the stability of atoms and the origin of line spectra had to await the augmentation of classical models by new quantum postulates.

There was, however, one piece of evidence that gave early atomic theorists hope that nature might yield her secrets to mathematical analysis. In 1885, Johann Balmer discovered that the wavelengths of the spectral lines of hydrogen followed a simple mathematical regularity [5], namely, that they could be computed from the formula

$$\lambda_n \; = \; 3646 \left(\frac{n^2}{n^2 - 4} \right) \text{Å}, \; n = 3, 4, 5, \dots . \tag{1}$$

Note that as $n \to \infty$, $\lambda_n \to 3646$ Å, the wavelength at which the hydrogen spectral lines "pile up" into a continuum.

Balmer's formula was purely empirical, with no model of an underlying physical mechanism. This does not diminish its value, though, for when a phenomenon can be

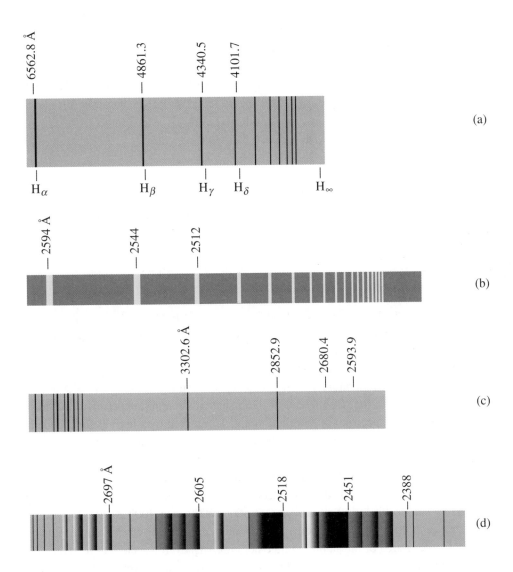

FIGURE 1.2 (a) Emission spectrum of hydrogen.
(b) Absorption spectrum of sodium.
(c) Emission spectrum of sodium.
(d) Spectrum of PN molecule.
Reproduced from G. Herzberg, *Atomic spectra and atomic structure*, Dover Publications, Inc., New York, 1944. Reprinted through the permission of the publisher.

fitted into a simple arithmetic scheme one is justified in having hope that a deeper understanding may not be far off. Indeed, Balmer's formula was a key clue for Niels Bohr's development of the first really successful theory of atomic structure.

We remark in passing that spectroscopists often refer to spectral lines by their reciprocal wavelengths. Balmer's formula can be rearranged to reflect this:

$$\frac{1}{\lambda_n} = R_H\left(\frac{1}{4} - \frac{1}{n^2}\right)\text{Å}^{-1}, \; n = 3, 4, 5, \ldots \; , \tag{2}$$

where R_H is known as the *Rydberg constant* for hydrogen; its experimental value is 109,678 cm^{-1}. With considerable success, Swedish physicist Johannes Rydberg suggested that the spectral lines of any element could be described by a generalized version of Equation (2):

$$\frac{1}{\lambda_{n,m}} = K\left(\frac{1}{m^2} - \frac{1}{n^2}\right) \; (n > m), \tag{3}$$

where K is a constant specific to the element involved. Different series of spectral lines are given by various values of n for a fixed value of m. We will return to this modified Balmer formula later in this chapter.

Continuous spectra also posed a challenge to classical physics. Experimentally, any solid body at a temperature T above absolute zero emits a continuous spectrum of electromagnetic radiation. By the end of the nineteenth century, experiment had also established that the spectrum of "thermal radiation" emitted by a body is independent of the nature of the body, depending only on T. These experiments were usually carried out with so-called "blackbody" cavities. This can be thought of as a heated, internally hollow lump of metal with a hole in it from which some of the thermal radiation can escape and so be sampled by a detector. Figure 1.3 shows spectra for the light emitted by such cavities at temperatures of 5000, 6000, and 7000 K over the wavelength range 2000–10,000 Ångstroms; what is plotted is the power emitted per square meter of surface area of the sampling hole per unit Ångstrom wavelength interval as a function of wavelength. (The range of human vision spans approximately 3500–7000 Å). As T increases, the wavelength of peak emission shifts to shorter (bluer) wavelengths. If you are familiar with some stellar astronomy, you may know that blue stars have hotter surfaces than yellow stars, which in turn are hotter than red-dwarf stars.

Attempts to find a mathematical description of thermal radiation based on classical models failed completely. The generally held concept was somewhat analogous to Thomson's oscillating electrons: each atom of a material body would be in constant motion, jostling about with its neighbors. When a charged particle oscillates at frequency ν (in, say, simple harmonic motion as studied in freshman-level physics

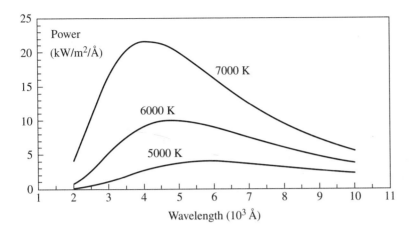

I FIGURE 1.3 Thermal Radiation Spectra.

classes), it will emit electromagnetic radiation at that same frequency; for this reason the atoms were abstracted as "oscillators." (Recall that, in 1900, knowledge of the detailed internal structure of atoms was essentially nil.) The cavity will fill with electromagnetic radiation bouncing around at the speed of light, and an equilibrium ("thermal equilibrium") will soon be established as the oscillators emit and absorb radiation. Like standing waves on a vibrating string, however, the cavity can only "support" electromagnetic waves of certain frequencies, depending on its dimensions. From Maxwell's theory, the number of possible "standing-wave" frequencies available between frequencies ν and $\nu + d\nu$, usually designated as $N(\nu)d\nu$, was given by

$$N(\nu)d\nu = \frac{8\pi V}{c^3} \nu^2 d\nu, \tag{4}$$

where V is the volume of the cavity and c is the speed of light. An approximate derivation of this expression is given in Section 6.1. Now, what is desired is an expression for the energy within the cavity (in the form of electromagnetic waves) in some specified range of frequencies: this is what the measurements ultimately sample. In effect, we need to know how many oscillators are oscillating at each available frequency and what amount of energy is associated with each mode of oscillation. In classical physics, however, there is no connection between the energy of an oscillator and its frequency. You can set the amplitude and frequency of a vibrating string separately to be whatever values you please. To build a connection to energy, the approach adopted was to appeal to the success of Maxwell and Boltzmann's work on statistical mechanics. Their research showed that if a particle is in an environment at absolute (Kelvin) temperature T, then the probability of it having energy between E and $E + dE$ is proportional to an exponential function of T:

$$p(E)dE = A e^{-E/kT} dE, \tag{5}$$

where A is a constant and k is Boltzmann's constant. To determine A we insist that if we add up probabilities over all possible energies they must sum to unity. This is equivalent to saying that the particle must have *some* energy between 0 and infinity. That is, we demand

$$\int_0^\infty p(E)dE = A \int_0^\infty e^{-E/kT} dE = 1.$$

This integral evaluates to kT, giving $A = 1/kT$. The *average* energy of a particle in such a situation is then given by the integral of probability-weighted energy:

$$\langle E \rangle = \int_0^\infty E p(E)dE = \frac{1}{kT} \int_0^\infty E e^{-E/kT} dE = kT. \tag{6}$$

(For a fuller elaboration of this averaging technique, see Section 4.2.) The assumption is now made that the number of oscillators wiggling about with frequencies between ν and $\nu + d\nu$ is given by Equation (4), and that the amount of radiant energy in the cavity between these frequencies is consequently given by this number times the average energy of an oscillator at temperature T, kT:

$$E(\nu)d\nu = \frac{8\pi V}{c^3} kT \nu^2 d\nu. \tag{7}$$

Despite these various assumptions, this relationship actually proved to be in good agreement with experimental data at low frequencies. At high frequencies, though, one has a disaster: The amount of energy in the cavity becomes infinite, a situation known as the ultraviolet catastrophe. Something was apparently wrong with either classical electromagnetism or statistical mechanics, or perhaps even both. It is probably fair to say that at the dawn of the twentieth century, thermal radiation was *the* outstanding problem of theoretical physics.

A way around this difficulty was found by Max Planck of the University of Berlin in late 1900, in a paper usually credited with marking the birth of quantum mechanics proper [6]. However, his solution came at a substantial price: abandoning the classical notion that the energy and frequency of an oscillator are independent. Planck proposed that the energy of an oscillator is restricted to only certain multiples of its frequency, namely, $E_n = nh\nu$, where n is an integer-valued "quantum number" ($n = 0, 1, 2, 3, ...$) and h is a constant of nature.

Maintaining the assumption of a Maxwellian exponential probability distribution, the probability of an oscillator having energy E is now given by

$$p(E) = A e^{-nh\nu/kT}, \tag{8}$$

where A is again a normalization constant. Note carefully that no "dE" appears in this expression: the idea now is that an oscillator has some probability of having a *particular* energy, as opposed to any arbitrary energy between E and $E + dE$. Forcing the probabilities to again add up to unity means that we must have

$$A \sum_{n=0}^{\infty} e^{-nh\nu/kT} = 1,$$

or

$$A \sum_{n=0}^{\infty} (e^{-h\nu/kT})^n = 1. \tag{9}$$

We are summing over *discrete* energy states as opposed to integrating over energy as a *continuous* variable. The sum appearing in Equation (9) is of the form Σx^n, where $x = e^{-h\nu/kT}$; that is, we have a geometric series. Such a sum evaluates to $(1 - x)^{-1}$, hence

$$A = (1 - e^{-h\nu/kT}), \tag{10}$$

and so the probability of an oscillator having energy E can be written as

$$p(E) = e^{-nh\nu/kT}(1 - e^{-h\nu/kT}). \tag{11}$$

With this new probability recipe, the average energy of oscillators of frequency ν becomes

$$\langle E \rangle = \sum_{n=0}^{\infty} E\,p(E) = \sum_{n=0}^{\infty} (nh\nu)\,p(E) = h\nu(1 - e^{-h\nu/kT}) \sum_{n=0}^{\infty} ne^{-nh\nu/kT}$$

$$= h\nu(1 - e^{-h\nu/kT}) \frac{e^{-h\nu/kT}}{(1 - e^{-h\nu/kT})^2} = \frac{h\nu}{(e^{h\nu/kT} - 1)}. \tag{12}$$

In working Equation (12), we have used another result from series analysis, namely

$$\sum_{n=0}^{\infty} n x^n = \frac{x}{(1-x)^2} \quad (|x| < 1),$$

where we again have $x = e^{-h\nu/kT}$. Again assuming that the number of oscillators with frequencies between ν and $\nu + d\nu$ is given by Equation (4), we find a new expression for the energy in the cavity between frequencies ν and $\nu + d\nu$:

$$E(\nu)d\nu = \frac{8\pi h V}{c^3} \frac{\nu^3}{(e^{h\nu/kT} - 1)} d\nu. \tag{13}$$

This is Planck's famous **blackbody radiation formula**. Note that frequency is still a *continuous* variable; the energy that an oscillator can have is *discretized* by $E = nh\nu$ once its frequency is specified. Planck found this expression to be a perfect match to the experimental data provided that the constant h is chosen suitably. This quantity is now known as **Planck's constant** and has the value

$$h = 6.626 \times 10^{-34} \text{ Joule-sec.}$$

Planck's assumption is now practically an element of popular culture. Hindsight tends to blind us to perceiving just how radical it was to his contemporaries. That electrical charges come in discrete units is one thing, but to suggest that the most venerable quantity in all of physics—energy itself—could be exchanged only in discrete lumps (in other words, that it is **quantized**) was to disavow two and a half centuries of accumulated wisdom. As with all fundamental postulates, the difficulty in understanding it and its consequences stems from just that: like $\mathbf{F} = m\mathbf{a}$ it is a postulate, not derivable from anything more fundamental. The justification for Planck's hypothesis is that it has never been found to lead to conclusions in conflict with experiment.

The development of blackbody theory actually spanned the better part of two decades, with Planck modifying his assumptions and calculations many times; the preceding description represents only a very cursory survey of the issue.[3]

Planck's hypothesis lay essentially dormant until 1905, when Einstein adapted it to explain the photoelectric effect, the emission of electrons from a metal surface being bombarded by light [7]. This phenomenon had proven impossible to understand when light was considered as a wave (as in the Maxwellian tradition), but became clear if the light were regarded instead as a stream of particles (**light-quanta** or **photons**) of energy $E = h\nu$, where ν is the frequency of the wave one would normally associate with the light. It was as if the incident light were colliding billiard-ball style with electrons, knocking them out of the metal. Although Einstein's work resolved the

---

[3]Readers interested in exploring more deeply this fundamental revolution in physics are directed to Thomas Kuhn's comprehensive *Black-Body Theory and the Quantum Discontinuity, 1894–1912*. Chicago: University of Chicago Press, 1978.

associate with the light. It was as if the incident light were colliding billiard-ball style with electrons, knocking them out of the metal. Although Einstein's work resolved the photoelectric effect, it thrust into the foreground an apparent paradox: Is light a wave or a stream of particles? On one hand it behaves optically as any sensible wave: it is refractable, diffractable, focusable, and so forth. On the other it can behave dynamically, like billiard balls. Which picture do we adopt? The answer is, we have to live with both. Although in some circumstances one can conveniently analyze an experiment with an explicitly wave picture in mind (for example, double-slit diffraction in classical optics), whereas in others a particle view provides for a convincing analysis (the photoelectric effect), the inescapable fact is that photons possess both wave and particle properties simultaneously (as do material particles such as electrons and entire atoms and molecules—see Section 1.4). Indeed, it has been amply experimentally verified that photons interfere with themselves even as they pass, one by one, through an optical system![4] We shall have more to say about this wave-particle duality in coming chapters.

The idea of light carrying momentum was not new. Indeed, Maxwell had predicted that electromagnetic radiation of energy E would possess momentum in the amount $p = E/c$. (If you are familiar with special relativity, recall the Einstein energy-momentum-rest mass relation $E^2 = p^2 c^2 + m_0^2 c^4$, and set the rest mass m_0 to be zero for a photon.) This can be expressed in terms of the frequency and wavelength of the light as $p = E/\lambda\nu$ since $c = \lambda\nu$. If light is also treated as consisting of particles characterized by the Planck relation $E = h\nu$, then $p = h/\lambda$ or

$$\lambda = \frac{h}{p}. \tag{14}$$

Equation (14) applies only to photons even though it was derived from a mixture of both classical and quantum concepts. Nevertheless, in the 1920s, Arthur H. Compton verified that photons and electrons indeed interact billiard-ball style, precisely as the equation predicts. This deceptively simple equation will figure in subsequent discussions.

The substitutions leading to Equation (14) are simple. Yet, it seems remarkable that the connection between Planck's quantized oscillator energies and the discrete wavelengths (= discrete energies) of light constituting spectral lines was not made for nearly another decade. This breakthrough had to await further experimental probing of the internal structure of atoms.

---

[4]For readers interested in learning about the details of such experiments and many other aspects of the fundamentals of quantum mechanics, George Greenstein and Arthur Zajonc's *The Quantum Challenge* (Sudbury, MA: Jones & Bartlett, Second Edition, 2006) is highly recommended.

In early 1911, Ernest Rutherford, in collaboration with Hans Geiger and Ernest Marsden, proposed a model of atomic structure radically different from Thomson's plum-pudding scenario [8]. Based on an analysis of the distribution of alpha-particles (helium nuclei) scattered through thin metal foils, they put forth a **nuclear** model of the atom wherein the positive charge (and with it most of the atomic mass) is concentrated in a tiny volume of space at the center of the atom, around which negative electrons orbit like planets about the Sun.[5] Their experiments indicated a size on the order of 10^{-14} meters for the positively charged nucleus: it was larger than an electron, but some four orders of magnitude smaller than the atom itself. Evidently, atoms are mostly empty space.

The stage was now set for a leap of logic of the sort alluded to at the end of Section 1.2. Planck had established that atoms constituting the source of thermal radiation from material bodies could exist only in certain discrete energy states. If Rutherford's planetary electrons were restricted to orbits of certain special energies, could electrons "transiting" from orbits of higher energy (say, E_2) to orbits of lower energy (say, E_1) be the source of spectra and thermal radiation, with the energy difference appearing as a photon of frequency ν_{21} given by Planck's hypothesis written in the form $E_2 - E_1 = h\nu_{21}$? These were among the assumptions made by a young Danish physicist, Niels Bohr, in a trilogy of papers published in the *Philosophical Magazine* in 1913 that marked the first truly successful theory of the inner workings of atoms [9].

Let us explore the consequences of Bohr's postulates for a simple model of the hydrogen atom. The situation is illustrated in Figure 1.4, where an electron of mass m_e and charge $-e$ is in a circular orbit of radius r and speed v around a central proton of charge $+e$.

---

[5]An excellent website on the life and work of Rutherford can be found at www.rutherford.org.nz.

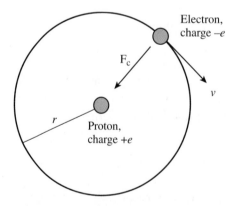

I FIGURE 1.4   Bohr Model for Hydrogen.

Bohr began by assuming that the energetics of the electron's orbit are dictated by the Newtonian dynamics of circular orbits, namely that if the electron is in a circular orbit, then it must experience a centripetal force of magnitude $m_e v^2/r$ toward the proton. Identifying as the source of this centripetal force the Coulomb attraction between electron and proton gives

$$magnitude \text{ of Coulomb force } = \frac{m_e v^2}{r} = \frac{e^2}{4\pi\epsilon_o r^2}. \tag{1}$$

A more refined version of this calculation accounts for the motion of the proton and the electron about their mutual center of mass. This can be effected by substituting the reduced mass of the system, $m_e m_p/(m_e + m_p)$ in place of the electron mass m_e wherever it appears; m_p is the mass of the proton. Also, the theory can be extended to include hydrogen-like ions; that is, systems wherein a single electron orbits a nucleus of charge $+Ze$ by replacing e^2 by Ze^2 wherever it appears.

Because the physically relevant quantities are wavelengths and energies, we start out by deriving an expression for the total energy (kinetic + potential) of the electron in its orbit. From Equation (1),

$$\text{Kinetic energy } = \frac{1}{2}m_e v^2 = \frac{e^2}{8\pi\epsilon_o r}. \tag{2}$$

The potential energy is just the electrostatic potential of an electron (charge $-e$) and a proton (charge $+e$) separated by distance r:

$$\text{Potential energy} = -\frac{e^2}{4\pi\epsilon_o r}. \tag{3}$$

From Equations (2) and (3) we find the total energy E_{total}:

$$E_{total} = KE + PE = -\frac{e^2}{8\pi\epsilon_o r}. \tag{4}$$

The interpretation of the negative sign is that positive energy must be supplied from some external source to dissociate the electron from the atom. We say that the electron is in a **bound energy state**. Curiously, the total energy is equal to one-half of the potential energy; this result is actually a specific case of a very general result known as the **virial theorem**, which is treated in Section 4.9.

Imagine the electron "falling" from infinity [$E = 0$ with $r = \infty$ in Equation (4)] down to an orbit of radius r about the proton. In doing so it would lose energy, which is assumed to appear as a photon of frequency ν. At this point, Bohr made two assumptions: (1) that this frequency is equal to one-half of the electron's final orbital frequency about the proton, and (2) consistent with Planck's hypothesis, the energy of the photon is given by $nh\nu$ where n is an integer and h is Planck's constant. For an electron in a circular orbit of speed v and radius r, the time for one orbit is $2\pi r/v$, hence the orbital frequency is $v/2\pi r$ and Bohr's hypotheses give

$$E_{photon} = |E_{total}| = nh\nu = \frac{nh}{2}\left(\frac{v}{2\pi r}\right) = \frac{e^2}{8\pi\epsilon_o r}. \tag{5}$$

Solving the last two members of this expression for v gives

$$v = \frac{e^2}{2\epsilon_o nh}. \tag{6}$$

Now solving Equation (2) for the orbital radius and substituting this result for v gives

$$r_n = \left(\frac{\epsilon_o h^2}{\pi m_e e^2}\right)n^2 = a_o n^2, \; (n = 1, 2, 3, \dots). \tag{7}$$

The interpretation of Equation (7) is that the electron is restricted to orbits of radius $a_o n^2$, where a_o, now known as the **Bohr radius**, represents the smallest permissible orbit (note that we cannot have $n = 0$, for this would imply $E = -\infty$ in Equation 4); n is called the **principal quantum number**.

Using the following modern values for the constants

$$\epsilon_o = 8.8542 \times 10^{-12} C^2/Nm^2,$$
$$h = 6.6261 \times 10^{-34} \text{ J-sec},$$
$$m_e = 9.1094 \times 10^{-31} \text{ kg},$$
$$e = 1.6022 \times 10^{-19} \text{ C},$$

one finds

$$a_o = 5.2918 \times 10^{-11} \text{ m} = 0.52918 \text{ Å}. \tag{8}$$

This is a remarkable result, exactly of the order of atomic dimensions as deduced in Section 1.1. Bohr's assumptions result in a theoretical explanation of the sizes of atoms, an otherwise empirical detail.

EXAMPLE 1.1

The lone proton in a hydrogen atom has an effective radius of about 10^{-15} m. Suppose that the entire atom is magnified so that the proton has a radius of 1 mm, about the size of a rather small pea. If the orbiting electron is in the $n = 1$ state in Equation (7), what would be the radius of its magnified orbit?

As a multiple of the proton's effective radius, the distance of the $n = 1$ Bohr orbit is $a_o/10^{-15}$ m ~ $(5.29 \times 10^{-11}$ m$)/10^{-15}$ m ~ 52,900. If the proton is expanded to a radius of 1 mm, then the electron will be orbiting at about (1 mm)(52,900) ~ 52.9 meters. In other words, if the expanded proton is placed at the center of a football field, the electron's orbit will reach to just beyond the goal lines!

More importantly, Equation (7) leads to an expression for the wavelengths of photon emitted when electrons transit between possible orbits, and to a theoretically predicted value of the Rydberg constant. To arrive at the wavelength expression, imagine that the electron falls from an initial orbital radius r_i to some final orbital radius r_f, with $r_f < r_i$. According to Equation (4), $E_f < E_i$ (both E_f and E_i are negative); if the energy lost by the electron is presumed to appear as a photon in accordance with Planck's hypothesis, then

$$E_{photon} = E_i - E_f = \frac{e^2}{8\pi\epsilon_o}\left(\frac{1}{r_f} - \frac{1}{r_i}\right) = h\nu_{i\to f}. \tag{9}$$

This would correspond to a photon of wavelength $\lambda = c/\nu$ or

$$\frac{1}{\lambda_{i\to f}} = \frac{e^2}{8\pi\epsilon_o hc}\left(\frac{1}{r_f} - \frac{1}{r_i}\right). \tag{10}$$

Substituting Equation (7) for the orbital radii gives

$$\frac{1}{\lambda_{n_i \to n_f}} = \frac{m_e e^4}{8\epsilon_o^2 h^3 c}\left(\frac{1}{n_f^2} - \frac{1}{n_i^2}\right) \quad (n_f < n_i).$$ (11)

Now recall the Balmer-Rydberg expression for the visible-region hydrogen-line wavelengths, Equation (1.2.2):

$$\frac{1}{\lambda_n} = R_H\left(\frac{1}{4} - \frac{1}{n^2}\right).$$ (12)

Equations (11) and (12) are remarkably similar in form; indeed, they correspond precisely if we take $n_f = 2$ and if the Rydberg constant is given by

$$R_H = \frac{m_e e^4}{8\epsilon_o^2 h^3 c}.$$ (13)

Substitution of the appropriate numerical values yields $R_H = 109{,}737$ cm^{-1}, in close agreement with the experimental value of $109{,}678$ cm^{-1}. The slight discrepancy (0.05%) can be accounted for by the motion of the electron and proton about their mutual center of mass (Problem 1–11). With this agreement it is clear that Equation (11) will produce the observed wavelengths of the Balmer lines when $n_f = 2$. According to the Bohr model, the Balmer series of hydrogen lines corresponds to electrons transiting to the $n = 2$ orbit from "higher" orbits.[6]

Equation (11) is quite general, and can be used to calculate the wavelengths of whole series of spectral lines for hydrogen. Inverting it gives the wavelengths directly:

$$\lambda_{n_i \to n_f} = \frac{8\epsilon_o^2 h^3 c}{m_e e^4}\left(\frac{1}{n_f^2} - \frac{1}{n_i^2}\right)^{-1} = 911.75\left(\frac{1}{n_f^2} - \frac{1}{n_i^2}\right)^{-1} \text{Å},$$ (14)

where the numerical value of 911.75 Å accounts for electron/proton center-of-mass motion.

---

[6] A website giving the energy levels of hydrogen and deuterium for states $n = 1$ to 200 for all allowed angular momentum states (see Chapter 6) is available through the National Institute of Standards and Technology at http://physics.nist.gov/PhysRefData/HDEL.

EXAMPLE 1.2

Compute the wavelength of the $7 \rightarrow 4$ transition for a hydrogen atom. What is the energy of the photon emitted in such a transition, in eV?

From Equation (14),

$$\lambda_{7 \rightarrow 2} = 911.75 \left(\frac{1}{4^2} - \frac{1}{7^2} \right)^{-1} \text{Å} = 911.75 \left(\frac{1}{16} - \frac{1}{49} \right)^{-1} \text{Å}$$

$$= 911.75 \left(\frac{33}{784} \right)^{-1} \text{Å} = 21{,}661 \text{ Å}.$$

With this wavelength, 2.166×10^{-6} m, such a photon would lie in the *infrared* part of the electromagnetic spectrum, far to the red of human visual response. The energy is

$$E = \frac{hc}{\lambda} = \frac{(6.6261 \times 10^{-34} \text{J} \cdot \text{sec})(2.9979 \times 10^8 \text{m/s})}{2.1661 \times 10^{-6} \text{m}}$$

$$= 9.171 \times 10^{-20} \text{J}.$$

With 1 eV $= 1.602 \times 10^{-19}$ J, this corresponds to about 0.57 eV.

Table 1.1 lists hydrogen spectral wavelengths computed from this formula for a number of (n_i, n_f) pairs. A group of lines corresponding to the same n_f is known as a **series** of lines. Each such series is characterized by a **series limit** corresponding to

Table 1.1 **Hydrogen Transition Wavelengths (Å)**

Final state	\multicolumn{6}{c}{Initial state}	
	2	3	4	5	6	Infinity	Series
1	1215.7	1025.7	972.5	949.7	937.8	911.8	Lyman
2		6564.6	4862.7	4341.7	4102.9	3647.0	Balmer
3			18756.0	12821.5	10941.0	8205.8	Paschen
4				40522.2	26258.4	14588.2	Bracket
5					74597.7	22794.3	Pfund
6						32824.2	Humphreys

$n_i = \infty$; the spacing of the lines decreases toward the series limits. As mentioned earlier, the range of human vision runs from about 3500–7000 Å; only the Balmer series lies entirely within these limits. The series corresponding to $n_f = 3$ lies in the infrared region of the spectrum, and had been observed in 1908 by Freidrich Paschen [10] to occur at exactly the wavelengths calculated by the Bohr formula. After publication of Bohr's theory the series corresponding to $n_f = 1, 4$, and 5 were discovered by Lyman (1914), Brackett (1922), and Pfund (1924) [11–13]. These discoveries lent immense credibility to Bohr's theory.

The energy of an electron in quantum state n in the Bohr model is given by combining Equations (4) and (7):

$$E_n = -\frac{m_e e^4}{8\epsilon_o^2 h^2 n^2} = -\frac{13.606}{n^2} \text{ eV} \quad (n = 1, 2, 3, \dots), \tag{15}$$

where the factor of 13.606 eV, known as the Rydberg energy, accounts for the electron/proton center-of-mass motion and the values of the various constants to five significant figures. This is one of the most famous results of early quantum mechanics. It tells us that to ionize a hydrogen atom from its **ground state** ($n = 1$) requires an expenditure of 13.6 eV of energy, precisely the observed value.

Figure 1.5 shows an **energy-level diagram** for hydrogen based on the Bohr model. Energy is plotted increasing upward on the vertical axis; the horizontal axis has no physical meaning and serves only to improve the readability of the figure. The arrows show a number of possible quantum jumps or *transitions*; their lengths are proportional to the frequencies of the corresponding emitted photons because $E = h\nu$. Electrons that are initially not bound to the atom (so-called free electrons with $E > 0$) can become so by releasing just enough energy to bring them into one of the stationary states; thus, there is a **continuum** of energy levels with $E > 0$.

An intriguing aspect of Bohr's model concerns the orbital angular momentum of the electron, usually designated L. Classically, a mass m in a circular orbit of radius r and speed v has angular momentum $L = mvr$. If we apply this to the electron in the Bohr model with the help of Equations (6) and (7),

$$L = m_e v r = m_e \left(\frac{e^2}{2\epsilon_o n h}\right)\left(\frac{\epsilon_o h^2}{\pi m_e e^2}\right)n^2 = \left(\frac{h}{2\pi}\right)n, \quad (n = 1, 2, 3, \dots). \tag{16}$$

the physical interpretation of the result is that the orbital angular momentum of the electron is quantized in units of $h/2\pi$. Planck's constant, which was originally introduced to explain thermal radiation, now appears as a fundamental unit of angular momentum. Many treatments of the Bohr model begin by assuming that angular

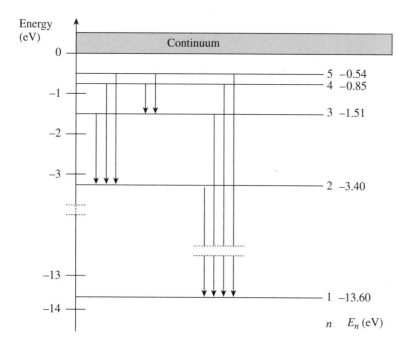

I FIGURE 1.5 Energy Level Diagram for Hydrogen.

momentum is quantized in this way. Whether one regards E or L as being the fundamentally quantized attribute is arbitrary; the relationship is symbiotic. The fundamental quantum of angular momentum, $h/2\pi$, is given its own symbol, $\hbar$, read as "h-bar":

$$\hbar = \frac{h}{2\pi} = 1.05459 \times 10^{-34} \, \text{Joule-sec.} \tag{17}$$

We will see in Chapter 7 that angular momentum plays a central role in the wave mechanics of the hydrogen atom.

At this point, it is useful to look back at the illustration of Kirchhoff's laws, (Figure 1.1), and relate it to Bohr's model. A cool gas will have most of its atoms in the lowest energy (ground) state. When light is passed through such a gas only those photons with energy equal to the various differences between the ground state and higher energy levels of the gas atoms will be absorbed out, causing certain wavelengths to be removed from the light beam. In the case of a hot gas, we will see photons emitted from de-excitations of the gas atoms: the reverse of the cool-gas excitation process. The continuous spectrum of a hot solid object (e.g., a lightbulb filament) is a manifestation of interactions between atoms.

EXAMPLE 1.3

One of the results of Planck's blackbody radiation theory is that any environment at absolute (Kelvin) temperature T will be teeming with photons of average energy $2.7kT$ where k is Boltzmann's constant. At room temperature (300 K), would this average energy be sufficient to ionize a hydrogen atom from the $n = 1$ state? If not, what temperature would result in such ionization?

The average photon energy evaluates as

$$< E > = 2.7 \, (1.381 \times 10^{-23} \text{ J/K})T = 3.729 \times 10^{-23} \, T \text{ (Joules)}$$

if T is in Kelvins. This is equivalent to $2.327 \times 10^{-4}T$ eV. At $T = 300$ K, $< E > = 0.07$ eV, far below the ionization energy of 13.6 eV. $< E > = 13.6$ eV would require $T \sim 58,000$ K. In cosmology, the time after the Big Bang at which the Universe had cooled to this temperature is known as the *recombination time*—the point at which neutral hydrogen could form.

In the years following its publication, Bohr's theory underwent a number of refinements. Inclusion of elliptical orbits and relativistic effects led to some understanding of the "fine structure" of spectral lines. Experimental work by Henry Moseley [14] on X-rays, and by James Franck and Gustav Hertz [15] on collisions of electrons with atomic and molecular gases, added compelling evidence for the existence of quantized energy levels. Despite its success and powerful intuitive appeal, though, Bohr's model was not without problems. First was the sheer arbitrariness of the orbital frequencies assumption: It clearly works, but was there any way a more fundamental understanding might be sought? Despite years of effort by Bohr and his colleagues to extend the theory to more complex atoms, they had only very limited success [16]. Deeper understanding of these matters had to await a wave formulation of quantum mechanics in 1926.

EXAMPLE 1.4

X-rays are photons with wavelengths from 0.06 to 125 Å. In 1913–14, Henry Moseley provided supporting evidence for the Bohr model by measuring the wavelengths of photons emitted from (among others) $2 \rightarrow 1$ electronic transitions for metals of a variety of atomic numbers Z. To what range of Z does the X-ray part of the spectrum correspond for $2 \rightarrow 1$ transitions in the Bohr model?

From Equation (1.3.14) and the comment given regarding incorporating different Z values following Equation (1.3.1), we can write the Bohr transition wavelengths as

$$\lambda_{n_i \to n_f} = \frac{912}{Z^2}\left(\frac{1}{n_f^2} - \frac{1}{n_i^2}\right)^{-1} \text{Å},$$

where we have rounded the Rydberg constant to the nearest Ångstrom. For $(n_i, n_f) = (2, 1)$ this becomes (again to the nearest Å)

$$\lambda_{2 \to 1} = \frac{1216}{Z^2} \text{ Å}.$$

For $\lambda = 125$ Å we find $Z \sim 3$, and for $\lambda = 0.06$ Å, $Z \sim 142$. Thus, essentially the whole of the periodic table was available to Moseley. Further details on Moseley's work appear in Section 1-10 of French and Taylor.[7]

■ 1.4 de Broglie Matter-Waves

In his 1924 Ph.D. thesis, French physicist Louis de Broglie (pronounced "de broy") proposed that if photons could behave like particles and transport momentum according to

$$p = \frac{h}{\lambda}, \tag{1}$$

then might material particles possessing momentum be accompanied by a **matter-wave** of wavelength given by inverting the relation: $\lambda = h/p = h/mv$?

The mathematical manipulation here is trivial, but the physical hypothesis seems absurd: We do not observe matter to be wavy; it is solid and localized. But just because we cannot see a particular phenomenon does not mean that it does not exist. The controlling factor in Equation (1) is the minuteness of Planck's constant. A mass of 1 kg moving at 1 meter/sec would have an associated **de Broglie wavelength** of $\sim 10^{-34}$ meters, some 20 orders of magnitude smaller than an atomic nucleus. We could scarcely hope to observe the "matter-wave" associated with such a macroscopic object. On the other hand, if an extremely tiny mass is involved, such as that of an electron, then it turns out that the associated wave can be comparable in size to its parent particle.

[7]A. P. French and E. F. Taylor, *An Introduction to Quantum Physics,* Boca Raton, FL: CRC Press, 1978.

Table 1.2	de Broglie Wavelengths.

Situation	λ(Å)	Comment
Electron, energy 1 eV	12.3	Molecular size
Proton, energy 1 keV	0.009	Subatomic size
800 kg car @ 20 m/sec	4.1×10^{-28}	$\ll$ Nuclear size

Table 1.2 shows a few de Broglie wavelengths computed via the relationship now named after him [17]:

$$\lambda = \frac{h}{mv} = \frac{h}{\sqrt{2Km}}, \quad (v \ll c), \tag{2}$$

where K is the kinetic energy of the mass involved.

If particles really do possess associated waves, then it is clear that we can hope to detect them only in atomic-scale phenomena. Leaving aside for the moment the question of what they mean, let us ask how such matter-waves might manifest themselves.

Waves can be diffracted to produce constructive and destructive interference patterns. According to de Broglie, then, electrons fired through a double-slit apparatus should somehow interfere with each other (and themselves!). The problem is that the slit separation must be on the order of the wavelength involved, far too small (at least in de Broglie's day) to be physically manufactured. However, as de Broglie himself pointed out, nature provides natural diffraction gratings with spacings on the order of Ångstroms: the regularly spaced rows of atoms in metallic crystals. Less than three years after de Broglie advanced his hypothesis, experimental verification came independently from American and British groups of researchers. Working at the Bell Telephone Laboratories in the U.S., Clinton Davisson and Lester Germer observed, by accident, interference effects with electrons scattering from crystals of nickel [18]. In Britain, George P. Thomson (J.J.'s son) verified the effect by scattering electrons through thin metallic foils [19]. In 1961, Claus Jonsson [20] demonstrated electron diffraction with a true double-slit arrangement, utilizing an elaborate array of electrostatic lenses to magnify the image. More recently, the wave properties of Carbon-60 "buckyball" molecules have been observed by similarly passing them through a series of slits,[8] as has the diffraction of electrons by a standing light wave.[9] All these experiments and many others have demonstrated that electrons, atoms, and molecules

---

[8]Physics Today 1992; 52(12):9.

[9]Physics Today 2002; 55(1):15.

behave in full agreement with de Broglie's hypothesis. The wave nature of electrons is put to stunning practical use in electron microscopy. The resolution of a microscope (the smallest distance by which two objects can be separated and still viewed as distinct) is proportional to the wavelength of light used. Because electrons behave as waves of wavelengths much shorter than that of visible light, much greater detail is resolvable. Images of individual molecules and atoms can be obtained in this way.

The evidence for de Broglie's matter-waves is incontrovertible. But what does it mean to say that a particle has a wave nature? How do we reconcile the classical point-mass view of matter with wave properties? As a schematic model, consider Figure 1.6.

The victim in this game of wavy particles is the classical idea that the position of the particle can be specified with an arbitrary degree of precision. In effect (but not in reality) the electron acts as if it is smeared out into a so-called wave packet that pervades all space. The amplitude of this wave, however, is not constant: it proves to be strongly peaked in the vicinity of the electron over a length scale Δx on the order of the size of the electron, as the figure suggests. For practical purposes, we can no longer specify with precision where the electron is; we can only speak meaningfully in terms of the *probability* of finding the electron at some position. (We will explore these "probability waves" further in subsequent chapters.) It is this wavy nature of matter that lies at the heart of the Heisenberg uncertainty principle, which we will examine in Chapter 4.

These considerations in no way invalidate the application of Newtonian dynamics to objects such as golf balls or planets. The de Broglie waves accompanying such masses are so infinitesimally small in comparison with their length-scales that we cannot hope to detect them. Only when the size of the system under study is comparable to $\lambda = h/mv$ will quantum effects become noticeable. As an example, refer to Table 1.2. A 1 keV proton incident on a hydrogen atom has a de Broglie wavelength much less than the size of the atom; for practical purposes, this will be a particle interaction. On the other hand, an electron of energy 1 eV

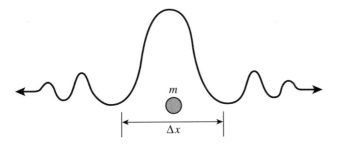

❘ FIGURE 1.6 A Particle and Its de Broglie Matter-Wave.

has a de Broglie wavelength on the order of the size of that same hydrogen atom: to an imaginary observer riding on the atom, the incoming electron would appear amorphous.

The "wave-particle duality" is perhaps the most counterintuitive aspect of quantum mechanics, and, not surprisingly, has inspired an extensive body of literature. An excellent discussion on this topic appears in the first two chapters of the third volume of Feynman's *Lectures on Physics* [21]. A very readable and humorous look at the situation appears in "Two lectures on wave-particle duality" by Mermin.[10]

EXAMPLE 1.5

What speed must an electron have if its de Broglie wavelength is 5000 Å? A photon of this wavelength would be in the visible part of the electromagnetic spectrum.

Putting $p = mv$ in Equation (1) and solving for v gives $v = h/m\lambda$, hence

$$v = \frac{h}{m\lambda} = \frac{(6.626 \times 10^{-34} \text{J} \cdot \text{s})}{(9.109 \times 10^{-31} \text{kg})(5 \times 10^{-7} \text{m})} = 1455 \text{ m/s}.$$

See Problem 1-20. If this speed were due to the electron's random thermal motion in an environment at absolute temperature T, the environment would be at $T \sim 0.04$ K. Electrons of such speed are thus characterized as "cold."

EXAMPLE 1.6

de Broglie further hypothesized that the allowed orbits for an electron in a hydrogen atom are given by the condition that an integral number "n" de Broglie wavelengths fit around the circumference of the orbit. Show that this condition leads to the Bohr quantization condition on angular momentum, Equation (1.3.16).

Let the electron have speed v in an orbit of radius r. The circumference of the orbit is then $2\pi r$. de Broglie's hypothesis is then that an integral number of wavelengths fit into this circumference:

$$\frac{2\pi r}{\lambda} = n.$$

---

[10]Mermin ND, *Physics Today* 1993; 46(1):9–11.

Setting $\lambda = h/m_e v$ gives

$$\frac{2\pi m_e v r}{h} = n.$$

However, $m_e v r$ is just the angular momentum of the electron in its orbit:

$$L = \left(\frac{h}{2\pi}\right) n = \hbar n,$$

precisely the Bohr quantization condition on L. If the condition on the electron's speed that emerged from Bohr's orbital frequency assumption is used here (Equation 1.3.6), the result is the same restriction on orbital radii and energies that emerged from his approach.

Figure 1.7 shows a sketch of what de Broglie had in mind: an integral number of wavelengths (in this case shown, $n = 4$) fitting around the circumference of an orbit like a standing wave. It should be emphasized that the amplitude of the wave shown in the sketch is purely arbitrary; de Broglie's relation gives no information on this.

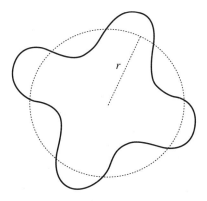

I FIGURE 1.7 de Broglie's Quantization Condition.

■ **Summary**

The need to introduce the hypothesis that some physical quantities (such as energy and angular momentum) are quantized grew out of the inability of classical physics to provide adequate understanding of phenomena such as thermal radiation, atomic spectra, and atomic structure. The way was led by Max Planck, who in 1900 proposed that one could model the mechanism of thermal radiation by assuming that the source of black-body radiation lay in "oscillators" restricted to possessing energies given by

$$E = nh\nu,$$

where n is an integer ($n = 1, 2, 3, ...$), h is Planck's constant, and ν is the frequency of vibration. Later, Niels Bohr used this assumption in conjunction with a semiclassical planetary electron model of the hydrogen atom. The essence of Bohr's model is that the orbiting electron is restricted to certain "stationary" energy states wherein it does not radiate. Atomic spectra are then presumed to be due to electrons executing transitions between different stationary states the difference in energy ΔE between the states appearing as a photon of energy $\Delta E = h\nu$ in accordance with Planck's hypothesis. The energy level of a Bohr atom in quantum state n ($n = 1, 2, 3, ...$) is given by

$$E_n = -\frac{m_e Z^2 e^4}{8\epsilon_o^2 h^2 n^2} = -13.595 \frac{Z^2}{n^2} \text{ eV} \quad (n = 1, 2, 3, \dots)$$

where Z is the number of protons in the nucleus. The wavelength of the photon emitted by an electron transiting from Bohr orbit n_i to orbit n_f ($n_i > n_f$) is given by

$$\lambda_{n_i \to n_f} = \frac{911.75}{Z^2}\left(\frac{1}{n_f^2} - \frac{1}{n_i^2}\right)^{-1} \text{\AA}.$$

A corollary of the Bohr model is that the orbital angular momentum of the electron is quantized in units of $h/2\pi$.

A central concept of the quantum aspect of nature is that of matter-waves, due to de Broglie. On the scale of atomic phenomena we are forced to abandon the notion of point particles in favor of treating them as being smeared out over a characteristic de Broglie wavelength given by

$$\lambda = \frac{h}{mv}.$$

The idea of matter-waves proves to be intimately related to the probability distribution interpretation of quantum mechanics.

■ Problems

1-1(E) The table gives densities and atomic weights for a number of common elements.

Use Equation (1.1.1) to calculate approximate sizes for these species.

Element	Density (g/cm³)	A (g/mol)
Al	2.7	27
Fe	7.88	56
Cu	8.96	64
Pb	11.34	207
Pt	21.45	195

1-2(E) Consider a gas of "classical" Maxwell-Boltzmann atoms whose energies are distributed in accordance with Equation (1.2.5). In an environment of $T = 6000$ K (the approximate temperature of the surface of the Sun), what is the ratio of the number of atoms with energies between $E + dE$ to those with energies between $2E$ and $2E + dE$, where $E = 5$ eV?

1-3(I) Equation (1.2.13) gives the amount of radiant energy $E(\nu)d\nu$ between frequencies ν and $\nu + d\nu$ within a blackbody cavity. According to Einstein, the energy of an individual photon of frequency ν is $E = h\nu$. If the radiant energy is presumed to be comprised of individual photons, then the number of photons with frequencies between ν and $\nu + d\nu$ in the cavity would be given by $n(\nu)d\nu = E(\nu)d\nu/h\nu$. The total number of photons within the cavity will then be given by the integral of this expression for $\nu = 0$ to ∞. Given that

$$\int_0^\infty \frac{x^2 dx}{(e^x - 1)} \sim 2.404,$$

determine the density of photons in a blackbody cavity at $T = 300$ K, about room temperature. Intergalactic space has a temperature of about 2.7 K; what is the density of photons in that environment?

1-4(E) To establish the relationship between Equation (1.2.13) and Figure 1.3 requires some knowledge of thermodynamics, which shows that the rate of energy escape (power) between wavelengths λ and $\lambda + d\lambda$ through a hole of area A in a blackbody cavity of temperature T is given by

$$P(\lambda)d\lambda = A\left\{\frac{2\pi hc^2}{\lambda^5(e^{hc/\lambda kT} - 1)}\right\}d\lambda.$$

Consider a blackbody at $T = 7000$ K. What is the power emitted through a hole of area 1 m^2 between $\lambda = 4000$ Å and 4001 Å? Does your result accord with Figure 1.3?

1-5(E) Derive an expression for the speed of an electron in Bohr orbit n in terms of the speed of light. Is it justifiable to neglect relativistic effects in the development of the Bohr model?

1-6(E) Repeat the derivation of the Bohr model for a lone electron orbiting a nucleus of Z protons. Use your results to compute ionization energies for a single electron orbiting nuclei of (a) helium, (b) carbon, and (c) uranium.

1-7(E) Derive an expression for the centripetal force experienced by the electron in Bohr orbit n as a function of n and physical constants. What is the value of the force when $n = 1$? Modern force-probe microscopes are capable of measuring nano-Newton scale forces.

1-8(E) An electron transits between two energy levels separated by energy E, emitting a photon of wavelength λ in accordance with the Planck/Bohr relation $E = hc/\lambda$.

(a) Show that if λ is given in units of Ångstroms, then $E = 12{,}398/\lambda$ electron-volts.

(b) As a consequence of some perturbing effect, the separation of the energy levels is altered by an amount dE electron-volts. Show that the corresponding change in the wavelength of the emitted photon is $d\lambda = -\lambda^2 dE/12{,}398$ Ångstroms. If a transition leading to a photon of wavelength 4000 Å is perturbed by $dE = 0.01$ eV, what is $d\lambda$?

1-9(I) The purpose of this question is to derive an educated guess at the classically expected "lifetime" of an electron in various Bohr orbits. According to classical electrodynamics, an accelerated charge e radiates energy at the rate $P = e^2 a^2/6\pi\epsilon_o c^3$ Joule/sec, where a is the acceleration (v^2/r for a circular orbit). Decay rate (DR; unit = sec^{-1}) can be defined to be the power radiated divided by the energy emitted during the decay. Use the Bohr model to derive an expression for DR for a decay from orbit n to orbit $n - 1$; for simplicity, use the acceleration for orbit n in the expression for P. The lifetime is given by the reciprocal of the decay rate; evaluate this numerically for $n = 2$.

1-10(E) Both Newton's gravitational law and Coulomb's law are inverse-square laws: The force of attraction between the Sun (S) and the Earth (E) has magnitude Gm_Sm_E/r^2, whereas the force of attraction between an electron and a proton in a hydrogen atom is $e^2/4\pi\epsilon_o r^2$. Derive an expression for the equivalent of the Bohr radius for the gravitational case. What is the value of the quantum number of Earth's orbit? Would distance differences between individual quantum states in the solar system be observable?

1-11(A) The text indicates how one can take into account the motions of the proton and electron around their mutual center of mass in the Bohr model. Using the condition that the center of mass of an isolated system must stay in the same place, derive the correction specified in the footnote, and hence derive the factor of 911.75 Å in Equation (1.3.14). *Hint:* Do not forget the kinetic energy of the proton about the electron/proton center of mass.

1-12(I) It is remarked in the text that the effect of the motions of the electron and proton around their common center of mass in the Bohr model can be accounted for by substituting the reduced mass of the system, $m_e m_p/(m_e + m_p)$ in place of the electron mass m_e wherever the latter appears. An atom of deuterium consists of a lone electron orbiting a nucleus consisting of a proton and a neutron fused together; such a nucleus has mass close to $2m_p$. Show that the difference in wavelength between the Balmer $3 \rightarrow 2$ transition for deuterium versus ordinary hydrogen is given by

$$(\lambda_h - \lambda_d)_{3 \rightarrow 2} \sim \frac{144}{5} \frac{\epsilon_o^2 h^3 c}{m_p e^4}.$$

Evaluate this result numerically. If you have available a spectrometer capable of resolving spectral lines that are separated by no less than 2 Å, would you see the deuterium and hydrogen lines as separate?

1-13(E) Write a computer program to compute the wavelengths of photons emitted by a single electron orbiting a hydrogen-like atom of nuclear charge $+Ze$ as it transits between any pair of states (n_i, n_f) (see Problem 1-6). Test your program by comparing your results with Table 1.1 for $Z = 1$. What are the wavelengths of the "Balmer series" for helium? For uranium?

1-14(I) Derive expressions for the lowest- and highest-possible wavelength photons emitted during transitions corresponding to a given series of spectral lines. Show that as a result, only the Lyman and Balmer series in hydrogen are not overlapped by lines from other series.

1-15(E) The *Ritz combination principle* was an empirical result that predated the Bohr model. This principle states that the inverse of the wavelength of a spectral line of some atomic species can often be predicted by computing the difference in the inverse wavelengths of two other spectral lines of the same species. Show that in the context of the Bohr model, hydrogen $p \rightarrow m$ transitions can be predicted form the $p \rightarrow n$ and $m \rightarrow n$ transitions according as

$$\frac{1}{\lambda_{p \rightarrow m}} = \frac{1}{\lambda_{p \rightarrow n}} - \frac{1}{\lambda_{m \rightarrow n}}.$$

Verify numerically by computing the $5 \rightarrow 3$ transition on the basis of the values for the $5 \rightarrow 1$ and $3 \rightarrow 1$ wavelengths given in Table 1.1.

1-16(I) A diatomic molecule (such as H_2) can be modeled as two point particles, each of mass m, joined by a rigid rod of length L. Assuming that the molecule rotates about an axis perpendicular to the rod through its midpoint and with angular momentum given by the Bohr condition (Equation 1.3.16), derive an expression for the quantized values of the rotational energy.

1-17(I) As another model of an atom, consider a solid sphere of mass M and radius R rotating about an axis through its center in accordance with the Bohr quantization condition on angular momentum. Show that the possible rotational energies are given by $E_n = 5n^2h^2/16\pi^2MR^2$, where n is the quantum number. From this result derive an expression for the wavelength of a photon emitted as this system undergoes a transition from state $n + 1$ to state n. Evaluate your answer numerically for the case of M equal to the mass of a proton (essentially the mass of a hydrogen atom), $R = 1$ Å, and $n = 2$. Approximately what value would n have to be to give wavelengths in the optical region of the spectrum, $\lambda \sim$ 5000 Å?

1-18(E) Compute the de Broglie wavelength for an electron of energy 1 keV. If this electron were interacting with a hydrogen atom, would classical mechanics suffice?

1-19(E) Particles in motion have associated de Broglie wavelengths. As a rule, if one is within a few de Broglie wavelengths of a particle, then the particle loses its identity as a particle and acts more like a wave. The result is that classical mechanics no longer suffices to describe collisions. Rutherford investigated the scattering of α-particles (helium nuclei) from stationary gold nuclei, using classical mechanics to analyze the collisions. This question investigates the issue from a wave-mechanics perspective.

(a) Determine the de Broglie wavelength of an α-particle of kinetic energy 6 million electron-volts.

(b) The electrical potential energy of charges Q_1 and Q_2 separated by distance r is given by $U = Q_1 Q_2 / 4\pi\epsilon_o r$. By equating the initial kinetic energy of the α-particle to the electrical potential energy, find the distance of closest approach of the α-particle to the gold nucleus, and so render a judgment as to how well-justified Rutherford was in his use of classical mechanics.

1-20(E) In kinetic theory, atoms are modeled as point masses of mass m, and the mean speed v of an atom in an environment at absolute temperature T is given by $mv^2 = 3kT$, where k is Boltzmann's constant. Derive an expression for the de Broglie wavelength for an atom of mass m at absolute temperature T in terms of h, k, T, and m. At room temperature, hydrogen atoms typically travel many thousands of Ångstroms between collisions; is it fair to treat them as effectively acting as point masses under such circumstances?

1-21(E) In a paper published in the October 14, 1999 edition of *Nature*,[11] a group at Universität Wien in Austria reported experimental detection of the de Broglie wave interference of Carbon-60 "buckyball" molecules. Such molecules consist of 60 carbon atoms arranged in a roughly spherical shape reminiscent of a soccer ball. In this experiment, the C-60 molecules had a most probable velocity of 220 m/s. Their data is well-fit by a de Broglie wavelength of 2.5 picometers. Verify this wavelength from the information given.

1-22(E) An atom of mass m is initially at rest with respect to an outside observer and has an electron in an excited state. The electron transits to a lower energy level, emitting a single photon of wavelength λ in the process. The emitted photon will have momentum $p = h/\lambda$. To conserve momentum, the atom must recoil with some speed v. Derive an expression giving the ratio of the

---

[11]*Nature* 1999; 401:680–682.

photon's energy to the kinetic energy of the recoiling atom in terms of λ, m, c, and h. A classical analysis will suffice for the recoiling atom. Evaluate the ratio numerically for a hydrogen atom emitting a photon of wavelength 5000 Å. Based on your result, do you think it was reasonable to neglect the energy involved with the recoiling atom in the derivation of the Bohr model? Along these lines, the momentum transferred to an atom upon its absorbing a photon has actually been measured.[12]

---

[12]*Physics Today* 2005; 58(7):9.

2 Schrödinger's Equation

From lines of evidence like those marshaled in Chapter 1, it became clear to physicists in the early part of the twentieth century that the laws of classical mechanics do not apply to physical systems on atomic scales. The problem then became how to modify classical mechanics to produce a "quantum mechanics" consistent with the microscopic characteristics of atoms and molecules that reverts to a form consistent with Newtonian mechanics on macroscopic scales. As the essence of classical physics is embodied in Newton's laws, the essence of quantum mechanics is embodied in Schrödinger's equation (SE).

At this point we could simply state Schrödinger's equation and say, "Here it is—let's see how to solve it in certain circumstances," just as you would use $F = ma$ with an applied force and some initial conditions to solve for the motion of a classical point mass. This would be convenient, but not aesthetically satisfying. Postulated physical laws, although derivable from nothing more fundamental, do not simply pop out of thin air: They are products of thinking processes conditioned by past successes, empirical facts, intuition, trial and error, and inspired guesses. In an effort to smooth the transition, we introduce Schrödinger's equation by means of a plausibility argument. This is a fancy way of saying that even though no rigorous derivation exists, it is possible to arrive at Schrödinger's equation by deftly combining some classical and quantum concepts. Of course, any equation could be concocted in this way; whether or not the result is useful is a matter for experiment.

We develop Schrödinger's equation in Sections 2.2 and 2.3 after first reviewing the classical wave equation in Section 2.1. In Section 2.4, we discuss what general constraints must be imposed upon solutions to Schrödinger's equation and how they are interpreted. We follow this procedure because the interpretation, like the equation itself, is fundamentally a postulate, and it seems sensible to gather postulates together in one place, independent of any particular example. Examples of setting up and solving Schrödinger's equation are reserved for subsequent chapters.

■ 2.1 The Classical Wave Equation

Any equation that purports to describe quantum physics must respect the incontrovertible fact that particles possess a fundamentally wavy nature. To physicists of the early twentieth century, this demand was familiar ground: waves in strings, water waves, sound waves, electromagnetic waves, and so forth were pervasive phenomena in classical physics. As a starting point, then, let us consider the classical wave equation and how one might modify it to accommodate the wave nature of individual particles.

As a classical model of a wave, consider a disturbance in a string. Figure 2.1(a) shows a sketch of such a disturbance at some particular time $t = 0$. Distance along the string from the origin is measured by x, whereas $y(x, t)$ measures the amplitude; that is, the up or down displacement of the string from its undisturbed position as a function of position and time. The pattern may in fact be quite complex, but we can describe it in principle by saying that at $t = 0$, $y = f(x)$.

The simplest wave pattern we can conceive is one that retains its shape as it propagates down the string. The speed at which the pattern flows through the string is determined by the tension T in the string and its mass per unit length μ: $v = \sqrt{T/\mu}$. In such a transverse wave, an individual point on the string oscillates up and down but does not shift left to right as the wave passes by. Figure 2.1(b) shows the wave pattern after time t has elapsed; the whole pattern has advanced a distance vt along the string. The vertical offset between the two patterns is for clarity only.

Now imagine two observers, O_1 and O_2, standing at fixed positions on the x-axis as shown; O_2 is at distance vt to the right of O_1. Distances measured by O_1 and O_2 along the x-axis are referred to as x and x', respectively. Assuming that the wave pat-

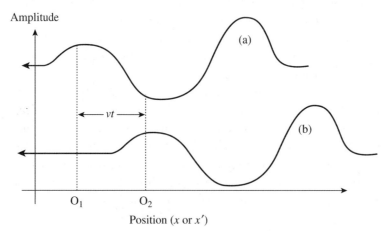

I FIGURE 2.1 Traveling Wave at Two Different Times.

tern retains its shape, each observer must describe the pattern with the same mathematical function of his or her distance coordinate:

$$y = f(x) = f(x'). \tag{1}$$

In addition, when $x' = 0$, $x = vt$. Thus x and x' are related as

$$x' = x - vt. \tag{2}$$

Substituting Equation (2) into Equation (1) gives

$$y = f(x) = f(x - vt). \tag{3}$$

The interpretation of this equation is that for the wave pattern to maintain its shape, x, v, and t must always appear in the combination $(x - vt)$. Examples of *acceptable* wave patterns would be

$$y = sin(x - vt),$$

$$y = e^{(x - vt)^{7/8}}$$

and

$$y = Tanh^{-1} [(x - vt)^{-4/3}].$$

On the other hand, a wave that would not maintain its shape is

$$y = cos [x^2 - (vt)^2].$$

Although these considerations establish a constraint on x, v, and t if waves are to maintain their shape, it is clear that we could write down an infinite variety of possible wave patterns $y(x)$, which are called *wavefunctions*. Is there any way we can express the constraint in more general terms without getting mixed up with an infinite number of functions? Inevitably, such generalized expressions of physical laws take the form of partial differential equations. Assuming that wave patterns must involve functions of the form $f(x - vt)$, it is possible to work out the general differential equation that any wave pattern must satisfy to be acceptable [1].

Now, we know that in general we can put

$$y(x, t) = f(x - vt) = f(z), \tag{4}$$

for which $z = (x - vt)$. From this definition (the velocity is assumed to be constant),

$$\frac{\partial y}{\partial x} = \frac{\partial y}{\partial z}\frac{\partial z}{\partial x} = \frac{\partial y}{\partial z}, \tag{5}$$

and

$$\frac{\partial y}{\partial t} = \frac{\partial y}{\partial z}\frac{\partial z}{\partial t} = -v\frac{\partial y}{\partial z}. \tag{6}$$

From these results we can form an identity:

$$\frac{\partial y}{\partial t} + v\frac{\partial y}{\partial x} = -v\frac{\partial y}{\partial z} + v\frac{\partial y}{\partial x} = 0. \tag{7}$$

Taking the partial derivative of Equation (7) with respect to time gives:

$$\frac{\partial}{\partial t}\left(\frac{\partial y}{\partial t} + v\frac{\partial y}{\partial x}\right) = \frac{\partial}{\partial t}(0),$$

that is,

$$\frac{\partial^2 y}{\partial t^2} + v\frac{\partial}{\partial t}\left(\frac{\partial y}{\partial x}\right) = 0.$$

or,

$$\frac{\partial^2 y}{\partial t^2} + v\frac{\partial}{\partial x}\left(\frac{\partial y}{\partial t}\right) = 0, \tag{8}$$

where the last step resulted from exchanging the order of the partial derivatives. From Equation (6) we can replace $(\partial y/\partial t)$ by $-v(\partial y/\partial z) = -v(\partial y/\partial x)$, hence

$$\frac{\partial^2 y}{\partial t^2} + v\frac{\partial}{\partial x}\left(-v\frac{\partial y}{\partial x}\right) = 0$$

or

$$\frac{\partial^2 y}{\partial t^2} = v^2\frac{\partial^2 y}{\partial x^2}. \tag{9}$$

Equation (9) is the **classical wave equation**. If you are familiar with some advanced mathematical physics, its solution in any particular case usually proceeds in terms of Fourier or Laplace transforms, but this will not concern us. The essential point for our purposes is that "classical wavefunctions" $y(x, t)$ must satisfy this equation.

EXAMPLE 2.1

Show that the function $y = e^{(x - vt)^{7/8}}$ satisfies the classical wave equation.

We have a function of the form e^z for which $z = (x - vt)^{7/8}$. It is helpful to recall that for any variable q,

$$\frac{d}{dq}[e^{z(q)}] = e^{z(q)}\frac{dz}{dq}.$$

Begin with the left side of the wave equation. Here we will have $q \equiv t$, and

$$\frac{dz}{dt} = \frac{7}{8}(x - vt)^{-1/8}(-v).$$

Hence

$$\frac{dy}{dt} = e^z\frac{dz}{dt} = -\frac{7}{8}(v)e^z(x - vt)^{-1/8}.$$

Remembering the chain rule of basic calculus, the second derivative goes as

$$\frac{d^2y}{dt^2} = -\frac{7}{8}(v)\frac{d}{dt}[e^z(x - vt)^{-1/8}]$$

$$= -\frac{7}{8}(v)\left[e^z\frac{dz}{dt}(x - vt)^{-1/8} - \frac{1}{8}e^z(x - vt)^{-9/8}(-v)\right]$$

$$= -\frac{7}{8}(v)\left[-\frac{7}{8}(v)e^z(x - vt)^{-1/4} - \frac{1}{8}e^z(x - vt)^{-9/8}(-v)\right]$$

$$= (v^2)\left[\frac{49}{64}(x - vt)^{-1/4} - \frac{7}{64}(x - vt)^{-9/8}\right]e^z.$$

Now look at the right side of the wave equation. Here $q \equiv x$, and we have

$$\frac{dz}{dx} = \frac{7}{8}(x - vt)^{-1/8}.$$

Hence

$$\frac{dy}{dx} = e^z \frac{dz}{dx} = \frac{7}{8}e^z(x - vt)^{-1/8}.$$

The second derivative develops as

$$\frac{d^2y}{dt^2} = \frac{7}{8}\frac{d}{dt}[e^z(x - vt)^{-1/8}]$$

$$= \frac{7}{8}\left[e^z \frac{dz}{dx}(x - vt)^{-1/8} - \frac{1}{8}e^z(x - vt)^{-9/8}\right]$$

$$= \frac{7}{8}\left[\frac{7}{8}e^z(x - vt)^{-1/4} - \frac{1}{8}e^z(x - vt)^{-9/8}\right]$$

$$= \left[\frac{49}{64}(x - vt)^{-1/4} - \frac{7}{64}(x - vt)^{-9/8}\right]e^z.$$

Comparing the second derivatives shows that the wave equation is satisfied.

Why didn't we stop at Equation (6), $(\partial y/\partial t) = -v(\partial y/\partial x)$, and call it the classical wave equation? The reason is that a wave equation should be space and time invariant; that is, insensitive to changes in the definition of the positive directions of x and t. Equation (9) has this property, whereas Equation (6) does not.

Aside from spatial (and temporal) invariance, Equation (9) has another important property: that of **linearity**. This means that wherever the dependent variable y appears, it does so only to the first power; there are no nonlinear terms such as e^y, $sin\,(y)$, or $y^{1/2}$. The result of this property is that if one has a number of independent solutions y_1, y_2, ..., y_n to the wave equation (all with the same speed v), then so, too, will be a function constructed by a linear sum of them; that is, a function of the form

$$y = a_1 y_1 + a_2 y_2 + \ldots + a_n y_n, \tag{10}$$

where the coefficients $a_1, a_2, \ldots, a_n$ are constants.

This linearity property is of great value in the following sense: In discussions of harmonic motion in elementary physics texts, one often encounters solutions of the wave equation of the form

$$y = A \sin(kx - \omega t), \tag{11}$$

where A is the amplitude of the wave, k is its wavenumber ($k = 2\pi/\lambda$, where λ is the wavelength), and ω its angular frequency ($\omega = 2\pi\nu$, where ν is the frequency in cycles per second, or Hertz). This expression corresponds to a wave pattern moving in the direction of the $+x$-axis; for one moving in the $-x$ direction, replace the $-$ sign inside the brackets with a $+$ sign. Now, it might happen in some particular problem that the solution to the wave equation is in fact more complicated than this. However, since Fourier analysis will always let us represent any function as a linear sum of sines and cosines, and because the wave equation is linear, we are guaranteed that such a sum will also be a solution. That is, we can always express any solution of the wave equation as a sum of sinusoidal functions of the form of Equation (11). By using Equation (11) as a prototype wave in our development of the Schrödinger equation, we can keep the mathematical manipulations fairly simple while sacrificing no generality.

■ 2.2 The Time-Independent Schrödinger Equation

How can the classical wave equation be modified to accommodate the characteristics of *quantum* matter-waves? This is by no means obvious. Strings exhibit wave phenomena as a whole; y and v in Equation (2.1.9) refer to pattern amplitude and speed, respectively. What we now desire is a wave equation applicable to individual particles. With no idea of what a quantum wave equation can be expected to look like, how should we proceed? It is at this point that our derivation becomes nonrigorous. What follows might at best be called a plausibility argument.[1]

Schrödinger was led by the assumption that the putative quantum wave equation should possess two properties. Experience with classical waves argued strongly in favor of a linear, second-order differential equation, and the success of the Bohr model argued for retaining the concept of energy conservation. In classical notation, conservation of mechanical energy is expressed as

$$E = \frac{p^2}{2m} + V(x), \tag{1}$$

---

[1]Readers interested in a detailed account of the development of quantum ideas and fundamental relationships are urged to look at Max Jammer's masterful *The Conceptual Development of Quantum Mechanics* (New York: McGraw-Hill, 1966).

where p is the momentum of the particle, and where $V(x)$ denotes the potential energy of the particle as a function of position x: the so-called *potential function*. Momentum will of course also be a function of position $p(x)$. We will derive the Schrödinger equation in one dimension and later generalize the result to three dimensions.

To make the connection from classical wave to quantum-mechanical matter-waves, recall the de Broglie relation between the momentum of a particle to its wavelength:

$$\lambda = \frac{h}{p}. \tag{2}$$

Substituting this into the prototype sinusoidal wavefunction introduced in the preceding section (Equation 2.1.11, along with $k = 2\pi/\lambda$) yields

$$y = A \sin\left(\frac{p}{\hbar}x - \omega t\right). \tag{3}$$

To impose the constraint of energy conservation without specifying any particular potential function $V(x)$, let us extract an expression for the momentum from this wavefunction. Differentiating Equation (3) twice with respect to x leads to

$$p^2 = -\frac{\hbar^2}{y}\left(\frac{d^2y}{dx^2}\right), \tag{4}$$

which, upon substitution into the law of conservation of energy (Equation 1), leads to a differential equation:

$$-\frac{\hbar^2}{2m}\frac{d^2y}{dx^2} + V(x)y = Ey. \tag{5}$$

Note how this derivation was carried out to yield a differential equation that bears no explicit trace of the form of the wavefunction that was assumed at the start! Equation (5) is the nonrelativistic, one-dimensional, time-independent Schrödinger equation (also known as the Schrödinger Wave Equation) for a particle of mass m. This equation and some of its fundamental applications were put forth by Erwin Schrödinger in a series of papers in 1926 [2]. Much of what we shall take up in the remainder of this book descends directly from these fundamental papers.

Mathematically, Equation (5) can be classified as a second-order linear differential equation with independent variable x and dependent variable y. As derived here, this equation involves only one spatial dimension, x. This is fine for a pulse traveling along a string, but atoms and molecules live in three dimensions. By intuition, let us accept that Equation (5) can be expressed in a three-dimensional form by adding second partial derivatives of the wave pattern with respect to y and z to the left side. This leads to a minor crisis of notation: confusion between the function representing the wave pattern and the coordinate y itself. Convention is to designate the time-independent wave pattern by the lowercase Greek letter psi (ψ). In this notation Schrödinger's equation becomes

$$-\frac{\hbar^2}{2m}\left(\frac{\partial^2\psi}{\partial x^2} + \frac{\partial^2\psi}{\partial y^2} + \frac{\partial^2\psi}{\partial z^2}\right) + V\psi = E\psi, \tag{6}$$

where we have written partial derivatives because ψ may be a function of some or all of (x, y, z) and, in anticipation of the following section, of time. Be sure to understand that both the potential function V and solution function ψ in this differential equation will in general be functions of all three coordinates (x, y, z).

The astute reader will have noticed three curious aspects regarding the foregoing derivation of the Schrödinger equation. The first is that the classical wave equation was in fact never used—only a prototype wavefunction. The second is that nowhere was the concept of quantization built into the development. Lastly, the total system energy E appears explicitly in the resulting differential equation. From the point of view of classical physics, this latter aspect is distinctly unusual. Newton's law $\boldsymbol{F} = m\boldsymbol{a}$ makes no mention of energy; that is something to be specified by supplying the initial position and speed of the particle involved after solving the differential equation for a particular force law, a process known as supplying "boundary conditions." We shall see that quantization is actually predicted by Schrödinger's equation on solving it for a given $V(x, y, z)$ and set of boundary conditions. Indeed, Schrödinger's equation is of a form known to mathematicians as an **eigenvalue equation**. Loosely interpreted, this means that for a given $V(x, y, z)$ and set of boundary conditions there exists a certain restricted set of functions $\psi(x, y, z)$ that satisfy the equation, and that to each of these functions corresponds a particular value of E. This set of values of E comprises the quantized energy states of the system.

Equation (6) is expressed in Cartesian coordinates. Coordinate systems are, however, a human construct; any true physical law should be expressible in a form that makes no mention of any particular coordinate system. In the case of the SE, we can satisfy this demand by writing it in the form

$$-\frac{\hbar^2}{2m}\nabla^2\psi(\mathbf{r}) + V(\mathbf{r})\psi(\mathbf{r}) = E\psi(\mathbf{r}), \tag{7}$$

where ∇^2 is the Laplacian operator and where r designates a general (x, y, z) dependence.

This coordinate-system independence is actually a rather profound point of fundamental physics. Coordinate systems are a human invention: physical laws must be independent of the location and orientation of the origin and axes of the coordinate systems we use for our descriptions of physical phenomena, and should transcend the choice of any particular coordinate system. To be sure, the Laplacian operator has different forms depending on the choice of coordinate system, but all of these forms express the same concept: a summation of second derivatives. The results of physical calculations cannot depend upon the coordinate system used to develop those calculations.

EXAMPLE 2.2

Suppose that the function $\psi(x) = Ae^{-\iota kx}$ where $\iota = \sqrt{-1}$, and where A and k are constants, is known to be a solution to the time-independent one-dimensional Schrödinger equation with energy E. What is the potential function $V(x)$?

The time-independent Schrödinger equation in one dimension appears as

$$-\frac{\hbar^2}{2m}\frac{d^2\psi}{dx^2} + V(x)\psi = E\psi.$$

The second derivative of the given function is $d^2\psi/dx^2 = (\iota k)^2 Ae^{-\iota kx} = -k^2\psi$. Hence we have

$$-\frac{\hbar^2}{2m}(-k^2\psi) + V(x)\psi = E\psi.$$

We can cancel the common factor of ψ to leave

$$V(x) = E - \frac{\hbar^2 k^2}{2m},$$

that is, $V(x) =$ constant. This case corresponds to that of a so-called *free* particle, one whose energy is in fact *un*restricted. We will see solutions of this form in Chapter 3. It is worth noting that the wavefunction $\psi(x) = Be^{+\iota kx}$ would lead to the same result for $V(x)$. In general, $V(x)$ is considered to be given and $\psi(x)$ sought; for the case of $V(x) =$ constant, we will see in Chapter 3 that the k's in both solutions will be the same. Hence the most general solution to this potential is $\psi(x) = Ae^{-\iota kx} + Be^{+\iota kx}$. All second-order differential equations have two families of solutions.

■ 2.3 The Time-Dependent Schrödinger Equation

Any sensible wave equation should be both space- and time-dependent. In the preceding derivation, time dependence was overlooked by concerning ourselves only with derivatives of y (or ψ) with respect to x. In doing so, any knowledge of the direction sense of the wave pattern was foregone. Because the vast majority of the problems that will be addressed in this book are time-independent, this represents no loss. It is worthwhile presenting a brief pseudo-derivation of the time-dependent SE, however, for sake of completeness, in order to touch on some historical issues and to establish some results we will use in Chapter 3. Also, the time-dependent SE is necessary for a complete proof of Heisenberg's famous Uncertainty Principle (Appendix A).

That we do not consider solutions of the time-dependent Schrödinger equation should not be interpreted to mean that it is somehow of lesser importance than its time-independent counterpart, which is referred to herein rather limitedly as *the* Schrödinger equation. The time-independent Schrödinger equation can ultimately only inform us of the permitted energy levels corresponding to a potential—what are known as the "stationary states." Indeed, particles that are actually changing position in time can only be modeled with solutions of the time-dependent SE, and an example of constructing such a "moving wave packet" is treated briefly in Section 4.8. Beyond this, one of the main applications of quantum mechanics is in calculating transition rates between stationary states, and for this one must also invoke the full machinery of time-dependence. (The scope of the material presented here is restricted to time-independent solutions, as the intention is an introductory treatment; developing and interpreting such solutions proves to be an area rich enough to fill several chapters. Even then, we will only scratch the surface of known time-independent solutions.)

Now, in deriving the SE, use was made of the concept of a particle as a wave ($\lambda = h/p$). For the time-dependent part of the wave pattern, let us play a similar game. Here the relationship that comes to mind is Planck's energy-frequency relation for oscillators,

$$E = h\nu. \tag{1}$$

This, along with the definition of angular frequency $\omega = 2\pi\nu$, renders the prototype wave pattern as (in ψ notation)

$$\psi = A \sin\left[\frac{1}{\hbar}(px - Et)\right]. \tag{2}$$

Proceeding as previously, we note that a factor of E appears in the energy-conservation expression (Equation 2.2.1); to express this in a differential form, we need only take a single time-derivative of Equation (2):

$$\frac{\partial \psi}{\partial t} = -\frac{E}{\hbar} A \cos \left[\frac{1}{\hbar}(px - Et) \right]. \tag{3}$$

However, this leads to a problem: If our wave equation is to represent a physical law it should be independent of the form of any of its particular solutions. That is, it should involve ψ only, not any particular function for ψ. Because only a first derivative is necessary to extract a factor of E, we are left with a cosine function as opposed to a sine function. One way to rectify this is to recall that the sum of a squared sine and cosine of an argument is unity; that is,

$$A^2 \sin^2 \left[\frac{1}{\hbar}(px - Et) \right] + A^2 \cos^2 \left[\frac{1}{\hbar}(px - Et) \right] = A^2. \tag{4}$$

Recognizing the first term in this expression as ψ^2, and rearranging to isolate the cosine term gives

$$A \cos \left[\frac{1}{\hbar}(px - Et) \right] = \pm \sqrt{A^2 - \psi^2}, \tag{5}$$

where the sign ambiguity arises on taking the square root. Substituting this into Equation (3) and solving for the energy gives

$$E = \frac{\mp \hbar}{\sqrt{A^2 - \psi^2}} \left(\frac{\partial \psi}{\partial t} \right), \tag{6}$$

which, upon substitution into the right side of the time-independent SE, renders it as

$$-\frac{\hbar^2}{2m} \frac{\partial^2 \psi}{\partial x^2} + V(x,t)\psi = \frac{\mp \hbar \psi}{\sqrt{A^2 - \psi^2}} \left(\frac{\partial \psi}{\partial t} \right). \tag{7}$$

Serious objections attend this result. The first is that the amplitude of the wave should not appear in what is presumed to be a general physical law: Amplitude, like energy, is presumably to be dictated by the boundary conditions relevant to a given problem. Worse, because of the presence of the square root in the denominator of the right side, this differential equation is not linear: A sum of independent solutions would not itself be a solution. In addition, there is a sign ambiguity.

One might argue that the amplitude objection could be circumvented by taking a second time derivative of the prototype waveform, which would return us to a sine function; that is, to the original ψ. However, this would lead to an expression involving E^2, with the result that the consequent differential equation would still be nonlinear because E appears only to the first power in the energy-conservation expression, necessitating taking a square root of $\partial^2\psi/\partial t^2$. We are forced to conclude that no conventional prototype wave expression will lead to a sensible time-dependent wave equation.

Faced with this situation, Schrödinger hit on the idea of modifying the wave expression to the imaginary exponential form

$$\psi(x,t) = A\exp\left[\frac{\iota}{\hbar}(px - Et)\right], \tag{8}$$

where $\iota = \sqrt{-1}$. The beauty of this assumption is that it leaves the time-independent SE unchanged (that is, we still have Equation 2.2.5—try it!), but leads to a more plausible time-dependent form. In this case, we find

$$E = -\frac{\hbar}{\iota\psi}\left(\frac{\partial\psi}{\partial t}\right) = \frac{\iota\hbar}{\psi}\left(\frac{\partial\psi}{\partial t}\right), \tag{9}$$

where we have used the fact that $1/\iota = -\iota$. Upon substituting this result into the right side of the time-independent SE, we find

$$-\frac{\hbar^2}{2m}\frac{\partial^2\psi}{\partial x^2} + V(x)\psi = \iota\hbar\left(\frac{\partial\psi}{\partial t}\right). \tag{10}$$

Equation (10) is the time-dependent Schrödinger equation.

Despite our success in arriving at a linear time-dependent differential equation, one final problem remains: We have played fast and loose with the form of the wavefunction in such a way that it now represents *neither* a wave to the right nor to the left. Indeed, recalling Euler's identity for expressing a sine function in terms of exponentials,

$$\sin\theta = \frac{1}{2\iota}(e^{\iota\theta} - e^{-\iota\theta}), \tag{11}$$

we see that a right-traveling "matter-wave" should be written as

$$\psi(x, t) = A\sin\left[\frac{1}{\hbar}(px - Et)\right] = \frac{A}{2\iota}\left[e^{\iota/\hbar(px - Et)} - e^{-\iota/\hbar(px - Et)}\right]. \tag{12}$$

Curiously, a purely right- (or left-) moving wave leads to an unacceptable time-dependent wave equation. On the other hand, either of the individual exponential components of which such a wave is composed does lead to a sensible differential equation, albeit with a change of sign.

Clearly, we cannot have *both* a sensible-looking wave equation and a classical left- or right-moving wave: something has to give. And yet, if we are to speak of particle-waves, there presumably must be some concept of direction of travel. To resolve this impasse Schrödinger proposed adopting one of the exponential terms in Equation (12) as arbitrarily representing a right-directed (that is, $+x$ direction) matter-wave, and the other to represent a left-moving matter-wave. By historical convention these are taken to be the first and second terms, respectively:

$$\psi_{\text{right}}(x, t) = A\,e^{\iota/\hbar(px - Et)}, \tag{13}$$

and

$$\psi_{\text{left}}(x, t) = A\,e^{-\iota/\hbar(px - Et)}, \tag{14}$$

where the factor of $1/2\iota$ has been absorbed into the amplitude. Experiment has shown that one can consistently adopt these prescriptions.

Actually, the decision to adopt Equations (13) and (14) as representing right- and left-moving waves is not wholly arbitrary, and can in fact be given some justification via the following argument.

Consider Equation (10), the time-dependent Schrödinger equation. By comparing it to the time-*independent* Schrödinger equation (2.2.5), it should be clear that the solution can in general be written as

$$\Psi(x,t) = \psi(x)\,e^{-\iota\omega t}$$

where $\psi(x)$ represents the solution to the time-independent SE and where $\omega = E/\hbar$. Now consider a wavefunction whose spatial part is of the form of the supposed right-moving wave, $\psi(x) = Ae^{\iota kx}$. The complete solution is then

$$\Psi(x,t) = Ae^{\iota(kx - \omega t)} = A\left[\cos(kx - \omega t) + \iota\sin(kx - \omega t)\right]. \tag{15}$$

Panels (a) and (b) of Figure 2.2, respectively, illustrate the real (cosine) and imaginary (sine) parts of Ψ at $t = 0$, and panels (c) and (d) illustrate them at a slightly later time Δt, presumed to be much less than the period of the wave. At the later time the maximum of the cosine function in the real part of Ψ is not reached until $x = \omega t/k$; likewise for the zero of the sine function in the imaginary part. The pattern for Ψ

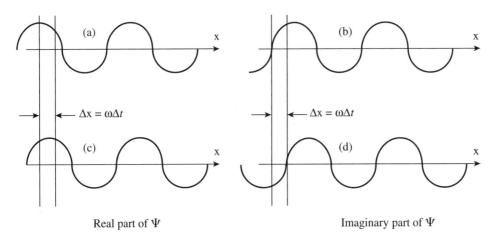

I FIGURE 2.2 Real and imaginary parts of $\Psi(x, t)$ at $t = 0$ and $t = \Delta t$.

behaves as if it has advanced slightly to the right between $t = 0$ and $t = \Delta t$. A similar construction for $\psi(x) = Ae^{-\iota kx}$ reveals a pattern whose "motion" is to the left.

Bear in mind that the preceding derivations are not rigorous. Although prototype waveforms and the de Broglie and Planck relations were used to set up the SE, we will find that its solutions will in general look nothing like simple sinusoidal or exponential functions.

■ 2.4 Interpretation of ψ: Probabilities and Boundary Conditions

For a wave on a string, the meaning of the wave pattern $y(x, t)$ is clear: it represents the vertical displacement of the string from its equilibrium position. How are we to interpret a quantum-mechanical wavefunction $\psi(x, y, z)$? Does an electron orbiting a nucleus actually "wave" in some way? Does it require some medium within which to do so? An interpretation of ψ in terms of probabilities was hinted at in Section 1.4. The precise recipe was postulated by German physicist Max Born in 1926 [3]. To state Born's result quantitatively requires an understanding of the concept of the complex conjugate of a quantity.

In general, the wavefunction $\psi(\mathbf{r})$ that satisfies the SE for some potential function $V(\mathbf{r})$ may be explicitly complex; that is, of the form $\psi = a + \iota b$, where a and b are real functions of (x, y, z). The complex conjugate of a function is formed by replacing ι by $-\iota$ wherever it appears and consequently designating the result with an asterisk: $\psi^* = a - \iota b$. The product of a function and its complex conjugate is always a purely real number:

$$\psi^*\psi = (a + \iota b)\,(a - \iota b) = a^2 + \iota ab - \iota ab - \iota^2 b^2 = a^2 + b^2,$$

because $\iota^2 = -1$. Thus, if ψ is complex (hence unphysical), we can construct a real quantity from it by computing $\psi^*\psi$. For brevity, $\psi^*\psi$ is often abbreviated as $|\psi|^2$, or simply ψ^2.

Born's interpretation of ψ can now be stated: The probability of finding the particle in a small volume of space $d\tau$ located at position r is given by $\psi^*(r)\psi(r)d\tau$. (The $d\tau$ notation is often used to designate an element of volume as opposed to the more common dV in order to avoid confusion with the potential function V.) This interpretation means that at any given time we cannot say exactly where the particle is; we are restricted to specifying only that at some time the probability of finding the particle between x and $x + dx$, y and $y + dy$, z and $z + dz$ is given by $\Psi^*(x, y, z, t)\ \Psi(x, y, z, t)\ dx\ dy\ dz$.[2]

This probabilistic interpretation of ψ is sometimes popularly misconstrued to imply that a particle can be in two or more places simultaneously. This is not so; particles are not assumed to lose their identity as (essentially) point objects. To make a macroscopic-scale analogy, suppose that a friend says, "There is a ten percent probability that I will be at home this afternoon, a sixty percent probability that I will be at school, and a thirty percent probability that I will be at work." This does not mean that your friend will be at all three places simultaneously, but rather that he or she is more likely to be at school than at home or at work.[3] Until you do some experiments to find out where your friend actually is at some time, your knowledge is limited to these probabilities.

A probabilistic interpretation of ψ implies a clear break with the sort of quantities one is familiar with computing in classical mechanics. Physicist and historian of science Abraham Pais has remarked that the concept of probability as an inherent feature of fundamental physical law may be the most dramatic scientific change of the twentieth century. Instead of being able to specify explicit recipes for the position and velocity of a particle, we can only predict the probability of finding the particle in some region of space or of its having momentum within certain limits. This probability will be greater in some places and less, perhaps even zero, in others. ψ itself has no physical reality; it is simply a mathematical construct used to keep account of

---

[2]Born is credited with coining the term "quantum mechanics"; see *Physics Today* 2001; 54(4):94 and 2001; 54(5):90.

[3]For a very readable treatment on other common quantum misconceptions, see "Common misconceptions regarding quantum mechanics," by Styer DF, *American Journal of Physics* 1996; 64:31.

probabilities. Particles are not actually "undulating" in space; the apparent "waviness" of matter is a consequence of its *probability distribution*.

Quantitatively, Born's interpretation can be expressed as

$$P(\boldsymbol{r})\,dV = \psi^*(\boldsymbol{r})\,\psi(\boldsymbol{r})\,dV. \tag{1}$$

Probabilities are dimensionless pure numbers. Inasmuch as an element of volume has units of (length)^3, $\psi^*\psi$ must have units of (length)$^{-3}$ to render dV dimensionless. Thus, $\psi^*\psi$ is known as a *probability density*; literally, this is the probability per cubic meter of space of finding the particle at a certain position (x, y, z). The position at which the particle has the greatest probability of being found (that which maximizes $\psi^*\psi$) is known as the most probable position, $\boldsymbol{r}_{\mathrm{mp}}$.

There is an important corollary to Born's interpretation. If one adds up the probabilities of finding a particle over the entire space it could possibly occupy, the total must be unity. That is, the probabilities must add up to a "whole particle." Mathematically, we express this as

$$\int \psi^*\psi\,dV = 1, \tag{2}$$

where, in practice, the limits of integration correspond to the limits of space to which the particle is restricted. Because this is an integral over volume, it is in general a triple integral. Any wavefunction for which this calculation can be performed is said to be **square-integrable**. In practice, this constraint represents a condition imposed on ψ that serves to pin down constants of integration that arise when solving the SE for a given potential function $V(\boldsymbol{r})$. Once those constants have been determined, a wavefunction is said to be **normalized**.

Schrödinger's equation is a second-order differential equation. Its solution for any particular $V(\boldsymbol{r})$ will in general lead to two constants of integration whose values become specified upon supplying boundary conditions. Boundary conditions are physical constraints applied to general mathematical solutions of differential equations; they are the means by which we specify the particular problem being solved. In general, one needs to supply as many boundary conditions as there are constants of integration: in our case, two. This is analogous to supplying the initial position and velocity of a particle in a Newton's law problem. In quantum-mechanical problems, however, these boundary conditions can be expressed very generally and independent of any particular example. Although the description of them that follows will make more sense in the context of solutions to the SE presented in subsequent chapters, this discussion appears here in order to tie them in with Schrödinger's equation.

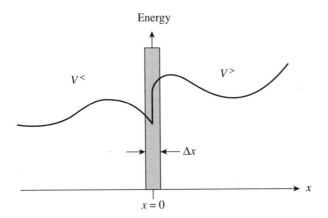

I FIGURE 2.3 Potential function with a discontinuity at $x = 0$.

Many quantum-mechanical problems involve different regions of space, each of which is described by its own potential function $V(r)$. In such cases, the SE is set up and solved independently for each region. These solutions may be *very* difficult to obtain, but this does not detract from the generality of the following argument. The boundary conditions can then be thought of as recipes for "patching together" the resulting wavefunctions at the boundaries where the different regions of space meet. We can discern the nature of these conditions by considering a general boundary between two one-dimensional regions, as shown in Figure 2.3. For simplicity, we can imagine the boundary to be at $x = 0$: functions referring to $x < 0$ are designated with superscript $<$, and those referring to $x > 0$ with superscript $>$. Thus, the potential function and wavefunction for $x < 0$ are designated $\{V^<(x), \psi^<(x)\}$, and those for $x > 0$ are designated $\{V^>(x), \psi^>(x)\}$. In general, there may or may not be a discontinuity in $V(x)$ at the boundary; one is shown in the figure for sake of generality. In reality, discontinuous potentials cannot exist (why?), but they can often be a very handy approximation for simplifying the description of a real potential. Because a particle must have a unique energy, the two solutions to the SE must refer to the same energy (we consider only time-independent wavefunctions and potentials here):

$$-\frac{\hbar^2}{2m}\frac{d^2\psi^<}{dx^2} + V^<(x)\psi^< = E\psi^< \tag{3}$$

and

$$-\frac{\hbar^2}{2m}\frac{d^2\psi^>}{dx^2} + V^>(x)\psi^> = E\psi^>. \tag{4}$$

The first general boundary condition is that the probabilistic interpretation of ψ can make sense only if each position in space has a unique probability associated with it. Thus, $\psi(x, y, z)$ **must be a continuous function**. In practice, this means forcing the two solutions to agree at the boundary; that is,

$$\psi^<(\text{boundary}) = \psi^>(\text{boundary}). \tag{5}$$

The second condition is somewhat more involved. What follows will not be a fully mathematically rigorous derivation, but rather one based on physical grounds.

We can rearrange the Schrödinger equation to read

$$\frac{d^2\psi}{dx^2} = -\left(\frac{2m}{\hbar^2}\right)[E - V(x)]\,\psi(x).$$

Now, imagine integrating this expression across the boundary:

$$\int_<^> \left(\frac{d^2\psi}{dx^2}\right)dx = -\left(\frac{2mE}{\hbar^2}\right)\int_<^> \psi(x)\,dx + \left(\frac{2m}{\hbar^2}\right)\int_<^> V(x)\psi(x)\,dx, \tag{6}$$

where the limits of integration are to represent points within the $\{<, >\}$ domains. In general, the integral of the second derivative of ψ will be its first derivative. Suppose that the limits of integration straddle the boundary with a narrow extent Δx as shown in the diagram; that is, we are integrating from $x = -\Delta x/2$ to $x = +\Delta x/2$ and will eventually let $\Delta x \to 0$. Because ψ must be continuous across the boundary [that is, $\psi^<(x) \to \psi^>(x) \to \psi_{x=0}$ as $x \to 0$], we have

$$\left(\frac{d\psi^>}{dx}\right)_{\substack{+\Delta x/2 \\ \Delta x \to 0}} - \left(\frac{d\psi^<}{dx}\right)_{\substack{-\Delta x/2 \\ \Delta x \to 0}} = -\left(\frac{2mE}{\hbar^2}\right)(\psi_{x=0}\Delta x)$$

$$+ \left(\frac{2m}{\hbar^2}\right)[V^>(0) - V^<(0)]\left(\psi_{x=0}\frac{\Delta x}{2}\right). \tag{7}$$

Now, as $\Delta x \to 0$, the first term on the right side of Equation (7) will always vanish if E and $\psi_{x=0}$ remain finite. For the second term, two circumstances are possible: If the potential is continuous or at worst finitely discontinuous across the boundary (that is, if $V^>(0)$ and $V^<(0)$ are equal or at most differ by a finite amount), then the second term will vanish as $\Delta x \to 0$. On the other hand, if the potential is infinitely discontinuous (that is, if $V^>(0)$ and $V^<(0)$ differ by an infinite amount), then the second term will be of the indeterminate form infinity times zero, in which case we can make no conclusion regarding the continuity (or not) of $d\psi/dx$. (Full disclosure: This statement is not true in a very pathological case involving a mathematical model for the potential known as a delta-function, but we will not encounter such a function in this book.) It is crucial to appreciate that it is *differences* in potentials that are important, not their absolute magnitudes: forces are given by $F = -dV/dx$ and are unaffected if the potential is changed by an additive constant.

To repeat: If $V(x)$ is continuous or finitely discontinuous across a boundary, then the first derivative of ψ must be made continuous across the boundary. If, however, $V(x)$ is infinitely discontinuous across the boundary, then no statement can be made regarding the continuity of $d\psi/dx$ across the boundary. Potential discontinuities cannot exist in reality as they would imply infinite forces, but such discontinuities are often assumed in model problems to simplify the analysis.

In summary, the three conditions that must be imposed on solutions of Schrödinger's equation are:

1. ψ must be square integrable: $\displaystyle\int \psi^* \psi \, dV = 1$.

2. ψ must be continuous everywhere.

3. $d\psi/dx$ must be made continuous across a finite potential discontinuity, but cannot be specified across an infinite potential discontinuity.

All of these conditions will be used in examples studied in Chapter 3.

In closing this chapter, a few quasiphilosophical remarks are appropriate. Schrödinger's equation is not in itself terribly imposing: classical physics is full of linear, second-order partial differential equations. It is the interpretation of the solutions and the constraints imposed upon them that are unlike anything that is familiar from Newtonian mechanics. The previously solid, deterministic Universe dissolves into fuzzy, intangible clouds of probability where there is no *yes* or *no*, but only *might be*. In the end, though, experiment arbitrates the correctness of physical theories, and we shall see that application of Schrödinger's equation to systems such as the hydrogen atom yields predictions entirely consistent with experiment.

EXAMPLE 2.3

Presume that the wavefunction $\psi(x) = Ae^{-kx}$ applies over the domain $0 \leq x \leq \infty$ (assume that $\psi = 0$ outside this domain). What must be the value of A in terms of k if this function is to be properly normalized? What is the probability of finding the particle between $x = 0$ and $x = 1/k$?

We must have $\int \psi^2 dx = 1$. In the present case this demands

$A^2 \int_0^\infty e^{-2kx} dx = 1$. Because $\int e^{-ax} dx = -\dfrac{1}{a} e^{-ax}$ (see Appendix C), we

have $(a = 2k)$

$$A^2 \int_0^\infty e^{-2kx} dx = 1 \Rightarrow A^2 \left[-\frac{1}{2k} e^{-2kx} \right]_0^\infty = 1,$$

or

$$A^2 \left[0 - \left(-\frac{1}{2k} \right) \right] = 1,$$

That is, $A = \sqrt{2k}$.

The probability of finding the particle between $x = 0$ and $x = 1/k$ is given by the integral of ψ^2 over these limits:

$$P(0, 1/k) = \int_0^{1/k} \psi^2 dx = A^2 \int_0^{1/k} e^{-2kx} dx$$

$$= 2(k) \left[-\frac{1}{2k} e^{-2kx} \right]_0^{1/k} = 1 - e^{-2} \sim 0.865.$$

The chance that the particle will be found between these limits is about 86.5%.

■ Summary

Inasmuch as no derivation-from-first-principles of the Schrödinger wave equation exists, there are almost an infinite number of ways of concocting it; the development given in this chapter is a common one.

The central relationship in quantum physics is Schrödinger's equation, which in one dimension appears as

$$-\frac{\hbar^2}{2m}\frac{d^2\psi}{dx^2} + V(x)\psi = E\psi.$$

This linear, second-order differential equation is to quantum mechanics what $F = ma$ is to Newtonian mechanics. In general, one solves this equation for the wavefunctions $\psi(x)$ and energy eigenvalues E for a system of mass m in an environment where the potential energy is given by $V(x)$; one need also apply the boundary conditions that follow. In itself, ψ has no physical meaning, but $\psi^*\psi\, dV$ is the probability of finding the system in a volume of space dV. More than anything else, it is this probability interpretation of quantum mechanics that implies a clear break with the sort of directly tangible quantities one is used to in Newtonian physics.

The boundary conditions that must be imposed on solutions of Schrödinger's equation are:

1. ψ must be square integrable.

2. ψ must be continuous everywhere.

3. $d\psi/dx$ must be made continuous across a finite potential discontinuity, but cannot be specified across an infinite potential discontinuity.

■ Problems

2-1(E) Verify that if one has a number of independent solutions y_1, y_2, ..., y_n of the classical wave equation (all of pattern speed v), then a linear sum of them (Equation 2.1.10) is also a solution.

2-2(E) Following Example 2.1, show that the wave pattern $y = Tanh^{-1}[(x - vt)^{-4/3}]$ satisfies the classical wave equation. $Tanh^{-1}(u)$ designates the inverse hyperbolic tangent of argument u. Derivatives of this function with respect to any variable q are given by

$$\frac{d}{dq}\{Tanh^{-1}[u(q)]\} = \left(\frac{1}{1 - u^2}\right)\frac{du}{dq}.$$

2-3(I) Schrödinger's equation is not the only possible differential wave equation consistent with the law of conservation of energy and the prototype waveform (2.2.3). Derive one other.

2-4(I) Suppose that the solution to Schrödinger's equation for some potential gives rise to three wavefunctions, $\psi_1(x)$, $\psi_2(x)$, and $\psi_3(x)$ of the forms and domains

$$\begin{cases} \psi_1(x) = Ae^{kx} & (-\infty \le x \le 0) \\ \psi_2(x) = Bx^2 + Cx + D & (0 \le x \le L) \\ \psi_3(x) = 0 & (x \ge L). \end{cases}$$

What values must B, C, and D take in terms of A in order that these solutions satisfy the continuity conditions discussed in Section 2.4? In Chapter 3 we will see that a solution of the form $\psi_3(x) = 0$ requires the presence of an infinitely discontinuous potential at $x = L$; consequently, you do not need to apply the continuity condition on $d\psi/dx$ there. Derive also an expression that A, B, C, D, k, and L must satisfy in order that the overall $(-\infty \le x \le +\infty)$ solution be normalized.

2-5(E) Given the wavefunction $\psi(x) = Axe^{-kx}$ $(0 \le x \le \infty; k > 0)$, what value must A take in terms of k in order that ψ be normalized? See Appendix C for the relevant integral.

2-6(E) Suppose that the wavefunction in Problem 2-5 is known to be a solution of Schrödinger's equation for some energy E. What is the corresponding potential function $V(x)$?

2-7(E) The wavefunction $\psi(x) = Ae^{-kx^2}$ $(-\infty \le x \le +\infty; k > 0)$ is known to be a solution of Schrödinger's equation for some energy E. What is the corresponding potential function $V(x)$? We will explore a potential like this in Chapter 5.

3 Solutions of Schrödinger's Equation in One Dimension

The purpose of this chapter is to investigate solutions of Schrödinger's equation for a variety of one-dimensional potential functions. Although such potentials have applications in areas such as modeling of real electronic devices such as CCD chips (Example 3.3) and understanding phenomena such as alpha-decay (Section 3.9), our reason for starting with them as opposed to two- or three-dimensional problems is that they exhibit many uniquely quantum effects with a minimum of mathematical complexity. Solving them will build a foundation for more involved problems in subsequent chapters.

This is a lengthy chapter, so an overview is given here to help orient the reader. Part I of this chapter, comprising Sections 3.1–3.6, is devoted to examining *potential wells*. Loosely defined, this means situations where a particle is trapped in some region of space by force barriers that, classically, it does not possess sufficient energy to "leap over" and escape from. Such situations lead to discrete bound-energy states analogous to those appearing in the Bohr model. We will begin our study of potential wells in Section 3.1 by reviewing certain characteristics of classical potential-energy functions that make for valuable points of contact with quantum-mechanical problems. In Section 3.2 we will actually solve the SE for the first time, for the case of a potential known as an infinite well. The solution of this highly idealized case illustrates how discrete wavefunctions and energies emerge upon application of the boundary conditions derived in Chapter 2. In Sections 3.3–3.5 we will consider a similar potential, the finite well. This case will help us to understand the phenomenon of *quantum tunneling*. Although this phenomenon has a classical analog for *massless* systems (penetration of electromagnetic waves through nonconducting media), we will see that, wave-mechanically, tunneling can happen as well for particles with mass. Section 3.6 discusses how the information gleaned from the infinite and finite-well solutions can be used to create guidelines for sketching approximate wavefunctions for *any* potential function. Part II, comprising Sections 3.7–3.10, is devoted to an analysis of *potential barriers*. Again speaking loosely, we can regard a potential barrier as a potential well that has been turned inside-out: instead of being trapped within a well, an "incoming" particle encounters a barrier from the outside, which it has some probability of penetrating through. Much of the mathematics involved in studying wells and barriers is similar, but the motivations and results are different; this is why these concepts are brought under the roof of one chapter but are housed, as it were, in separate but adjacent (and communicating) apartments. Potential barriers are of interest, for example, to nuclear physicists who probe the structure and energy levels of nuclei by scattering accelerated subatomic particles from them. Results built up in Sections 3.7 and 3.8 are applied in Section 3.9 to the phenomenon of *alpha decay*, a quantum tunneling effect whose explanation was one of the first great successes of quantum mechanics. Section 3.10 briefly discusses some further aspects of scattering experiments; it could have been included with potential wells in Part I, but as the emphasis is on scattering (a concept first studied in detail in Section 3.7) we put it with Part II. Problems for all sections appear at the end of the chapter.

Part I: Potential Wells

■ 3.1 Concept of a Potential Well

In Newtonian mechanics the "object of the exercise" is often to establish expressions giving the position r and velocity v of a body of mass m as a function of time. To do this one supplies the initial position and velocity and a description of the forces to which the mass is subject. The forces can be expressed either directly or in the form of a **potential energy function** $V(r)$; the force on the body is given by the negative gradient of V, $F = -\nabla V$, and the motion follows from Newton's second law: $F = ma$. In problems where quantum physics is applicable, the environment also enters through $V(r)$, but one solves for the wavefunctions and corresponding energy eigenvalues that satisfy Schrödinger's equation.

Two constructs that we shall use extensively are **energy-level diagrams** and **potential wells**. To introduce these concepts it is helpful to consider a simple Newtonian example. Consider a car of mass m on a roller coaster track as shown in Figure 3.1.

If the car starts from height h above the ground, its potential energy is given by $V = mgh$. If the height of the track as a function of position is given by $h(x)$, then we can write $V(x) = mgh(x)$. $V(x)$ and $h(x)$ are equivalent but for a factor of mg; the curve in Figure 3.1 can be regarded either as a sideways view of the track or, more abstractly, as a plot of the potential energy of the car as a function of position. We could label the vertical axis interchangeably as "height in meters" or as "energy in Joules." If the car is released from rest at position x_0 as shown, its total energy would be $E = mgh(x_0)$. In the energy/position version of Figure 3.1, this value defines a horizontal line as shown. In the absence of any friction or air resistance, E will remain constant at this

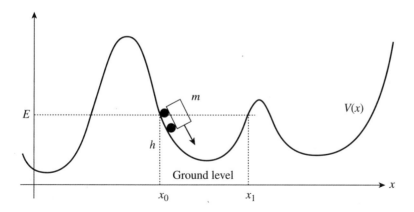

I FIGURE 3.1   Car on a roller-coaster track.

level, which defines a "valley" or "well" between x_0 and x_1. When the car is released it will accelerate, reach a maximum speed at the bottom of the valley, and then climb up the other side until it comes to rest momentarily at the same vertical height or *energy level* from which it was released. Destined to roll back and forth between x_0 and x_1, the car is constrained within a so-called **potential well** and is said to be in a **bound energy state**. Technically, a bound state is one whose total energy is less than $V(x)$ as $x \rightarrow \infty$. Points x_0 and x_1 are known as "classical turning points," positions at which the particle stops momentarily and reverses its direction of motion. If the car were released from x_0 with some nonzero speed, the total energy line would **not** cut the curve at x_0 because of the contribution of the initial kinetic energy: $E = mv_0^2/2 + mgh(x_0)$. In this event it would find itself in a new bound state, as illustrated in Figure 3.2.

Another possibility is that if the track to the right of the release point is always lower than the vertical level of the release point, the car will eventually arrive at $x = +\infty$. Figure 3.3 illustrates such an **unbound** energy state.

The preceding comments possess broad applicability. Figures 3.1–3.3 illustrate what are known as **potential diagrams**. In these figures the x-axis always corresponds to a position coordinate and the y-axis to energy; in general, the vertical axes in these diagrams will *not* be equivalent to a vertical height. The potential energy function for the system is typically plotted as a solid line in such diagrams.

Classically, the total energy of a system is in principle unrestricted; E does not appear explicitly in Newton's second law. Quantum-mechanically, it does enter Schrödinger's equation explicitly and solutions to that equation for a given potential

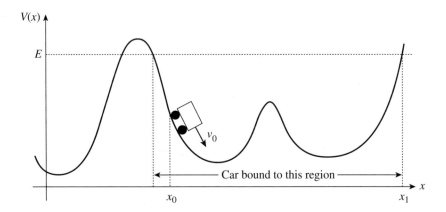

▌ FIGURE 3.2   Car in a bound energy state.

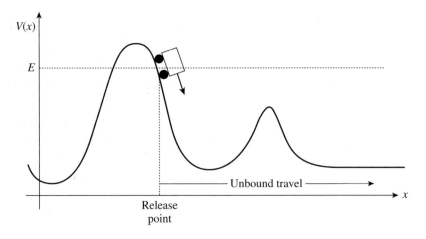

▌ FIGURE 3.3   Car in an unbound energy state.

will involve E directly as a parameter. With these general ideas in mind, let us now set up and solve the SE for some simple one-dimensional potentials.

■ 3.2 The Infinite Potential Well

The simplest quantum environment imaginable for a particle is one in which it is trapped between walls so energetically high that it would require an infinite amount of energy to leap over them. The potential diagram for such a situation is shown in Figure 3.4: a particle of mass m moves in an infinitely deep potential well between

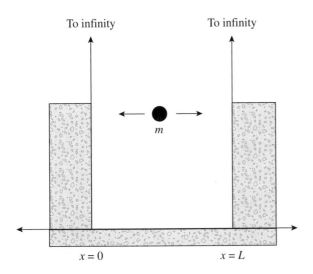

To infinity   To infinity

$x = 0$ $x = L$

| FIGURE 3.4 Infinite square well.

$x = 0$ and $x = L$. Such a construct is known variously as an **infinite potential well**, **infinite rectangular well**, or **infinite square well**.

In Figure 3.4 and subsequent similar diagrams, shading designates potential "walls." Analytically, the infinite potential well is defined by

$$V(x) = \begin{cases} 0, & 0 \le x \le L \\ \infty, & x < 0, x > L. \end{cases} \tag{1}$$

The walls need not (and in general will not) be physical barriers; Figure 3.5 shows how one might construct an electronic potential well by trapping an electron between strong electric fields in an evacuated chamber.[1]

In reality, the electric fields cannot be made infinitely strong, but the idea should be clear: As soon as the electron tries to penetrate to the left of $x = 0$ or to the right of $x = L$, it will experience a strong opposing force that turns it back. We refer to the regions defined by $x < 0$ and $x > L$ as being "outside" the well and that defined by $0 \le x \le L$ as being "inside." We seek bound-state solutions with $E > 0$.

In the outside regions, the SE takes the form

$$-\frac{\hbar^2}{2m}\frac{d^2\psi}{dx^2} + (\infty)\psi = E\psi, \quad (x < 0, x > L). \tag{2}$$

---

[1]Figure 3.5 adapted from *An Introduction to Quantum Physics* by A. P. French and Edwin F. Taylor. Copyright © 1978 by the Massachusetts Institute of Technology. Used by permission of W. W. Norton & Company, Inc.

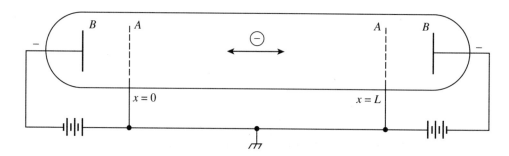

FIGURE 3.5 Schematic diagram of an electron trapped in a one-dimensional "box" made of electrodes and grids in an evacuated tube. From *An Introduction to Quantum Physics* by A. P. French and Edwin F. Taylor. Copyright © 1978 by the Massachusetts Institute of Technology. Used by permission of W. W. Norton & Company, Inc.

This equation can only be satisfied if $\psi = 0$ everywhere outside the well. This is so because E must presumably be finite.

Inside the well the story is different. Here $V(x) = 0$, and

$$-\frac{\hbar^2}{2m}\frac{d^2\psi}{dx^2} = E\psi, \quad (0 \le x \le L). \tag{3}$$

Rearrange this equation to read

$$\frac{d^2\psi}{dx^2} = -k^2\psi, \tag{4}$$

where

$$k^2 = \frac{2mE}{\hbar^2}. \tag{5}$$

In general, the solution of Equation (4) is a sum of exponential functions with imaginary arguments:

$$\psi(x) = Ae^{\iota kx} + Be^{-\iota kx}, \tag{6}$$

where $\iota = \sqrt{-1}$ and where A and B are constants of integration.

We saw in Chapter 2 that three boundary conditions must be applied to solutions of Schrödinger's equation:

1. they must be normalizable by being square-integrable.

2. ψ must be continuous everywhere.

3. $d\psi/dx$ must be made continuous across potential discontinuities unless the discontinuity is infinite.

It is generally easiest to consider the latter two conditions first. In the present case, condition (3) cannot be used because we do in fact have infinite potential discontinuities. Condition (2) demands

$$\psi(x) = 0 \text{ at } x = 0 \tag{7}$$

and

$$\psi(x) = 0 \text{ at } x = L. \tag{8}$$

On substituting $x = 0$ into Equation (6) we find that it reduces to $A + B = 0$ or $B = -A$. Thus the general solution can be cast as

$$\psi(x) = A(e^{\iota kx} - e^{-\iota kx}) = (2\iota A)\sin(kx). \tag{9}$$

At $x = L$, we must then have

$$(2\iota A)\sin(kL) = 0. \tag{10}$$

There are two possibilities: either $A = 0$ or $\sin(kL) = 0$. If $A = 0$, the wavefunction vanishes entirely, an unphysical solution because we cannot normalize it. The second possibility is much more interesting: $\sin(kL)$ will vanish if (and only if) $kL = n\pi$, where n is an integer. This restricts k to values such that $k = n\pi/L$; from Equation (5) this sets a restriction on the permissible values for the total energy of the particle:

$$E_n = \left(\frac{\pi^2 \hbar^2}{2mL^2}\right)n^2. \tag{11}$$

Strictly, n can be any nonzero integer and is known as the **principal quantum number** of the system. Because E is proportional to n^2, however, negative integers give rise to no different **energy eigenvalues** than do their positive counterparts; for practical purposes we can restrict ourselves to $n = 1, 2, 3, \dots$. The **ground-state** energy corresponds to $n = 1$. (Note that $n = 0$ leads to a null solution. In this case $E = k = 0$, and Equation (4) would imply $\psi = ax + b$. This solution can only be made to satisfy the boundary conditions if the constants a and b are set to zero.)

The important concept here is that *application of the quantum-mechanical boundary conditions has led to quantized energy levels. This is characteristic of all bound-state solutions to the SE.* It is customary to label the value of the energy corresponding to its quantum number n as we have done in Equation (11). To each energy E_n corresponds a wavefunction ψ_n:

$$\psi_n(x) = (2\iota A)\sin\left(\frac{n\pi}{L}x\right), \tag{12}$$

where we have replaced k in Equation (9) with $n\pi/L$. Note that negative quantum numbers give rise to different wavefunctions than their positive counterparts: $\psi_n(x) = -\psi_{-n}(x)$. A given energy eigenvalue can therefore refer to two possible wavefunctions; such a system is said to be **doubly degenerate**. In this case, however, this feature has no observable consequence as only $\psi * \psi$ has any connection to physical reality, and $\psi_n^2(x) = +\psi_{-n}^2(x)$. This degeneracy is really mathematical as opposed to physical. In Chapters 6 and 7 we will explore potentials that give rise to true physical degeneracy.

What of the constant of integration A? There is one constraint we have not yet imposed: that ψ *must be normalized*; that is, the probability distribution of the particle, when integrated over the well, must be unity. Thus, for every possible value of n,

$$\int_0^L \psi_n^*(x)\psi_n(x)\,dx = 1. \tag{13}$$

In the present case, $\psi_n^*(x)\psi_n(x) = 4A^2\sin^2(kx)$, so the normalization condition proceeds as

$$\int_0^L \psi_n^*(x)\psi_n(x)\,dx = 4A^2\int_0^L \sin^2\left(\frac{n\pi}{L}x\right)dx$$

$$= 4A^2\left[\frac{x}{2} - \frac{\sin(2n\pi x/L)}{4(n\pi/L)}\right]_0^L = A^2\left\{\left[\frac{L}{2} - \frac{\sin(2n\pi)}{4(n\pi/L)}\right] - \left[0 - \frac{\sin(0)}{4(n\pi/L)}\right]\right\}$$

$$= 4A^2\left(\frac{L}{2}\right) = 2A^2L.$$

Forcing this result to be equal to unity gives

$$A = \sqrt{\frac{1}{2L}}. \tag{14}$$

Combining Equations (12) and (14) gives the normalized infinite rectangular well wavefunctions:

$$\psi_n(x) = \iota\sqrt{\frac{2}{L}}\sin\left(\frac{n\pi}{L}x\right), \quad (0 \le x \le L), \quad n = 1, 2, 3, \ldots. \tag{15}$$

Note that A depends only on the length of the well, and not on the quantum state n. This will prove to be an exception rather than the rule. The energy levels generally depend on the quantum state involved, the mass of the particle, the width of the well, and Planck's constant.

Because only $\psi_n^*(x)\psi_n(x)$ has physical meaning, we will usually drop the factor of ι when discussing infinite well wavefunctions and treat them as purely real.

It is worthwhile reiterating two key lessons from this solution to the SE:

1. **Quantized energy levels** (also known as **energy eigenvalues**) arise naturally from the imposition of **boundary conditions** on solutions of the SE, and lead to **quantum numbers** that can be used to label the energy eigenvalues. Compare the natural way that energy quantization emerges from Schrödinger's equation as opposed to its ad-hoc introduction by Bohr in his model of the hydrogen atom.

2. To each energy eigenvalue corresponds a **wavefunction** (or **eigenfunction**) $\psi_n(x)$ that dictates the **probability distribution** of the system when it possesses total energy E_n.

Figure 3.6 shows sketches of $|\psi_n|$ and $|\psi_n|^2$ for the three lowest-energy infinite rectangular well wavefunctions. The $n = 1$ state is known as the **ground state** or

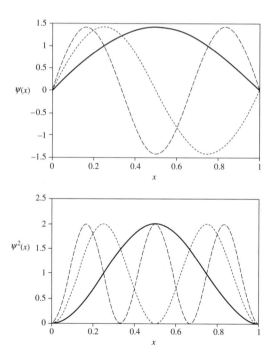

FIGURE 3.6 Top: Infinite-well wavefunctions $\psi(x)=\sqrt{2/L}\sin(n\pi x/L)$ for $L = 1$ for $n = 1$ (solid curve), $n = 2$ (short-dashed curve) and $n = 3$ (long-dashed curve). Bottom: As top figure but showing $\psi^2(x)$.

normal state of the system. In the plots of $|\psi_n|^2$, the peaks correspond to positions where there is a high probability of finding the particle. The valleys correspond to positions of low probability. The number of extrema in the wavefunction is equal to n. There are a number of positions—so-called **nodes**—where $\psi = 0$; that is, where we would *never* expect to find the particle. Including the boundaries of the well, the number of nodes in state n is $n + 1$.

The wavefunctions sketched in Figure 3.6 are reminiscent of standing waves on a string. In fact, the problems are mathematically identical in that an integral number of half-wavelengths fit between the boundaries in each case. For the string this results in a constraint on the possible vibrational frequencies; for a particle in the infinite well this translates to a constraint on possible energies via the de Broglie relation.

If we accept the probability-distribution interpretation of quantum mechanics, why, then, do we not detect a wavy nature for matter in everyday life? The answer lies in the differing orders of magnitude of the quantum numbers involved in atomic-scale and macroscopic-scale phenomena. To illustrate this we consider two cases. Case A is the quantum case: an electron of energy 20 eV ($= 3.20 \times 10^{-18}$ J) trapped in an atomic-scale potential well of width $L = 1$ Å ($= 10^{-10}$ m). Case B is a mass of 1 kilogram and energy 1 Joule trapped in a potential well of width 1 meter. Then

$$n_A = \sqrt{\frac{8 m_A L_A^2 E_A}{h^2}} = \sqrt{\frac{8(9.11 \times 10^{-31}\,\text{kg})(10^{-10}\text{m})^2(3.20 \times 10^{-18}\text{J})}{(6.626 \times 10^{-34}\text{J sec})^2}} = 0.73$$

and

$$n_B = \sqrt{\frac{8 m_B L_B^2 E_B}{h^2}} = \sqrt{\frac{8(1\,\text{kg})(1\,\text{m})^2(1\,\text{J})}{(6.626 \times 10^{-34}\text{J sec})^2}} = 4.3 \times 10^{33}.$$

The n's should of course work out to be integers; the fact that n_A did not means that mutually incompatible values of m, L, and E were chosen. But the important point is that in the atomic-scale problem ψ would have on the order of only one maximum over the length-scale of the problem, whereas in the macroscopic case there would be some 10^{33} maxima in the space of one meter. The distance between probability maxima in the latter case would be about 10^{-33} meters, some 20 orders of magnitude smaller than a nucleus, and hence unresolvable from each other. This means that for practical purposes, the 1 kg mass can be located anywhere in the 1-meter box with almost unlimited precision. On a macroscopic scale we do not notice the "bumpiness" of the probability distribution.

Pursuing this example further, consider the spacing between energy levels as a function of energy. From Equation (11),

$$\frac{dE_n}{dn} = 2\left(\frac{\pi^2 \hbar^2}{2mL^2}\right)n = \frac{2E_n}{n}.$$

From this result we find that the spacing between the first and second levels in the macroscopic and atomic cases are, respectively, about 3×10^{-15} eV and 54.8 eV. In macroscopic phenomena the spacing between energy levels is always much less than the typical system energy and impossibly small to detect: energy will appear to be a continuous quantity, as it is in Newtonian mechanics. In atomic-scale phenomena the spacing can be on the same order as the system energy.

EXAMPLE 3.1

Determine the probability of finding a particle of mass m between $x = 0$ and $x = L/10$ if it is in the $n = 3$ state of an infinite rectangular well.

We know that the probability of finding the particle in an infinitesimal region of space dx at position x is given by Equation (2.4.1), $(\psi^*\psi)dx$. The answer to this question is then given by integrating this probability over the desired range:

$$P(0, L/10) = \int_0^{L/10} \psi_3^*(x)\psi_3(x)dx = \frac{2}{L}\int_0^{L/10} \sin^2\left(\frac{3\pi}{L}x\right)dx$$

$$= \frac{2}{L}\left[\frac{x}{2} - \frac{\sin(6\pi x/L)}{(12\pi/L)}\right]_0^{L/10} = \frac{2}{L}\left[\frac{L}{20} - \frac{\sin(3\pi/5)}{(12\pi/L)}\right] = 0.0496,$$

or about 5%.

It is important to remember that *probabilities have meaning only in a statistical sense*. In practice, you would have to measure the positions of particles in a number of identically prepared infinite wells and then somehow determine what fraction of them were found between $x = 0$ and $x = L/10$.

In questions of the type of Example 3.1 a shortcut can often be used. We began from the fact that the probability of finding the particle between x and $x + dx$ when dx is infinitesimally small is given by

$$P(x, x + dx) = \psi_n^*(x)\psi_n(x)dx. \tag{16}$$

To compute the probability of finding the particle within some *finite* range Δx it was necessary to integrate. However, if the desired range is small in comparison to the length scale over which ψ changes appreciably, one can assume that ψ remains approximately constant over Δx and write

$$P(x, x + \Delta x) \sim \psi_n^*(x)\psi_n(x)\Delta x.$$

For the present example, we have $\Delta x = L/10$. Evaluating ψ at the midpoint of the range, $x = L/20$, gives

$$P(0, L/10) \sim \frac{2}{L}\sin^2\left(\frac{3\pi}{20}\right)\left(\frac{L}{10}\right) \sim 0.041,$$

which compares favorably with the exact result obtained by integration.

■ 3.3 The Finite Potential Well

We now consider a particle of mass m trapped in a potential well of **finite** depth. This is a somewhat more realistic problem than that of the infinite well, corresponding, for example, to an electron trapped near the surface of a metal in a photoelectric-effect experiment and needing only a few electron-volts of energy to escape. The situation is illustrated in Figure 3.7. This situation is commonly referred to as the finite rectangular well or finite square well.

We take the well to have a depth of V_0 Joules and width $2L$, symmetric about $x = 0$. (This arrangement is different from that used in the infinite well, but ultimately makes the mathematics easier.) The well is described by

$$V(x) = \begin{cases} 0 & (-L \le x \le L) \\ V_0 & (|x| > L). \end{cases} \tag{1}$$

We again divide space into inside ($|x| \le L$) and outside ($|x| > L$) regions. Inside the well, $V(x) = 0$, and the SE reduces to the same form as that inside the infinite rectangular well:

$$-\frac{\hbar^2}{2m}\frac{d^2\psi_{in}}{dx^2} = E\psi_{in}. \tag{2}$$

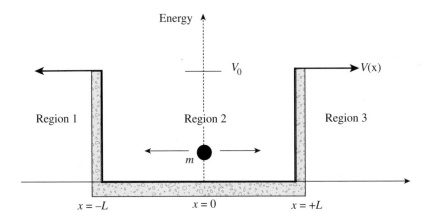

| FIGURE 3.7 Finite rectangular well.

Outside the well, $V(x) = V_0$, and

$$-\frac{\hbar^2}{2m}\frac{d^2\psi_{out}}{dx^2} = (E - V_0)\psi_{out}. \tag{3}$$

Equation (3) expresses the first difference from the infinite-well case: ψ outside the well need not (and in general will not) be zero. To be precise, there are two outside regions, one with $x \leq -L$ and the other with $x \geq +L$. However, the SE is identical in both, and we can address this complication later. As a notational convenience, label the regions as 1 through 3 from left to right, as shown in Figure 3.7. These region numbers will be used as subscripts on the corresponding wavefunctions. (Note that they *do not* designate energy levels!) Once again, we are seeking *bound energy states*; that is, ones with $E < V_0$.

We can write Equations (2) and (3) more compactly as

$$\frac{d^2\psi_{in}}{dx^2} = -k_2^2\psi_{in} \tag{4}$$

and

$$\frac{d^2\psi_{out}}{dx^2} = k_1^2\psi_{out}, \tag{5}$$

where

$$k_1^2 = \frac{2m}{\hbar^2}(V_0 - E) \tag{6}$$

and

$$k_2^2 = \frac{2mE}{\hbar^2}. \tag{7}$$

Because the bottom of the well is at $V = 0$ and we are seeking bound states with $V_0 > E$; both k_1 and k_2 are positive real. Note that the subscripts on the k's refer to the regions to which they apply. Because the value of k in region 3 is equal to that in region 1, we can put $k_3 = k_1$.

The solution to Equation (4) is of the same general form as that for the inside of the infinite rectangular well:

$$\psi_{in}(x) = A e^{ik_2 x} + B e^{-ik_2 x}. \tag{8}$$

The solution to Equation (5) is in general

$$\psi_{out}(x) = C e^{k_1 x} + D e^{-k_1 x}, \tag{9}$$

where C and D are constants of integration.

As alluded to previously, Equation (9) actually applies to the two separate outside regions; to be formally correct we should write down two versions of Equation (9), each with its own constants of integration. Hence we put

$$\begin{cases} \psi_1(x) = C e^{k_1 x} + D e^{-k_1 x} & (x \le -L) \\ \psi_2(x) = A e^{ik_2 x} + B e^{-ik_2 x} & (-L \le x \le L) \\ \psi_3(x) = G e^{k_1 x} + F e^{-k_1 x} & (x \ge L), \end{cases} \tag{10}$$

where we subscript the wavefunctions according to the regions to which they apply. We do not use E as a constant of integration, as that symbol is used to represent energy.

The problem now is to apply the general boundary conditions derived in Chapter 2. Here the potential discontinuities at $x = -L$ and $x = +L$ are not infinite, so we must force continuity of both the wavefunctions and their derivatives at the boundaries. That is, we must demand

$$\psi_1(x) = \psi_2(x) \text{ at } x = -L, \tag{11}$$

$$\psi_2(x) = \psi_3(x) \text{ at } x = +L, \tag{12}$$

$$\left. \frac{d\psi_1}{dx} \right|_{-L} = \left. \frac{d\psi_2}{dx} \right|_{-L}, \tag{13}$$

and

$$\frac{d\psi_2}{dx}\bigg|_{+L} = \frac{d\psi_3}{dx}\bigg|_{+L}. \tag{14}$$

Before applying these, we can simplify matters somewhat by considering the nature of the third boundary condition: that ψ be normalizable by being square integrable. In practice, this means that $\psi^*\psi$ must integrate to unity. This demands

$$\int_{-\infty}^{-L} \psi_1^* \psi_1 dx + \int_{-L}^{L} \psi_2^* \psi_2 dx + \int_{L}^{\infty} \psi_3^* \psi_3 dx = 1.$$

Note that the square of each wavefunction is integrated only over the region within which it applies.

This square integrability demand presents a problem. Consider the wavefunction in region 1, ψ_1, the first of Equations (10). As $x \rightarrow -\infty$, $\psi_1(x)$ diverges due to the $De^{-k_1 x}$ term, with the result that the integral of $\psi_1^* \psi_1$ would never converge! A similar problem arises with the first term of $\psi_3(x)$ as $x \rightarrow \infty$. The only way to alleviate this catastrophe is to insist that if the domain of a wavefunction includes $\pm\infty$, then we must insist that $\psi \rightarrow 0$ asymptotically:

$$\psi_1(x) \rightarrow 0 \, as \, x \rightarrow -\infty \tag{15}$$

and

$$\psi_3(x) \rightarrow 0 \, as \, x \rightarrow +\infty. \tag{16}$$

These conditions require that $D = G = 0$ in Equations (10). This reduces the solution at once to

$$\begin{cases} \psi_1(x) = C e^{k_1 x} & (x < -L) \\ \psi_2(x) = A e^{\imath k_2 x} + B e^{-\imath k_2 x} & (-L \leq x \leq L) \\ \psi_3(x) = F e^{-k_1 x} & (x > L). \end{cases} \tag{17}$$

All seems well: we have four constants to determine (A, B, C, F), and four conditions to apply: Equations (11) through (14). But this is not the whole story: after applying Equations (11) through (14), we still have to actually apply the square-integrability condition, so we actually have an overdetermined system of five conditions on four constants! The resolution of this apparent difficulty will become clear shortly, when we address Equation (37).

Applying conditions (11) through (14) yields:

$$A e^{-\imath k_2 L} + B e^{\imath k_2 L} = C e^{-k_1 L} \tag{18}$$

$$\iota k_2 A e^{-\iota k_2 L} - \iota k_2 B e^{\iota k_2 L} = k_1 C e^{-k_1 L} \tag{19}$$

$$A e^{\iota k_2 L} + B e^{-\iota k_2 L} = F e^{-k_1 L} \tag{20}$$

$$\iota k_2 A e^{\iota k_2 L} - \iota k_2 B e^{-\iota k_2 L} = -k_1 F e^{-k_1 L}, \tag{21}$$

Equations (18) and (19) derive from Equations (11) and (13); similarly, (20) and (21) derive from (12) and (14). The dimensionless products $k_1 L$ and $k_2 L$ appear frequently in these equations, which suggests defining two new constants,

$$\eta = k_1 L = \sqrt{\frac{2m(V_0 - E)}{\hbar^2}} L \tag{22}$$

and

$$\xi = k_2 L = \sqrt{\frac{2mE}{\hbar^2}} L. \tag{23}$$

With these definitions, we can write Equations (18) through (21) as

$$A e^{-\iota \xi} + B e^{\iota \xi} = C e^{-\eta}, \tag{24}$$

$$\iota A e^{-\iota \xi} - \iota B e^{\iota \xi} = (\eta/\xi) C e^{-\eta}, \tag{25}$$

$$A e^{\iota \xi} + B e^{-\iota \xi} = F e^{-\eta}, \tag{26}$$

$$\iota A e^{\iota \xi} - \iota B e^{-\iota \xi} = -(\eta/\xi) F e^{-\eta}. \tag{27}$$

We treat these as four equations in four unknowns. Solving Equation (24) for A gives

$$A = e^{\iota \xi}(C e^{-\eta} - B e^{\iota \xi}). \tag{28}$$

Substituting this result into Equation (25) and isolating B gives

$$B = (\iota/2) C e^{-\iota \xi} e^{-\eta}(\eta/\xi - \iota), \tag{29}$$

Back-substituting Equation (29) into Equation (28) gives A in terms of C alone:

$$A = \frac{1}{2} C e^{-\eta} e^{\iota \xi}[1 - \iota(\eta/\xi)]. \tag{30}$$

Eliminating A and B in Equations (26) and (27) via Equations (29) and (30) gives, after some manipulation,

$$F = C[\cos(2\xi) + (\eta/\xi)\sin(2\xi)], \tag{31}$$

and

$$F = -C[\cos(2\xi) - (\xi/\eta)\sin(2\xi)], \tag{32}$$

where we have used the Euler identities. Equating these two expressions gives a condition on η and ξ:

$$2\cos(2\xi) + (\eta/\xi - \xi/\eta)\sin(2\xi) = 0. \tag{33}$$

A, B, C, and F have disappeared. The meaning of Equation (33) can be elucidated by noting that ξ and η are not independent. From Equations (22) and (23), we have

$$\xi^2 + \eta^2 = \frac{2mV_0L^2}{\hbar^2} = \text{constant} = K^2. \tag{34}$$

K is known as the **strength parameter** of the well. Expressing η as $\sqrt{K^2 - \xi^2}$, we can cast Equation (33) into the form of a constraint on ξ alone:

$$f(\xi, K) = (K^2 - 2\xi^2)\sin(2\xi) + 2\xi\sqrt{K^2 - \xi^2}\cos(2\xi) = 0. \tag{35}$$

For a given value of K, only certain values of ξ will satisfy Equation (35); from Equation (22) or (23), these will correspond to particular values of the energy of the particle. *The roots of Equation (35) correspond to the energy eigenvalues of the finite potential well.* If we label the roots of Equation (35) as ξ_n, then the energy levels are given by $E_n = \xi_n^2\hbar^2/2mL^2$. Now, if either of Equations (31) or (32) is squared and Equation (35) is used to eliminate $\sin(2\xi)$ or $\cos(2\xi)$, the result is $F^2 = C^2$, that is, $F = \pm C$. If $F = +C$, then Equations (24) and (26) reduce to $A = B$; in this case $\psi_2(x) = (2A)\cos(k_2x)$, and the overall wavefunction has **even parity**: $\psi(x) = \psi(-x)$. On the other hand, if $F = -C$, Equations (25) and (27) reduce to $A = -B$, and one finds $\psi_2(x) = (2\iota A)\sin(k_2x)$, that is, the overall wavefunction is of **odd parity**: $\psi(x) = -\psi(-x)$. Evidently, there exist two separate families of solutions to the finite rectangular well problem. These are referred to as the even and odd solution sets:

$$\left.\begin{array}{l} B = A \\ F = C \end{array}\right\} \text{even solutions}, \tag{36}$$

$$\left.\begin{array}{l} B = -A \\ F = -C \end{array}\right\} \text{odd solutions}. \tag{37}$$

The value of making the well symmetric about $x = 0$ is that it causes the solution to separate naturally into families of different parity. Equation (35) is valid for *all* of the energy eigenvalues, however. Odd and even-parity solutions to the SE will always be the case whenever a symmetric potential is involved; this is discussed further in Section 3.6.

The presence of two solution-families resolves the dilemma alluded to in the paragraph following Equation (17): not all of the boundary conditions can be satisfied simultaneously.

An important aspect of the finite potential well is that *there is some probability of finding the particle beyond the walls of the well, where, classically, it cannot be found.* This behavior, known as **tunneling** or **barrier penetration**, is, like quantized energies, a purely quantum-mechanical phenomenon that arises due to the wave nature of particles. *Particles can penetrate into and through potential barriers that they cannot surmount in classical physics.* A **characteristic tunneling length** for a given energy is given by the reciprocal of k_1. An engaging account of the discovery of tunneling appears in an article by Merzbacher, in which he wrote that "... among all the successes of quantum mechanics as it evolved in the third decade of the 20th century, none was more impressive than the understanding of the tunnel effect—the penetration of matter waves and the transmission of particles through a high potential barrier."[2]

Figure 3.8 shows sketches of the three lowest energy finite-well wavefunctions; again, we normally plot $|\psi|$, suppressing any explicitly complex nature of the wavefunction. Note the alternating parities and tunneling phenomena; the number of maxima in the wavefunctions again corresponds to n.

The finite well illustrates a number of concepts that apply generally for any potential well. Inside a well—that is, wherever $E > V(x)$—the wavefunction will always have the oscillatory form of the second of Equations (3.3.10). In regions where $E < V(x)$, the solution will have the form of an exponential decay that corresponds to the tunneling effect. The wavefunction and its first derivative must be continuous everywhere, and ψ must often be forced to vanish at the limits of its domain if those limits go to $\pm \infty$. The number of maxima in the wavefunction is equal to the quantum number of the system, and can be used to label the various possible states.

Before closing this section, it is worthwhile to elaborate briefly on the energy-eigenvalue condition, Equation (35). As it stands, this expression conotates no quantum number "n" to number the bound states in the way Equation (3.2.11) does for the infinite well. A quantum number for the finite well can be introduced through the following manipulation [1].

---

[2]Merzbacher E. The early history of quantum tunneling. *Physics Today* 2002; 55(8):44–49.

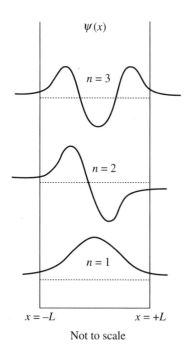

Not to scale

I FIGURE 3.8 Finite rectangular well wavefunctions (not to scale).

First, extract a factor of K^2 from both terms in Equation (35) to cast the eigenvalue condition as

$$[1 - 2(\xi/K)^2] \sin(2\xi) + 2(\xi/K)\sqrt{1 - (\xi/K)^2}\cos(2\xi) = 0. \tag{38}$$

Now, define the quantity Φ by

$$\Phi = \mathrm{Sin}^{-1}(\xi/K). \tag{39}$$

From this definition, it follows that

$$\cos^2\Phi = 1 - (\xi/K)^2, \tag{40}$$

so that

$$\cos(2\Phi) = \cos^2\Phi - \sin^2\Phi = 1 - 2(\xi/K)^2 \tag{41}$$

and

$$\sin(2\Phi) = 2\sin\Phi\cos\Phi = 2(\xi/K)\sqrt{1 - (\xi/K)^2}. \tag{42}$$

Now consider the quantity

$$\sin(2\xi + 2\Phi) = \sin(2\xi)\cos(2\Phi) + \cos(2\xi)\sin(2\Phi). \tag{43}$$

Substituting Equations (41) and (42) into Equation (43) gives

$$\sin(2\xi + 2\Phi) = [1 - 2(\xi/K)^2]\sin(2\xi) + 2(\xi/K)\sqrt{1 - (\xi/K)^2}\cos(2\xi). \tag{44}$$

Compare Equations (38) and (44): they are identical. This means that we can write the eigenvalue equation for the finite well as

$$\sin(2\xi + 2\Phi) = 0. \tag{45}$$

The sine of any angle will be zero only when that angle is equal to an integer number of π radians; that is, we must have

$$2(\xi + \Phi) = n\pi,$$

or

$$\xi + \text{Sin}^{-1}\left(\frac{\xi}{K}\right) = \frac{n\pi}{2}. \tag{46}$$

Equation (46) is the recast eigenvalue condition for the finite well: in this considerably simplified version, an integer quantum number appears explicitly.

EXAMPLE 3.2

Given an electron in a finite well of depth 100 eV and $L = 1$ Å, find the bound energy states. We have, from Equation (34),

$$K^2 = \frac{2mV_0L^2}{\hbar^2} = \frac{2(9.1095 \times 10^{-31}kg)(1.6022 \times 10^{-17}J)(10^{-10}m)^2}{(1.0546 \times 10^{-34}J - sec)^2} = 26.2462.$$

Figure 3.9 shows $f(\xi, K)$ [Equation (35)] vs. ξ for this value of K^2; note that, from Equations (34) and (35), ξ cannot exceed K since both η and ξ must be positive real numbers. By solving either Equation (35) or Equation (46), one finds that there are four bound states. They lie at $\xi = 1.3118$, 2.6076, 3.8593, and 4.9630, and correspond to energies of 6.56, 25.91, 56.75, and 93.85 eV, respectively [Equation (23)].

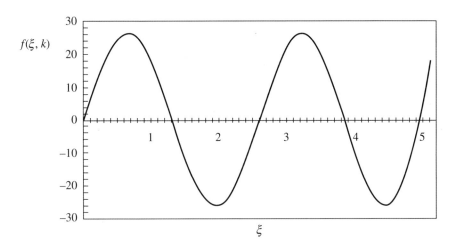

FIGURE 3.9 Example 3.2.

■ 3.4 Finite Rectangular Well—Even Solutions

Let us explore the even-parity solutions to the finite rectangular well in more detail. With $B = A$ and $F = C$, Equations (3.3.17) become

$$
\begin{cases}
\psi_1(x) = C e^{k_1 x} & (x < -L) \\
\psi_2(x) = 2A \cos(k_2 x) & (-L \le x \le L) \\
\psi_3(x) = C e^{-k_1 x} & (x > L).
\end{cases}
\tag{1}
$$

Similarly, Equations (3.3.24) through (3.3.27) reduce to two conditions:

$$
2A \cos \xi = C e^{-\eta}
\tag{2}
$$

and

$$
2A \sin \xi = (\eta/\xi) C e^{-\eta}.
\tag{3}
$$

Normalization demands

$$
\int_{-\infty}^{-L} \psi_1^* \psi_1 \, dx + \int_{-L}^{L} \psi_2^* \psi_2 \, dx + \int_{L}^{\infty} \psi_3^* \psi_3 \, dx = 1.
\tag{4}
$$

Again, note that each wavefunction is integrated only over the domain wherein it applies. Because we are dealing with even-parity states, the first and third integrals are equal and reduce to

$$
\int_{-\infty}^{-L} \psi_1^* \psi_1 \, dx = \int_{L}^{\infty} \psi_3^* \psi_3 \, dx = C^2 \int_{L}^{\infty} e^{2k_1 x} \, dx = \frac{C^2 e^{-2\eta}}{2k_1}.
\tag{5}
$$

The middle integral evaluates as

$$\int_{-L}^{L} \psi_2^* \psi_2 \, dx = 4A^2 \int_{-L}^{L} \cos^2(k_2 x)\, dx = 4A^2 \left[\frac{x}{2} + \frac{\sin(2k_2 x)}{4k_2} \right]_{-L}^{L}$$

$$= 4A^2 \left[\frac{\sin(2\xi)}{2k_2} + L \right]. \tag{6}$$

Hence we have

$$\frac{C^2 e^{-2\eta}}{k_1} + 4A^2 \left[\frac{\sin(2\xi)}{2k_2} + L \right] = 1. \tag{7}$$

Eliminating C via either of Equations (2) or (3) gives

$$4A^2 \left[\frac{\cos^2 \xi}{k_1} + \frac{\sin(2\xi)}{2k_2} + L \right] = 1, \tag{8}$$

which, on substituting for ξ and η in favor of k_1 and k_2, reduces to

$$4A^2 = \frac{\eta \xi}{L[\xi \cos^2 \xi + \eta \sin \xi \cos \xi + \eta \xi]}. \tag{9}$$

Hence, from Equation (2),

$$C^2 = \frac{\eta \xi e^{2\eta} \cos^2 \xi}{L[\xi \cos^2 \xi + \eta \sin \xi \cos \xi + \eta \xi]} = \frac{\eta \xi e^{2\eta}}{L[\xi + \eta \tan \xi + \eta \xi \sec^2 \xi]}. \tag{10}$$

Equations (1), (9), and (10) specify the even-parity wavefunctions of the finite rectangular well: once a given energy state ξ_n is specified, A and C can be computed. Unlike the case of the infinite well, the normalization constants depend on the energy eigenvalue involved.

The probability of finding the particle outside the well is given by

$$P_{\text{out}}^{\text{even}} = \int_{-\infty}^{-L} \psi_1^* \psi_1 \, dx + \int_{L}^{\infty} \psi_3^* \psi_3 \, dx = \frac{C^2 e^{-2\eta}}{k_1} = \frac{\xi}{[\xi + \eta \tan \xi + \eta \xi \sec^2 \xi]}. \tag{11}$$

Note that the probability is dimensionless and independent of A or C, depending only on the energy eigenvalue.

One might think the idea of building atomic-scale finite potential wells to be a fantasy. However, thanks to scanning tunneling microscopy, it is now possible to manipulate atoms one at a time, and in doing so cause electrons to be confined within corrals of atoms. The resulting probability distributions for the electrons are in excellent agreement with what is predicted from solutions of Schrödinger's equation (see the discussion of Figure 3.11).

■ 3.5 Number of Bound States in a Finite Potential Well

In Example 3.2 we saw that a finite rectangular well of strength $K = 5.12$ was capable of binding four energy states, the most energetic of which was close to the top of the well. From the form of the eigenvalue Equation (3.3.35) as exemplified in Figure 3.9, one might infer (correctly as it turns out) that a well with a larger K would likely bind more states. Is there any way to tell in advance how many states a well of a given K can bind without having to solve the eigenvalue equation in detail? The answer is yes.

To see this, it is convenient to rearrange the eigenvalue equation into the equivalent form

$$\tan(2\xi) = -\frac{2\xi\sqrt{K^2 - \xi^2}}{K^2 - 2\xi^2} = g(\xi, K). \tag{1}$$

This expression indicates another way one might solve for the eigenvalues: by finding the intersections of the function $g(\xi, K)$ with branches of the function $\tan(2\xi)$. This is illustrated in Figure 3.10 for the case of $K = 10$.

A plot of $\tan(2\xi)$ consists of a number of nearly vertical branches with zeros at $\xi = 0, \pi/2, \pi, 3\pi/2, \dots$. These branches approach positive infinity as ξ approaches

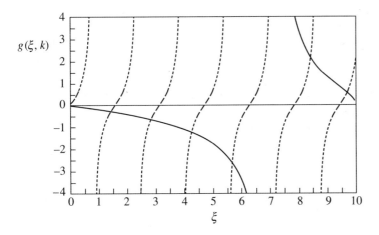

I FIGURE 3.10   Tangent and eigenvalue functions for K = 10 finite well.

$\pi/4$, $3\pi/4$, $5\pi/4$, ... , and increase toward zero from negative infinity when ξ is just past $\pi/4$, $3\pi/4$, $5\pi/4$, ... The function $g(\xi, K)$ has two branches: initially, as ξ increases from zero (recall that the range of ξ is $0 \le \xi \le K$), $g(\xi, K)$ decreases from zero to negative infinity as ξ approaches $K/\sqrt{2}$, and then decreases from positive infinity just past $\xi = K/\sqrt{2}$ down to zero at $\xi = K$. Although the figure shows six intersections (eigenvalues!) between the branches of $\tan(2\xi)$ and the two branches of $g(\xi, K)$, there are actually seven: one lies below the plot at $\xi \sim 7.07$.

It should be clear that no matter what value of K one is dealing with, $g(\xi, K)$ will always be of the form shown in Figure 3.10: two descending branches separated by a break at $K/\sqrt{2}$, one branch of negative values and one of positive, with $g(\xi, K) \rightarrow 0^+$ as $\xi \rightarrow K$.

As you look at Figure 3.10, imagine decreasing K: the branches of $g(\xi, K)$ will shrink toward the left edge of the figure while the branches of $\tan(2\xi)$ remain unchanged. No matter how small the value of K is, the second branch of the $g(\xi, K)$ function will always at least cut the first branch of the $\tan(2\xi)$ function, so we can conclude that *a finite rectangular well will always support at least one bound state*.

What can we say of the total number of bound states for a given value of K? The branches of $\tan(2\xi)$ have zeroes at $\xi = 0$, $\pi/2$, π, $3\pi/2$, ... Imagine, now, increasing K, so that the $g(\xi, K)$ curve begins to stretch out to the right. If K is less than $\pi/2$, there will be only one eigenvalue, the one corresponding to the positive-descending branch of $g(\xi, K)$ cutting the first branch of $\tan(2\xi)$ (the one that begins at $\xi = 0$). As soon as K exceeds $\pi/2$, there will be a second eigenvalue, where the positive-descending branch of $g(\xi, K)$ cuts the second branch of $\tan(2\xi)$. The pattern is clear: as K increases, and as it successively exceeds $2\pi/2$, $3\pi/2$, $4\pi/2$, $5\pi/2$, ..., we will have 3, 4, 5, 6, ... , eigenvalues. Study the figure carefully and convince yourself that because the branches of $\tan(2\xi)$ go to $\pm\infty$, we are guaranteed that $g(\xi, K)$ is bound to cut all of the ones that lie below the terminus of the $g(\xi, K)$ curve and that extend into $\tan(2\xi) > 0$.

We can summarize these conclusions by writing the number of eigenvalues N for a given value of K as

$$N(K) = 1 + \left[\frac{2K}{\pi} \right], \tag{2}$$

where $[2K/\pi]$ designates the largest integer less than or equal to $2K/\pi$. For $K = 10$, this gives $N = 7$, as expected.

Finite potential wells find practical use in a number of everyday devices. Digital cameras obtain their images with a two-dimensional grid of potential wells known as a charge-coupled-device or "CCD chip." Made from light-sensitive materials, these devices detect incident photons when they strike and liberate electrons from the material. The electrons are trapped in electronic potential wells. Each well is known as a picture element or "pixel." After the exposure is complete, the image is read out by suitably lowering and raising the potential "walls" to march the electrons off of the chip, thus clearing it for the next exposure. The now-ubiquitous "flash" drives used for transferring information between computers work similarly.

EXAMPLE 3.3

A manufacturer of CCD cameras for amateur telescopes advertises that one of its products uses a chip with "9-micron pixels" that have a "full well" of 60,000 electrons. This means that each tiny potential well is 9 by 9 microns (1 micron = $1\mu = 10^{-6}$ m) in size and that they can hold 60,000 electrons before becoming full. (Each energy level can hold two electrons, one each of opposite spin; see Chapter 8.) Suppose, for simplicity, that the pixels are one-dimensional finite rectangular wells. What must be their depth V_0?

With $N = 30,000$, the factor of unity on the right side of Equation (2) can be neglected:

$$K = \frac{N\pi}{2}.$$

Combining this with Equation (3.3.34) and solving for V_0 gives

$$V_0 = \frac{(N\pi\hbar)^2}{8mL^2},$$

where L is the half-width of the well; that is, $L = 4.5$ microns. Putting in the numbers,

$$V_0 = \frac{[30,000\,\pi\,(1.055 \times 10^{-34}\mathrm{J\,sec})]^2}{8(9.109 \times 10^{-31}\,\mathrm{kg})(4.5 \times 10^{-6}\,\mathrm{m})^2} = 6.70 \times 10^{-19}\ \mathrm{Joules},$$

about 4.18 eV. Such a device can easily be battery-powered, a necessity for astronomers at remote sites with no access to power.

The probability distribution of electrons trapped in an atomic-scale two-dimensional potential well has actually been measured via **scanning tunneling microscopy** (STM), a technique invented in 1981 by Gerd Binning and Heinrich Rohrer of IBM's Zurich Laboratory, and for which they shared the 1986 Nobel Prize for Physics. In this technique, a very tiny metallic probe tip (ideally, only one atom wide at the tip) is positioned close (within a few atomic diameters) to a conducting surface. A small voltage applied between the surface and the tip sets up a potential barrier through which electrons can tunnel. (We shall have much more to say about tunneling in Sections 3.7–3.9.) The resulting "tunneling current" is very sensitive to the barrier width (see Problem 3-18); consequently, by adjusting the tip/surface separation to maintain a constant current, the surface can be mapped at the atomic level; a resolution of about 0.2 nanometers is possible. A related technique, **atomic force microscopy** (AFM), makes it possible to actually move individual atoms around on a substrate to create nano-scale structures. Figure 3.11 shows a scanning-tunneling microscope "image" of a "quantum corral" constructed by atomic force microscopy. The image shows 48 iron atoms deposited on a copper surface. The diameter of the corral is about 143 Å; the wavelike ripples within the corral reflect the probability distribution of surface-state electrons. As Crommie et al. show, this electron distribution is dominated by the eigenstate density expected for an electron trapped in a round two-dimensional box. This striking image is direct evidence for the atomic-scale probability distributions predicted by quantum mechanics.[3]

---

[3]A good introduction to the physics of atomic force microscopy is the article "Atomic force microscopy" by Rugar D and Hansma P, *Physics Today* 1990; 43(10):23–30; also recommended is "Fifty years of seeing atoms" by Tsong TT, *Physics Today* 2006; 59(3):31–37 and "Exploring the nanoworld with atomic force microscopy" by Giessibl FJ and Quate CF, *Physics Today* 2006; 59(12):44–50. Tunneling also plays a central role in the design of devices such as transistors; a good treatment of some of the engineering details can be found in Levi AFJ, *Applied Quantum Mechanics*, Cambridge, UK: Cambridge University Press, 2003.

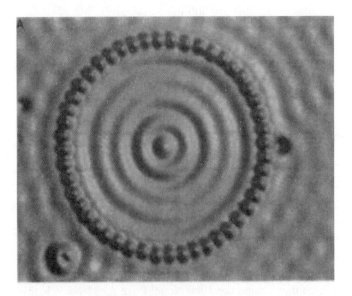

FIGURE 3.11   Quantum corral of iron atoms on a copper surface. Reprinted with permission from Confinement of Electrons to Quantum Corrals on a Metal Surface by M. F. Crommie, C. P. Lutz, and D. M. Eigler, Science 262, 218–220 1993. Copyright 1993 AAAS.

■ 3.6 Sketching Wavefunctions

The finite potential well is a simple, symmetric potential, yet its solution possesses a number of subtleties. It is easy to imagine that more complex potentials could involve intractable or impossible algebra. Indeed, closed analytic solutions to the SE are obtainable only for a very limited number of potentials; in many cases an appeal must be made to brute-force series solutions, approximation methods, or numerical integration. It is, however, possible to make **qualitative** sketches of plausible wavefunctions for complex potentials based on a few simple rules. This is instructive in its own right, and can be helpful as a guide as to what form an analytic solution might take.

Figure 3.12 shows a hypothetical example. We wish to get an idea of the form of the wavefunction corresponding to a particle of mass m and total energy E moving in the potential shown. The points where the total-energy line cuts $V(x)$ are known as the **classical turning points** of the motion; these points serve to delimit the inside and outside regions wherein the solutions will be of sinusoidal and exponential-decay form, respectively.

At any position we can divide the total energy into potential and kinetic contributions as shown. At positions where the well is deep, the kinetic energy will be relatively large. According to de Broglie's hypothesis, this will correspond to a smaller wavelength because $\lambda = h/p$. This is the first rule for sketching wavefunctions: deeper well $\rightarrow$ shorter λ. Further, wavefunctions with more nodes (points where $\psi(x) = 0$) exhibit shorter characteristic wavelengths, meaning higher energies. The ground state wavefunction has no nodes, the first excited state one, the second excited state two, and so on.

What of the amplitude of ψ as the well shallows or deepens? This question can also be addressed from an energy argument. At a position where the kinetic energy is large, the velocity of the particle will be high; hence it will spend less time in deeper

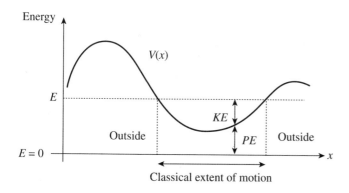

FIGURE 3.12 A hypothetical potential well.

parts of the well than in shallower regions. That is, there should be a lower chance of finding it where the well is deep. Because the probability of finding the particle at some position is proportional to ψ, the amplitude of ψ must decrease where the well deepens. This is the second rule for sketching wavefunctions: deeper well → smaller amplitude for ψ.

To get a deeper sense of the behavior of solutions to Schrödinger's equation in the various regions, it is helpful to look at some of its purely mathematical aspects. The discussion that follows is adapted from Eisberg and Resnick [2]. We can write Schrödinger's equation as

$$\frac{d^2\psi}{dx^2} = \frac{2m}{\hbar^2}[V(x) - E]\psi(x).$$

Consider an outside region where $[V(x) - E] > 0$. If $\psi > 0$ at some point, then $d^2\psi/dx^2$ must be > 0, whereas if $\psi < 0$ then $d^2\psi/dx^2$ will be < 0. For an inside region, $d^2\psi/dx^2$ must be < 0 (> 0) if $\psi > 0$ (< 0) because $[V(x) - E]$ is < 0. From elementary calculus, we know that functions with $d^2\psi/dx^2 > 0$ must be concave upward, whereas those with $d^2\psi/dx^2 < 0$ must be concave downward. Such functions are sketched for the inside and outside regions in Figure 3.13.

Imagine that you are inside the well at the point where the inside and left-outside regions meet, and that $\psi > 0$ with $d\psi/dx < 0$ [or > 0] at this point. If you proceed leftward and enter the outside region, ψ must have the form typical of such regions: a sum of positive and negative exponentials (Equation 3.3.9). ψ would initially decrease [or increase] in value, but will eventually begin to turn away from the $\psi = 0$ line [or diverge even more rapidly from it] because $d^2\psi/dx^2 > 0$. If the domain

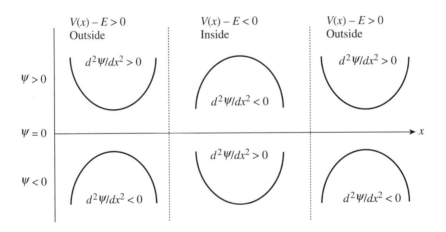

FIGURE 3.13   Nature of ψ functions.

of the potential goes to $x \to \infty$, the divergent part of ψ will have to be arbitrarily suppressed to prevent an infinite divergence. Similar logic applies to the right-outside region. If, on the other hand, you proceed rightward (toward the inside of the well), ψ will always tend to turn toward the $\psi = 0$ line whether the initial values of ψ and its first derivative be positive or negative. This behavior will always ensure the oscillatory-form solutions characteristic of the infinite and finite wells.

Inasmuch as they derive from considerations of fundamental quantum relationships and Schrödinger's equation, these comments regarding the wavelength and the number of nodes and curvature of wavefunctions are quite general for any potential. Other factors to keep in mind are that that the number of extrema in the wavefunction is equal to the quantum number of the state involved, and that if the well is symmetric the wavefunctions will alternate parity. Figure 3.14 illustrates an application of these rules.

When sketching such figures, it is conventional to superimpose the sketch of the wavefunction over the sketch of the well at the vertical level of the energy of the wavefunction.

Although the preceding argument for the amplitude of ψ based on potential and kinetic energy sounds plausible, it can in fact lead to erroneous predictions regarding what ψ should look like. An example is provided by the ground state of the parabolic-shaped harmonic oscillator potential $V(x) = kx^2/2$ discussed in Chapter 5, where $\psi(x)$ in fact has its greatest amplitude where the potential well is deepest (see Figures 5.1 and 5.2). This is because the above reasoning is based on classical concepts. The deeper well $\to$ smaller amplitude reasoning is correct for high-n energy levels, where the correspondence principle tells us that the results of classical and quantum computations must agree, but fails completely for the lowest energy levels. "High," however, need not mean "terribly high." As shown in Figure 5.2, the wavefunction for the fourth excited state of the harmonic oscillator potential concurs with what the energy argument would indicate. One must always be careful in applying classical concepts to quantum situations.

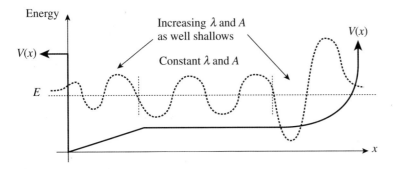

❙ FIGURE 3.14 Hypothetical $n = 9$ wavefunction.

Finally, it was remarked in Section 3.3 that a symmetric potential will always lead to odd- and even-parity solutions to the SE. This can be understood on the basis of some simple arguments. We can always define the coordinate system such that $x = 0$ is the symmetry axis of the potential; that is, such that the potential is described by $V(x) = V(-x)$. Because the two sides of the potential are indistinguishable, we can expect that the particle should have no preference for being found on one side or the other; that is, that the *probability* of finding the particle should also be symmetric about $x = 0$: $\psi^2(x) = \psi^2(-x)$. Taking the square root of this gives $\psi(x) = \pm\psi(-x)$; that is, $\psi(x)$ must be of either even or odd parity. If ψ is of even parity, then it must have either a local maximum or minimum at the symmetry point, with $d\psi/dx = 0$ there. If ψ is of odd parity, then we must have $\psi = 0$ at $x = 0$ and $d\psi/dx \neq 0$ there. By sketching a few even and odd-parity functions, you should be able to convince yourself of some further conclusions. One is that the lowest energy state for a symmetric potential must be of even parity. For an $n = 1$ state we expect one maximum; no odd-parity function can have only one maximum and still satisfy the usual boundary conditions $\psi \rightarrow 0$ as $x \rightarrow \pm\infty$, whereas a single-maximum even-parity function must always behave in this way. Ground-state wavefunctions of symmetric potentials will thus always have an appearance similar to that for the $n = 1$ state of a finite rectangular well in Figure 3.8.

As to the higher energy states of symmetric potentials, consider first those corresponding to odd quantum numbers, $n = 3, 5, 7 \ldots$. To achieve both the desired symmetry and have an odd number of maxima, ψ must have an extremum at $x = 0$. This can *only* be satisfied by an even-parity function. (An odd-parity function must have $d\psi/dx \neq 0$ at $x = 0$; it is impossible to satisfy that requirement *and* the demands of symmetry and an odd number of maxima simultaneously.) For states with even quantum numbers $n = 2, 4, 6, \ldots$, one can always easily sketch a suitable odd-parity solution, because a symmetric odd-parity function satisfying $\psi \rightarrow 0$ as $x \rightarrow \pm\infty$ must have a total number of maxima that is even. Even-parity functions are possible in this circumstance *but only* if they have a minimum at $x = 0$. This cannot be demanded, however, as this would be asking to impose a further boundary condition on the solution. For these reasons, solutions to symmetric potentials will alternate parity in the sequence even, odd, even, odd, and so forth. The harmonic-oscillator potential discussed in Chapter 5 is another example of a symmetric potential.

Part II: Potential Barriers and Scattering

■ 3.7 Potential Barriers

We now turn our attention to what might be called inside-out potential wells, the so-called potential barriers.

The general situation is depicted in Figure 3.15, where a matter-wave of energy E propagating from the left encounters a rectangular potential barrier of height V_0 Joules

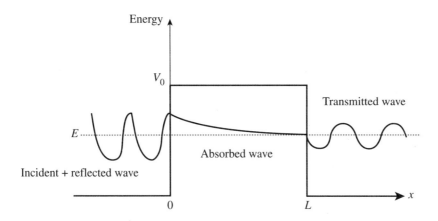

I FIGURE 3.15 Rectangular barrier penetration.

and thickness L. A simple classical analog is a ball rolling up a hill of height h: If the energy of the ball is greater than mgh (that is, $E > V_0$), then the ball will scale the hill and roll down the other side; if not, it will roll back toward the direction from which it came. The presence of tunneling phenomena in potential-well problems, however, hints that the quantum-mechanical situation could be quite different: there may be some probability of the matter wave penetrating through the barrier, even if $E < V_0$.

As a result of such a reflection process, the region to the left of the barrier would presumably contain a combination of incident and partially reflected waves and the region to the right a transmitted or scattered wave; within the barrier itself would be an absorbed component composed of exponential growth and decay terms of the form of Equation (3.3.9). Intuitively, we might expect the amplitude of the transmitted wave to depend on E, V_0, L, and the amplitude of the incident wave.

Potential-barrier problems have considerable practical application. Essentially all we know of atomic and nuclear structure derives from experiments wherein some incident probe matter-wave is fired at the atom or nucleus under study. From the intensity and spatial distribution of the scattered wave, much can be inferred as to the size and structure of the target object. In reality these experiments are of course three-dimensional, but many of the important features can be gleaned from a one-dimensional analysis.

In principle, a number of situations are possible. One could have particles with $E > V_0$, or $E < V_0$. The incident energy could be in the form of a spatially isolated wave packet or a continuous, time-independent stream of monoenergetic particles. The barrier could be thick or thin compared to the de Broglie wavelength of the incident particles. Because we will be analyzing the situation via time-independent wavefunctions like those used in our studies of potential wells, we are restricted to dealing with only a steady-state situation; that is, the case of a steady stream of particles of energy $E < V_0$ incident on the barrier. (Intuitively appealing as they are, it is misleading to invoke terms such as "incident," "reflected," and "transmitted," as these imply that some particles are time-dependently burrowing their way through the barrier to emerge on the other side. What we really have is a time-independent probability distribution whose amplitude varies across the barrier.) We will first work out the general situation for a barrier of arbitrary thickness, and then specialize our results to a few particularly interesting cases.

The potential for the case depicted in Figure 3.15 is

$$V(x) = \begin{cases} V_0 & (0 \le x \le L) \\ 0 & \text{otherwise.} \end{cases} \tag{1}$$

We divide space into three regions as shown in the figure. In the first region, where $V = 0$, the solution to the SE will be of the same form as that inside an infinite or finite rectangular well:

$$\psi_1(x) = A_0 e^{\iota k_1 x} + A e^{-\iota k_1 x}, \tag{2}$$

where

$$k_1^2 = \frac{2mE}{\hbar^2}, \tag{3}$$

and where A_0 and A are constants of integration.

Equation (2) can be interpreted as the sum of two waves: an incident matter-wave of amplitude A_0 propagating to the right, and a reflected one of amplitude A propagating to the left, corresponding to any partial reflection arising from the barrier at $x = 0$. Amplitude A_0 would be set experimentally.

In region 2, where $E < V_0$, the wavefunction will be of the form

$$\psi_2(x) = B e^{-k_2 x} + C e^{k_2 x}, \tag{4}$$

where

$$k_2^2 = \frac{2m(V_0 - E)}{\hbar^2}. \tag{5}$$

Neither B nor C can be eliminated from Equation (4), as the barrier does not extend to infinity; both terms must be retained for complete generality.

In region 3 we again have $V = 0$, but there is nothing for the transmitted wave to reflect back from. In this region, then, we take the solution to be of the form of a matter-wave propagating to the right:

$$\psi_3(x) = D e^{\iota k_1 x}. \tag{6}$$

Note that the wave number k is the same in regions 1 and 3 as V is the same for both regions. That fraction of the original incident wave that emerges from the barrier does so with the same energy that it entered with, but with a different, presumably smaller, amplitude. (Radio signals generated by your favorite station do not differ in frequency inside and outside of your house!)

Experimentally, one would measure the transmitted amplitude D as a function of the amplitude of the incident wave, A_0, presumably over a range of incident energies k_1. To get D in terms of A_0 it is necessary to apply the usual boundary conditions to Equations (2) through (6), with the exception that we cannot force $\psi \rightarrow 0$ as $x \rightarrow \pm\infty$ because the (incoming + reflected) and transmitted waves propagate to infinity in both directions; the dimensions of a laboratory are likely to be large in comparison with the size of a nucleus. Demanding the continuity of the wavefunctions and their derivatives at $x = 0$ and $x = L$ gives four conditions:

$$A_0 + A = B + C \tag{7}$$

$$\iota k_1 A_0 - \iota k_1 A = -k_2 B + k_2 C \tag{8}$$

$$B e^{-k_2 L} + C e^{k_2 L} = D e^{\iota k_1 L} \tag{9}$$

$$-k_2 B e^{-k_2 L} + k_2 C e^{k_2 L} = \iota k_1 D e^{\iota k_1 L}. \tag{10}$$

Taking A_0 to be fixed, we can treat Equations (7) through (10) as four equations in four unknowns: A, B, C, and D. Solving for D in terms of A_0 is tedious but straightforward, and follows the same sort of logic as was applied in the study of the finite rectangular well in Section 3.3. After eliminating A, B, and C, the result is

$$D = \frac{4 \iota k_1 k_2 e^{-\iota k_1 L}}{\left[(k_2 + \iota k_1)^2 e^{-k_2 L} - (k_2 - \iota k_1)^2 e^{k_2 L} \right]} A_0. \tag{11}$$

D/A_0 is the amplitude of the scattered-wave probability density as a fraction of that of the incident wave. The squared magnitude of this number, $(D/A_0)(D/A_0)^*$, is then a measure of the fraction of matter waves that penetrate the barrier and emerge on the other side. This is known as the **transmission coefficient** T:

$$T = D^*D, \tag{12}$$

where we have taken $A_0 = 1$ for simplicity. To expedite the algebra involved in computing T, it is helpful to extract a factor of $e^{k_2 L}$ from the denominator of Equation (11):

$$D = \frac{4\iota k_1 k_2 e^{-\iota k_1 L} e^{-k_2 L}}{[(k_2 + \iota k_1)^2 e^{-2k_2 L} - (k_2 - \iota k_1)^2]}.$$

Computing T is another exercise in algebra. One finds

$$T = \frac{16 k_1^2 k_2^2 e^{-2k_2 L}}{[(k_1^2 + k_2^2)^2 (1 + e^{-4k_2 L}) - e^{-2k_2 L}(2k_1^4 - 12 k_1^2 k_2^2 + 2 k_2^4)]}. \tag{13}$$

Equation (13) is quite general for our $E < V_0$ rectangular barrier, but also rather awkward. In the following subsections we consider two cases where simplifying approximations can be made. If you are familiar with hyperbolic trigonometric functions, Equation (13) can be expressed as

$$T = \left[1 + \left(\frac{k_1^2 + k_2^2}{2k_1 k_2}\right)^2 \sinh^2(k_2 L)\right]^{-1},$$

but Equation (13) as we have written it will suffice for our purposes.

(a) Thick Barrier Approximation

In cases where the width of the barrier is large compared to the wavelength $\lambda = 2\pi/k_2$, we can put $k_2 L \gg 1$, or

$$\frac{2 m L^2 (V_0 - E)}{\hbar^2} \gg 1. \tag{14}$$

In this event, the $e^{-4k_2 L}$ and $e^{-2k_2 L}$ terms in Equation (13) approach zero; the second term in the denominator drops away to give

$$T_{\text{THICK}} \approx \frac{16 k_1^2 k_2^2 e^{-2k_2 L}}{(k_1^2 + k_2^2)^2},$$

or, on replacing k_1 and k_2 via Equations (3) and (5),

$$T_{\text{THICK}} \approx 16\left(\frac{E}{V_0}\right)\left(1 - \frac{E}{V_0}\right)e^{-\frac{2L}{\hbar}\sqrt{2m(V_0 - E)}}. \tag{15}$$

Given Equation (14), the term being exponentiated will be large and negative, which will make T_{THICK} exceedingly small. This is demonstrated in the following example.

EXAMPLE 3.4

Electrons of energy $E = 1$ eV are incident on a barrier of height $V_0 = 50$ eV and width $L = 10$ Å. What is the transmission coefficient?

First we verify that the thick barrier approximation is valid:

$$k_2 L = \frac{L\sqrt{2m(V_0 - E)}}{\hbar} = \frac{(10^{-9}\text{ m})\sqrt{2(9.11 \times 10^{-31}\text{ kg})(7.850 \times 10^{-18}\text{ J})}}{1.055 \times 10^{-34}\text{ J} \cdot \text{sec}} = 35.85,$$

which we can regard as $\gg 1$ for the purpose of this example. Hence

$$T \approx 16\left(\frac{1}{50}\right)\left(\frac{49}{50}\right)e^{-71.7} \approx 2.29 \times 10^{-32}.$$

The chance of an electron penetrating the barrier is remote. If 10^6 electrons are incident per second, one would have to wait, on average, some 1.4×10^{18} years for a penetration to occur. This is some eight orders of magnitude greater than the estimated age of the universe. However, such calculations are not without practical value: if the electrons have higher energy, or if the barrier is thinner, tunneling is much more likely. An electronic device known as a Josephson junction depends on quantum tunneling to control tiny currents very precisely by raising and lowering potential differences appropriately.

A variant of the thick barrier scenario is the so-called semi-infinite potential step. In this situation, the thickness of the barrier in Figure 3.15 is allowed to become infinite: $L \to \infty$. The transmission coefficient in this case goes identically to zero: a particle may penetrate into the barrier, but will eventually be turned back.

(b) Thin Barrier Approximation

In this case the thickness of the barrier is assumed to be small with respect to the wavelength of the absorbed wave; that is, $k_2 L \ll 1$. This means that the incoming wave will hardly notice the barrier at all; we can expect $T \sim 1$. Because $e^{-2k_2L} \approx e^{-4k_2L} \sim 1$, the denominator of Equation (13) reduces to $16(k_1^2 k_2^2)$, leaving

$$T_{\text{THIN}} \approx e^{-2k_2L}. \tag{16}$$

Inasmuch as $k_2 L \ll 1$, T_{THIN} will be only slightly less than 1. In itself, this result is not particularly noteworthy. We put it to much more interesting use in the following section.

■ 3.8 Penetration of Arbitrarily Shaped Barriers

Equation (16) gives the transmission coefficient for a matter-wave incident on a thin rectangular barrier of height V_0 and thickness L. In reality, we are not likely to encounter such a barrier; for example, the potential presented by a nucleus to an incoming test particle is likely to have some more complex shape. However, it is possible to derive an expression for the penetration probability in the case of a particle encountering an arbitrarily-shaped barrier by considering the barrier to be comprised of a number of thin barriers placed back to back.

Figure 3.16 illustrates such a case. A particle of mass m and energy E is incident on some potential barrier described by the function $V(x)$.

We divide the barrier into a large number of back-to-back rectangular barriers, each of width Δx. Because each thin barrier has a different height $V(x)$, it will have a different k in Equation (3.7.16):

$$k(x) = \sqrt{\frac{2m\left[V(x) - E\right]}{\hbar^2}}. \tag{1}$$

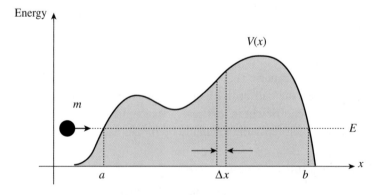

I FIGURE 3.16 General barrier penetration.

If the entire barrier is divided into n sub-barriers, the probability of traversing the entire barrier is just the product of penetrating each sub-barrier in turn:

$$P \sim \left(e^{-2k_1\Delta x}\right)\left(e^{-2k_2\Delta x}\right)\cdots\left(e^{-2k_n\Delta x}\right), \tag{2}$$

where the subscripts now refer to particular sub-barriers. Equation (2) can be expressed more compactly as

$$P \sim e^{-2(k_1+k_2+\cdots+k_n)\Delta x} \sim e^{-2\sum_{i=1}^{n}k_i(x)\Delta x}. \tag{3}$$

The k's are written as functions of x as a reminder to use Equation (1) for each sub-barrier. In the limit of $n \to \infty$, Equation (3) can be replaced by an integral over the entire barrier:

$$P_{\text{PENETRATE}} \sim e^{-2\int k(x)dx},$$

or, on using Equation (1),

$$P_{\text{PENETRATE}} \sim e^{-\frac{2\sqrt{2m}}{\hbar}\int_a^b \sqrt{V(x)-E}\,dx}. \tag{4}$$

The limits of integration in Equation (4) are taken to be the points at which E cuts the $V(x)$ curve (see Figure 3.16). In reality, an incoming particle would time-dependently sense the barrier before striking it, so these limits are an approximation—a complication we ignore.

The presence of the square root in Equation (4) limits the number of cases that can be handled analytically; one often has to resort to numerical integration, as demonstrated in the following example.

EXAMPLE 3.5

A electron of energy $E = A/2$ is incident on a potential barrier given by

$$V(x) = A\,e^{-(x/x_0)^2}.$$

If $A = 1$ eV and $x_0 = 1$ Å, what is the probability of it penetrating the barrier? (Figure 3.17)

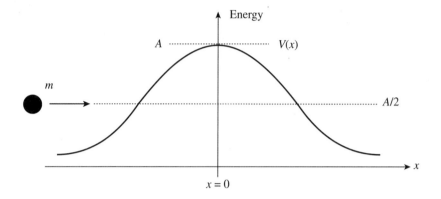

FIGURE 3.17   Example 3.5.

Equation (4) gives

$$\ln P \sim -\frac{2\sqrt{2m}}{\hbar} \int \sqrt{Ae^{-(x/x_0)^2} - E}\; dx.$$

Substituting $E = A/2$ and extracting a common factor of A gives

$$\ln P \sim -\frac{2\sqrt{2mA}}{\hbar} \int \sqrt{e^{-(x/x_0)^2} - 1/2}\; dx.$$

For a reason that will become clear momentarily, it is helpful to define the change of variable $z = x/x_0$, giving

$$\ln P \sim -\frac{2x_0\sqrt{2mA}}{\hbar} \int \sqrt{e^{-z^2} - 1/2}\; dz.$$

The limits of integration correspond to the points at which E cuts the $V(x)$ curve, namely $x = \pm x_0\sqrt{\ln 2}$, or $z = \pm\sqrt{\ln 2}$. Recognizing that the integral is symmetric about $z = 0$, we have

$$\ln P \sim -\frac{4x_0\sqrt{2mA}}{\hbar} \int_0^{\sqrt{\ln 2}} \sqrt{e^{-z^2} - 1/2}\; dz.$$

The advantage of changing variables from x to z is now clear: The integral itself has been rendered dimensionless, a significant convenience inasmuch as it can only be solved numerically. The reader should verify that it evaluates to 0.4416, giving

$$ln\ P \sim -2.498\frac{x_0\sqrt{mA}}{\hbar}.$$

For $A = 1$ eV and $x_0 = 1$ Å, $P \sim 0.4047$, a distinctly nonnegligible result. Techniques of numerical integration are discussed in Chapter 4 of Press et al.[4]

■ 3.9 Alpha-Decay as a Barrier Penetration Effect

Historically, one of the first great successes of quantum mechanics beyond reproducing the energy levels of the hydrogen atom (see Chapter 7) was the explanation of alpha-decay as a barrier penetration process, work published independently by George Gamow and the team of Ronald Gurney and Edward Condon in 1928 [3]. Alpha-decay is a natural process wherein a nucleus spontaneously decays by emitting an alpha-particle, a synonymous term for a helium nucleus. The resulting *daughter nucleus*, having two fewer protons than the original nucleus, is thus an isotope of an element two places lower in the periodic table than the *parent nucleus*. Half-lives for this process vary from microseconds to billions of years, a range of over 20 orders of magnitude. The emitted alpha-particles range in energy from about 4 to 9 MeV, with more energetic decays being accompanied by shorter half-lives. A good example is provided by the decay of the common isotope of uranium, U-238, into thorium-234:

$$^{238}_{92}U \rightarrow ^{234}_{90}Th + ^{4}_{2}He.$$

The half-life of this process is about 4.47 billion years; the α-particle emerges with a kinetic energy of about 4.2 MeV. (It was this particular decay process that led Henri Bequerel to the discovery of radioactivity in early 1896. Although we will refer to this particular case in what follows for sake of specificity, our analysis will be quite general and will ultimately be applied in detail to decay of thorium isotopes.) In papers published in 1911 and 1912, Hans Geiger and John Nutall found a relation between the logarithm of the half-life and the decay energy [4],

$$\ln(t_{1/2}) = a + \frac{b}{\sqrt{E_\alpha}},\qquad(1)$$

---

[4]*Numerical Recipes: The Art of Scientific Computing* by William H. Press, Brian P. Flannery, Saul A. Tuekolsky, and William T. Vetterling (Cambridge, UK: Cambridge University Press, 1986).

where the constants a and b depend on the element involved. Treating α-decay as a barrier penetration process provided an understanding of this otherwise purely empirical result.

The dilemma in trying to understand alpha-decay lay in what was known of nuclear forces. To hold nuclei together against the tremendous repulsive Coulomb forces between protons requires the existence of short-range ($\sim 10^{-15}$ m) but very strongly attractive *nuclear forces* that act between nucleons; the resulting potential can be modeled as a very deep potential well with a spatial extent on the scale of the size of the nucleus [5]. This is sketched in Figure 3.18, where the nuclear potential is represented by a rectangular well of width R; an alpha-particle of charge $+2e$ is trapped within this potential. (In reality, nuclei live in three dimensions. The x-axis in the Figure 3.18 represents a radial coordinate measured from the center of the original nucleus, so x is not defined for $x < 0$. We represent the potential as an infinite wall at $x = 0$, but this will not affect the argument that follows.)

The circles at the base of the figure represent the post-decay nucleus and emitted alpha-particle; we take R to be defined by their center-to-center distance when they are just in contact. After the alpha is emitted it will be strongly repelled by the inverse-square Coulomb force of the daughter nucleus; this is represented by the decreasing curved part of the potential function (the Coulomb potential behaves as $1/r$; see the upcoming

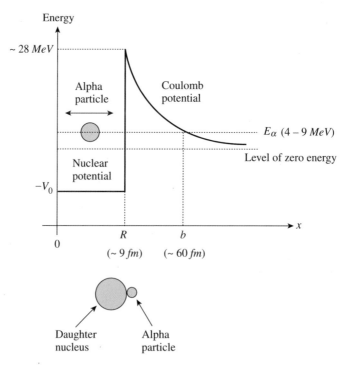

| FIGURE 3.18 Alpha-decay.

Equation (2).) The difficulty in understanding alpha-decay was that nuclear potentials were known to be some tens of MeV deep. How could an alpha-particle of an energy of only a few MeV energy possibly jump out of such a well? Gamow, Gurney, and Condon modeled alpha-decay as a penetration through the nuclear-plus-Coulomb barrier.

To get a sense of the distance scale involved, it is helpful to know that nuclei can be modeled as spheres whose radii depend on their number of nucleons A: $r \sim r_0 A^{1/3}$, where r_0 is empirically known from scattering experiments to be ~ 1.2 fm. (1 fm = 1 femtometer = 10^{-15} m; a femtometer is also known as a Fermi, in honor of Enrico Fermi.) For our thorium-alpha system, for example,

$$R \sim r_0(A_{\mathrm{Th}}^{1/3} + A_{\alpha}^{1/3}) \sim (1.2 \text{ fm})(234^{1/3} + 4^{1/3}) \sim 9.3 \text{ fm}.$$

The potential energy of this system when they are just in contact is given by the Coulomb potential. If Z is the atomic number of the post-decay daughter nucleus, then

$$V(R) = \frac{Q_Z Q_\alpha}{4\pi\epsilon_o R} = \frac{2Ze^2}{4\pi\epsilon_o R}, \tag{2}$$

because the alpha-particle has a charge of $Q_\alpha = 2e$. The combination of constants $e^2/4\pi\epsilon_0$ can be put into more convenient units as

$$\beta = \frac{e^2}{4\pi\epsilon_o} = \frac{(1.6022 \times 10^{-19}\,\mathrm{C})}{4\pi(8.8542 \times 10^{-12}\,\mathrm{C^2/Nm^2})} = 2.3071 \times 10^{-28}\,(\mathrm{J \cdot m})$$

$$= 1.440\,(\mathrm{MeV \cdot fm}). \tag{3}$$

For our post-decay thorium-alpha system, the potential at contact is then

$$V(R) = \frac{2\beta Z}{R} \sim 27.9 \text{ MeV},$$

where we have used $Z = 90$ for the thorium nucleus. The height of the (nuclear + Coulomb) barrier at R is then about 28 MeV, as indicated in Figure 3.18. To reinforce your appreciation of why alpha-decay could not be understood on the basis of classical energetics, imagine running the process in reverse: Fire an α-particle towards a fixed thorium nucleus. If the alpha has only 4.2 MeV of kinetic energy, it would be classically impossible for it to scale the 28-MeV high Coulomb barrier to the point where it would be drawn into and fuse with the nucleus via the effects of nuclear forces. Quantum-mechanically, however, there is a slight probability that the alpha could penetrate through the Coulomb barrier. (An actual alpha-decay is the reverse of this process, but this makes no difference to understanding the situation: Any fundamental physical process should be time-reversible; whether we imagine the α-particle as incoming or escaping makes no difference to the calculation.)

Classically, in the fusion scenario, if the incoming alpha has kinetic energy E_α, then it should be able to approach no more closely to a target nucleus of charge Z than distance b given by

$$b = \frac{2\beta Z}{E_\alpha}.$$
(4)

For the thorium-alpha system with $E_\alpha = 4.2$ MeV, this evaluates (check it!) to $b \sim 62$ fm, or $b \sim 6.6R$; this distance is sketched in Figure 3.18.

We are now ready to proceed with the penetration probability calculation. The potential barrier is described by Equations (2) and (3). For algebraic convenience we work with the natural logarithm of the penetration probability:

$$\ln P_\alpha \sim -\frac{2\sqrt{2m_\alpha}}{\hbar} \int_R^b \sqrt{\frac{2\beta Z}{x} - E_\alpha}\, dx.$$
(5)

Because R is fairly small compared to b, we invoke the approximation $R \sim 0$. Extracting a factor of E_α from within the radical and defining the change of variable $y = x/b$ casts Equation (5) into the form

$$\ln P_\alpha \sim -\frac{2\sqrt{2m_\alpha E_\alpha}\, b}{\hbar} \int_0^1 \sqrt{\frac{1}{y} - 1}\, dy.$$

Substituting for b from Equation (4) and defining another change of variable to $y = \sin^2 w$ gives

$$\ln P_\alpha \sim -\left(\frac{8\beta Z \sqrt{2m_\alpha}}{\hbar \sqrt{E_\alpha}}\right) \int_0^{\pi/2} \cos^2 w\, dw.$$

This integral evaluates to $\pi/4$, giving

$$\ln P_\alpha \sim -\left(\frac{2\beta Z \sqrt{2m_\alpha}\, \pi}{\hbar}\right) \frac{1}{\sqrt{E_\alpha}} \sim -\frac{K}{\sqrt{E_\alpha}},$$
(6)

The constant K defined here is known as the **Gamow factor** for alpha-decay.

To connect this result to the Geiger-Nutall law, we make the following argument: Imagine that the alpha-particle is trapped within the parent nucleus, making N escape attempts per second. The number of successful escapes per second would then be NP_α, and the average time τ between escapes would be the reciprocal of this, $1/(NP_\alpha)$, or $\tau \sim (1/N)\, e^{K/E_\alpha^{1/2}}$. If τ is in some way identifiable with the half-life, we would predict

$$\ln t_{1/2} \sim \ln\left(\frac{1}{N}\right) + \frac{K}{\sqrt{E_\alpha}}. \tag{7}$$

This expression has exactly the same energy dependence as the Geiger-Nutall law! (Strictly, we should imagine a large number of nuclei, each containing an alpha rattling around inside it that is attempting to escape; τ would then represent an average time to escape.) Although reproducing the form of the Geiger-Nutall law is impressive, we can also show that this calculation yields predicted values of K in remarkably good accord with experiment [5].

Table 3.1 lists half-lives and decay energies for seven isotopes of thorium; this element makes for a good test case in view of the tremendous range of half-lives involved, from 10^{-5} seconds to nearly 14 billion years. Thorium decays to radium, which has $Z = 88$. These data are plotted in Figure 3.19.

The straight line in Figure 3.19 is a least-squares fit to the data (E_α is taken to be in MeV and $t_{1/2}$ in seconds):

$$\ln t_{1/2} = -119.84 + \frac{323.87}{\sqrt{E_\alpha}}. \tag{8}$$

Table 3.1   Thorium alpha-decays

Mass number A	E_α (MeV)	Half-life (sec)
220	8.95	10^{-5}
222	8.13	2.18×10^3
224	7.31	1.04
226	6.45	1854
228	5.52	6.0×10^7
230	4.77	2.5×10^{12}
232	4.08	4.4×10^{17}

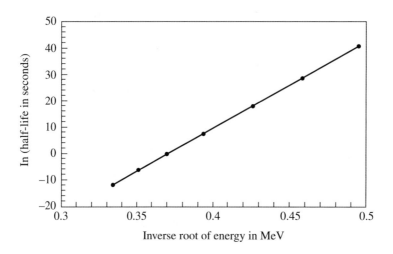

I FIGURE 3.19   Observed and predicted thorium $t_{1/2}$ vs. E_α relationship.

The units of K here are $MeV^{1/2}$. We can get a predicted value of K from Equation (6). To do this, it is helpful to write the mass of an α-particle as an energy equivalent, $m_\alpha = \mu_\alpha/c^2$ where $\mu_\alpha = 3727.38$ MeV. Hence

$$K = \frac{2\beta Z \sqrt{2m_\alpha}\,\pi}{\hbar} = \frac{2\beta Z \sqrt{2\mu_\alpha}\,\pi}{\hbar c}.$$

Now, $\hbar c = 3.1616 \times 10^{-26}$ J $\cdot$ m $\equiv 197.33$ MeV $\cdot$ fm. With the value of β from Equation (3) and $Z = 88$, we predict

$$K = \frac{2(1.440)(88)\sqrt{2(3727.38)}\,\pi}{197.33} = 348.38 \text{ MeV}^{1/2},$$

only about 7.5% high compared to the experimental value. On considering the assumptions that went into this model (modeling a three-dimensional phenomenon as one-dimensional, ignorance of the precise shape of nuclear potentials, and taking $R \sim 0$), this is remarkably good agreement. *The key point is that treating alpha-decay as a barrier-penetration effect provides a natural explanation of the Geiger-Nutall law.* Few physical theories give results even qualitatively consistent with experiment over so many orders of magnitude. The Gamow-Gurney-Condon analysis provided a convincing example of the veracity of wave mechanics and showed at the same time that it is valid *within* nuclei.

■ 3.10 Scattering by One-Dimensional Potential Wells

The last phenomenon we consider in this chapter is the scattering of matter waves from potential wells; that is, a situation wherein a matter-wave encounters a region of lower potential. The situation is illustrated in Figure 3.20.

For convenience we put the top of the well at zero energy; if it is of depth V_0, the bottom of the well will be at $V(x) = -V_0$. The well has width L, with one side located at $x = 0$. A matter-wave of energy $E > 0$ is incident from the left and experiences sudden changes of potential at $x = 0$ and $x = L$, leading to partial reflection and transmission at those positions. In regions 1 and 2 there will be waves propagating both right and left, whereas only a transmitted rightward-propagating wave will presumably be present in region 3. The analysis parallels that of Section 3.7. We can write the wavefunctions as

$$\psi_1(x) = A_0 e^{\iota k_1 x} + A e^{-\iota k_1 x}, \tag{1}$$

$$\psi_2(x) = B e^{\iota k_2 x} + C e^{-\iota k_2 x}, \tag{2}$$

and

$$\psi_3(x) = D e^{\iota k_1 x}, \tag{3}$$

with

$$k_1^2 = \frac{2mE}{\hbar^2} \tag{4}$$

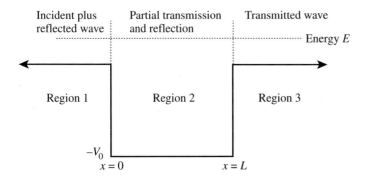

FIGURE 3.20 Scattering by a one-dimensional potential well.

and

$$k_2^2 = \frac{2m(E + V_0)}{\hbar^2}. \tag{5}$$

The difference in sign between Equations (5) and (3.7.5) is due to the fact that the top of the well is now at zero energy. Classically, the incoming particle has sufficient energy to climb back out of the well once it has fallen in. Quantum-mechanically, we will see that there is a nonzero probability of the particle becoming "trapped" inside the well in that the transmission probability need not be unity.

A_0 is again presumed to be experimentally set; the goal is to express D in terms of A_0 and then compute the transmission coefficient $T = D*D$. Applying the usual boundary conditions on the continuity of ψ and its first derivative at $x = 0$ and $x = L$ gives four conditions:

$$A_0 + A = B + C \tag{6}$$

$$\iota k_1 A_0 - \iota k_1 A = \iota k_2 B - \iota k_2 C \tag{7}$$

$$B e^{\iota k_2 L} + C e^{-\iota k_2 L} = D e^{\iota k_1 L} \tag{8}$$

$$\iota k_2 B e^{\iota k_2 L} - \iota k_2 C e^{-\iota k_2 L} = \iota k_1 D e^{\iota k_1 L}. \tag{9}$$

Taking $A_0 = 1$ and solving for D yields, after some algebra,

$$D = \frac{4 k_1 k_2 e^{-\iota k_1 L}}{[(k_1 + k_2)^2 e^{-\iota k_2 L} - (k_2 - k_1)^2 e^{\iota k_2 L}]}. \tag{10}$$

The transmission coefficient $T = D*D$ is given by

$$T = \frac{16 k_1^2 k_2^2}{(k_1 + k_2)^4 - (k_2^2 - k_1^2)^2 (e^{2\iota k_2 L} + e^{-2\iota k_2 L}) + (k_2 - k_1)^4}.$$

This result can be simplified as follows: The first and last terms in the denominator can be expanded and combined to give $2(k_1^4 + 6 k_1^2 k_2^2 + k_2^4)$. The sum of the exponential functions in the middle term can be expressed as $2 \cos(2k_2 L)$ via Euler's identity. Hence

$$T = \frac{16 k_1^2 k_2^2}{2(k_1^4 + 6 k_1^2 k_2^2 + k_2^4) - 2(k_2^2 - k_1^2)^2 \cos(2k_2 L)}.$$

On substituting $\cos(2k_2L) = 2\cos^2(k_2L) - 1$, further simplification results, leaving a fairly compact final result:

$$T = \frac{4k_1^2 k_2^2}{(k_1^2 + k_2^2)^2 - (k_2^2 - k_1^2)^2 \cos^2(k_2L)}. \tag{11}$$

Three interesting cases follow.

(a) Low-Energy Scattering

Here the idea is that the incoming particle is of very low energy compared to the depth of the well: $E \ll V_0$; that is $k_1 \ll k_2$. With $E \sim 0$, we can regard k_1 as effectively zero; k_2 will then have only a weak dependence on E. Setting $k_1 \sim 0$ in the denominator of Equation (11) gives

$$T(E \ll V_0) \sim \frac{4k_1^2}{k_2^2 \sin^2(k_2L)}. \tag{12}$$

The energy-dependence of this result resides primarily in k_1. Because $k_1 \propto \sqrt{E}$, we can conclude that *at low energies the transmission coefficient is proportional to the energy of the incident wave*. As $E \to 0$, the incoming particles are essentially captured by the well.

(b) High-Energy Scattering

In the case of a high-energy incident wave, we have $E \gg V_0$; that is, $k_1 \sim k_2$. In this case, Equation (11) reduces to

$$T(E \gg V_0) \sim 1. \tag{13}$$

This is not surprising: high energy particles barely notice the well.

(c) Resonance Scattering

It would appear from the preceding approximations that perfect transmission ($T = 1$) is never possible. In fact, this is not the case: There are certain energies for which $T = 1$ exactly.

Consider a case where $k_2L = n\pi$, with n an integer. In this event, $\cos^2(k_2L) = 1$, and the denominator of Equation (11) reduces to exactly $4k_1^2 k_2^2$, giving

$$T(k_2L = n\pi) = 1. \tag{14}$$

This is known as a **resonance condition**. At certain energies, the well becomes transparent to the incident matter-wave. The necessary condition is that the width of the well correspond exactly to an integral number of half-wavelengths of the matter-wave (recall that $k = 2\pi/\lambda$). This effect, known as Ramsauer-Townsend scattering [6], manifests itself in the form of a minimum in the scattering cross-section presented by noble-gas atoms to incident electrons. Because noble-gas atoms consist of closed electron shells (Chapter 8), they present a fairly sharply defined force to a bombarding particle.

Combining the condition $k_2 L = n\pi$ with the definition of k_2 gives an explicit expression for the resonance-scattering energies:

$$E_{\text{resonance}} = \frac{1}{2m}\left(\frac{n\pi\hbar}{L}\right)^2 - V_0, \quad (n = 1, 2, 3, \dots). \tag{15}$$

As an example, consider $n = 1$, $m = m_e$, $L = 2$ Å, and $E_{\text{res}} = 1$ eV. These give $V_0 = 8.41$ eV, a quite reasonable number on an atomic scale. The increase of T with E predicted by Equation (11) is, however, so sharp that T remains very close to unity after the first maximum is reached.

■ Summary

The energy levels of the infinite rectangular well are given by

$$E_n = \left(\frac{\pi^2 \hbar^2}{2mL^2}\right)n^2.$$

In general, in any region where $V = $ constant and $E > V$, solutions of the SE take the form

$$\psi(x) = Ae^{\imath kx} + Be^{-\imath kx},$$

where k is given by

$$k^2 = \frac{2m}{\hbar^2}(E - V).$$

When $V = $ constant and $E < V$, then

$$\psi(x) = Ce^{kx} + De^{-kx},$$

with k^2 replaced by $-k^2$. If $V(x)$ is a symmetric function, there will be two families of solutions whose energy levels interleave, one family each of even and odd parity.

The energy levels for a particle of mass m moving in a finite rectangular well of width $2L$ and depth V_0 are given by solving

$$f(\xi, K) = (K^2 - 2\xi^2) \sin(2\xi) + 2\xi \sqrt{K^2 - \xi^2} \cos(2\xi) = 0,$$

where

$$K^2 = \frac{2mV_0L^2}{\hbar^2}$$

is the strength parameter of the well and where

$$\xi = \sqrt{\frac{2mE}{\hbar^2}} L.$$

The number of bound states that can be supported by such a well is given by

$$N(K) = 1 + \left[\frac{2K}{\pi}\right].$$

Solutions to the SE when $E < V$ give rise to the phenomenon of barrier penetration. The probability of finding the particle at a distance x within the barrier decreases exponentially with a characteristic decay length given by

$$\lambda_{\text{tunneling}} \sim \frac{\hbar}{2\sqrt{2m[V(x) - E]}}.$$

The probability of a particle of mass m and energy E penetrating through a rectangular barrier of height V and thickness L depends in a complicated way on all these parameters. For a barrier of arbitrary shape defined by $V(x)$, the penetration probability P is given by

$$P_{\text{PENETRATE}} \sim e^{-\frac{2\sqrt{2m}}{\hbar} \int_a^b \sqrt{V(x) - E}\, dx},$$

where the limits of integration are given by where E cuts the $V(x)$ curve. The half-life of various isotopes to alpha-decay may be understood as a barrier penetration effect.

For a particle of mass m incident on a rectangular potential well of width L and depth $V = -V_0$, 100% transmission will occur at various *resonance energies*, which are given by

$$E_{\text{resonance}} = \frac{1}{2m}\left(\frac{n\pi\hbar}{L}\right)^2 - V_0, \quad (n = 1, 2, 3, \dots).$$

■ Problems

3-1(E) A possible alternate version of Schrödinger's equation is.

$$-\left(\frac{\hbar^2}{2m}\right)\left(\frac{d\psi}{dx}\right)^2 + V\psi^2 = E\psi^2.$$

(*Hint:* See Problem 2–3.) Show that this equation admits no plausible solution for the case of the infinite potential well.

3-2(I) Write a computer program to calculate values for E_n, ψ_n, and ψ_n^2 for an electron in an infinite rectangular well with $L = 10$ Å. Plot separately, to scale, ψ_n and ψ_n^2 for $n = 1$ to 6. What are the energies of these states?

3-3(E) Using classical arguments, derive an expression for the speed v of a particle in a one-dimensional infinite potential well. Apply your result to the case of an electron in a well with $L = 1$ Å. For what value of n does v exceed the speed of light? To what energy does this correspond?

3-4(I) An experimental physicist submits a proposal to a granting agency requesting support to construct an infinite potential well analogous to the one shown in Figure 3.5. Specifically, the proposal is to build a well with $L = 1$ mm, inject some electrons into it, and then measure the wavelengths of photons emitted during low-n transitions via optical spectroscopy. As an expert on quantum mechanics, you are asked to evaluate the proposal. What is your recommendation?

3-5(E) A particle in some potential is described by the wavefunction $\psi(x) = Axe^{-kx}$ ($0 \le x \le \infty$; $k > 0$; see Problem 2–5). If $k = 0.5$ Å^{-1}, what is the probability of finding the particle between $x = 2.0$ and 2.1 Å?

3-6(I) Verify the derivation of Equation (35) in Section 3.3, starting from the wavefunctions given in Equation (3.3.17), and the appropriate boundary conditions.

3-7(I) Verify the assertions leading to Equations (3.3.36) and (3.3.37).

3-8(I) By sketching a few even and odd-parity functions, convince yourself of the assertions in Section 3.6 regarding the parity of solutions for symmetric potentials.

3-9(E) A proton is moving within a nuclear potential of depth 25 MeV and full width $2L = 10^{-14}$ meters. If the potential can be modeled as a finite rectangular well, how many energy states are available to the proton?

3-10(I) Write a computer program to calculate and plot tan (2ξ) and $g(\xi, K)$ as a function of x for various values of K, as shown in Figure 3.10. Verify by comparing against Example 3.2. Run your program for a variety of combinations of m, V_0, and L. Can you discover any trends?

3-11(I) Consider a particle of mass m moving in the semi-infinite potential well illustrated in the following figure. Set up and solve the SE for this system; assume $E < V_0$. Apply the appropriate boundary conditions at $x = 0$ and $x = L$ to derive an expression for the permissible energy eigenvalues. With $V_0 = 10$ eV, $L = 5$ Å and $m = m_{\text{electron}}$, compute the values of the energy (in eV) for the two lowest-energy bound states.

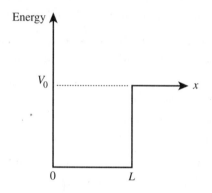

I FIGURE P3.11   Problem 3-11.

3-12(I) Derive an expression analogous to Equation (3.4.11) for the odd-parity states of the finite rectangular well.

3-13(I) **(a)** Show that the eigenvalue condition for the even-parity states of a finite square well can be written as $\xi^2 \tan^2 \xi = K^2(1 - \varepsilon)$, where K is as defined in Equation (3.3.34) and $\varepsilon = E/V_0$.

(b) For low-energy states, ξ will be very small. From your result in part (a), derive an expression for the ξ-values of such states. Apply your result to a case where $K = 1.5$ and compare your result with the exact value.

3-14(E) For the system discussed in Example 3.2, determine the probability of finding the particle outside the well for each of the four possible bound states.

3-15(I) For the potential well illustrated in the following figure, sketch a plausible form for a wavefunction corresponding to energy E.

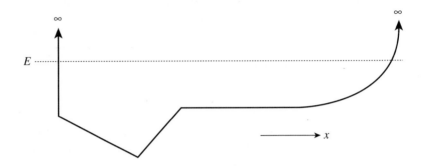

I FIGURE P3.15   Problem 3-15.

3-16(I) Verify the expressions given for D and T in the derivation of the rectangular potential barrier, Equations (3.7.11) and (3.7.13).

3-17(E) Electrons of energy 10 eV are incident on a rectangular potential barrier of height 20 eV and width 50 Å. What is the transmission coefficient?

3-18(E) In quantum tunneling, the penetration probability is sensitive to slight changes in the height and/or width of the barrier. Consider an electron with $V(x) - E = 10$ eV incident on a rectangular barrier of width 20 Å. By what factor does the penetration probability change if the width is increased to 21 Å?

3-19(I) Write a computer program to numerically integrate the barrier-penetration probability Equation (3.8.4) for any m, E, and $V(x)$. Verify by comparing with example 3.5. For this same problem, generate a plot of P vs. E for $E = 0.1A, 0.2A, \ldots, 0.9A$.

3-20(I) A potential barrier is defined by $V(x) = \sqrt{A^2 - \alpha^2 x^2}$, $|x| \leq (A/\alpha)$.

(a) Sketch $V(x)$.

(b) A particle of mass m and energy E ($< A$) is incident on this barrier. Derive an integral expression for the probability of penetration in terms of $\beta = E/A$ and $\sin(y) = \alpha x/A$.

(c) Evaluate your expression in part (b) numerically for $\beta = 0.1$ to 1.0 in steps of 0.1 for an electron striking such a barrier with $A = 10$ eV and $\alpha = 2$ eV/Å. Plot your result.

3-21(I) A potential barrier is defined by $V(x) = V_0 (1 - x/A)$ for $0 \leq x \leq A$; $V(x) = 0$ otherwise. A particle of mass m and energy E ($< V_0$) is incident on this barrier from the left. Derive an expression for the penetration probability. Evaluate your result numerically for an electron incident on such a barrier with $V_0 = 5$ eV, $E = 2$ eV, and $A = 12$ Å. Potentials of this form are used to model the spontaneous escape of electrons from metal surfaces subjected to electric fields, a process known as cold emission. The expression for the transmission probability is known as the *Fowler-Nordheim* formula.

3-22(I) A potential barrier is defined as

$$V(x) = \begin{cases} (V_0/L^2)x^2 & 0 \le x \le L \\ 0 & x < 0; x > L. \end{cases}$$

A particle of mass m and energy $V_0/2$ is incident on this barrier from $x < 0$. Derive an expression for the penetration probability. Evaluate your expression numerically for an electron striking such a barrier with $L = 10$ Å and $V_0 = 5$ eV.

3-23(E) A sprinter of mass 70 kg running at 5 m/s does not have enough kinetic energy to leap a wall of height 5 meters, even if all of that kinetic energy could be directed into an upward leap. If the wall is 0.2 meters thick, estimate the probability of the sprinter being able to "quantum tunnel" through it rather than leaping over it.

3-24(E) From the information given in Section 3.9, compute the approximate number of escape attempts per second for an alpha particle trapped within a thorium nucleus.

3-25(I) The following table gives a list of alpha-decay energies and half-lives for various isotopes of radium, element 88. Does radium follows the Gamow model for α-decay?

Mass number A	E_α (MeV)	Half-life
214	7.136	2.46 sec
220	7.46	0.019 sec
221	6.608	29 sec
222	6.656	38 sec
223	5.716	11.435 days
224	5.686	3.66 days
226	4.784	1599 years

3-26(E) Some nuclei decay by beta-decay, the emission of an ordinary electron. By examining the development of the Gamow factor, would you expect the beta-decay probability for a given nucleus to be greater or less than that for alpha decay, all other factors being equal?

3-27(I) Verify the expression for the transmission coefficient for scattering by a potential well, Equation (3.10.11).

3-28(E) In an experiment involving electron scattering from a finite rectangular well of depth 4 eV, it is found that electrons of energy 5 eV are completely transmitted. What must be the width of the well? At what next higher energy can one expect to again observe $T = 1$?

4 Operators, Expectation Values, and the Uncertainty Principle

In this chapter we consider certain aspects of Schrödinger's equation and matter-waves pertinent to the interpretation of quantum mechanics. The purpose here is not to explore new solutions of the SE, but rather to broaden understanding of how solutions are interpreted. As many of our points are postulates or require much more background to prove rigorously, we will sometimes resort to intuitive justifications.

We begin in Section 4.1 by considering the concept of a mathematical **operator**. By showing how the SE can be expressed in **operator notation**, we gain insight as to what is meant by an **eigenvalue equation**. This leads to a discussion of how mathematical operators relate to physically observable quantities. In Section 4.2 we discuss **expectation values**. The purpose of doing any calculation is, presumably, to compute something that can be compared with experiment, and it is via expectation values that quantum mechanics informs us of its predictions. In Sections 4.3 and 4.4 we give a semi-intuitive justification of the famous **Heisenberg uncertainty principle** and elucidate the recipe by which one can determine whether two quantities will be linked by an uncertainty relation. Section 4.5 is devoted to **Ehrenfest's theorem**, which shows how suitably defined average values of quantities in quantum mechanics agree with the predictions of Newtonian mechanics. Section 4.6 develops the **orthogonality principle**, which will prove to be of great value in the development of perturbation theory in Chapter 9. In Section 4.7 we take up the **superposition theorem**, which will also prove to be of value in developing the perturbation theory in Chapter 9. As an example of an application of this theorem, we construct in Section 4.8 a representation of a moving particle trapped in an infinite rectangular potential well via a time-dependent summation of two infinite-well states. Finally, in Section 4.9, we derive the **virial theorem**, a relationship between the expectation values of kinetic and potential energy for any potential.

■ 4.1 Properties of Operators

Consider again the one-dimensional time-independent Schrödinger equation:

$$\left(-\frac{\hbar^2}{2m}\frac{d^2}{dx^2} + V(x)\right)\psi(x) = E\psi(x). \tag{1}$$

On the left side appears the second derivative of $\psi(x)$(times a constant), plus $V(x)\psi(x)$. The result of this calculation is $E\psi(x)$. The term in large brackets on the left side can be said to perform an operation on $\psi(x)$ and return $E\psi(x)$. Inasmuch as we interpret E as the energy corresponding to $\psi(x)$, this term acts as a **total energy operator**. As in classical physics this is known as the **Hamiltonian operator**, designated by **H**:

$$\mathbf{H} = -\frac{\hbar^2}{2m}\frac{d^2}{dx^2} + V(x). \tag{2}$$

In **operator notation**, then, the SE can be expressed as

$$\mathbf{H}\psi(x) = E\psi(x). \tag{3}$$

An **operator** is an entity that does something to a function and returns a result, not unlike a subroutine in a computer program that processes an input value or function and returns an output value. The operation performed could be to multiply the input function by a constant, differentiate it, integrate it, exponentiate it, add something to it, or so on. There are many possible everyday examples of operators; for example, you can imagine an operator called "tax" that operates on your salary to return the amount of tax to be paid. In isolation an operator is meaningless; only an expression wherein an operator acts on a function has any meaning. Do not make the mistake of thinking that the ψ's in Equation (3) can be canceled out.

We know that only certain functions $\psi(x)$ will satisfy the SE for a given potential $V(x)$. These are known as the **eigenfunctions** corresponding to $V(x)$, and the corresponding constants E are known as the **eigenvalues** corresponding to these eigenfunctions. The general form of an **eigenvalue equation** is

(Operator) (Eigenfunction) = (Eigenvalue) (Eigenfunction). $\qquad$ (4)

As in conventional algebra, the operator acts on whatever quantity or function appears immediately to the right of it, but only if the operator is acting on one of its eigensolutions will the form of Equation (4) be valid. Returning to Equation (1), we can consider the total energy operator to be the sum of individual kinetic-energy and potential-energy operators:

$$KE_{op} = -\frac{\hbar^2}{2m}\frac{d^2}{dx^2} \tag{5}$$

$$PE_{op} = V(x). \tag{6}$$

An example of operator algebra is provided by the infinite-well wavefunctions:

$$\psi_n(x) = \sqrt{\frac{2}{L}}\sin\left(\frac{n\pi x}{L}\right).$$

In this case $V(x) = 0$, so

$$H\psi_n(x) = -\frac{\hbar^2}{2m}\frac{d^2\psi_n(x)}{dx^2}$$

$$= -\frac{\hbar^2}{2m}\frac{d^2}{dx^2}\left(\sqrt{\frac{2}{L}}\sin\left(\frac{n\pi x}{L}\right)\right) = \frac{\hbar^2}{2m}\frac{n^2\pi^2}{L^2}\left(\sqrt{\frac{2}{L}}\sin\left(\frac{n\pi x}{L}\right)\right)$$

$$= E_n\psi_n(x),$$

where we have used Equation (3.2.11).

Aside from energy, there are other **dynamical variables** whose values we may be interested in computing—for example, position, momentum, or angular momentum. What are the operators corresponding to these quantities? That there is an operator corresponding to every observable quantity is a fundamental postulate of quantum mechanics. In simple cases such as position (x), the operator is simply x itself (in three dimensions $\mathbf{r} = x\mathbf{x} + y\mathbf{y} + z\mathbf{z}$ where $\mathbf{x}$, $\mathbf{y}$, and $\mathbf{z}$ are the Cartesian-coordinate unit vectors). The operator for linear momentum can be deduced by considering the expression given in Chapter 2 for a right- or left-propagating matter-wave:

$$\psi(x, t) = Ae^{\pm\frac{i}{\hbar}(px - Et)},$$

Extracting a factor of p by differentiating gives

$$\frac{\partial \psi}{\partial x} = \pm \left(\frac{\iota}{\hbar}\right) p \left\{ A e^{\pm \frac{\iota}{\hbar}(px - Et)} \right\} = \pm \left(\frac{\iota}{\hbar}\right) p \psi,$$

or

$$p\psi \equiv \pm \left(\frac{\hbar}{\iota}\right) \frac{\partial \psi}{\partial x} = \left(\mp \iota \hbar \frac{\partial}{\partial x}\right) \psi,$$

where we have used $1/\iota = -\iota$. The sign ambiguity can be resolved by arguing that, in a wave to the right (or left) we choose the same sign (upper/lower) as is used in the description of the wave. Hence we have

$$(p_x)_{op} = -\iota \hbar \frac{\partial}{\partial x}. \tag{7}$$

Similarly, for the y and z directions, we infer

$$(p_y)_{op} = -\iota \hbar \frac{\partial}{\partial y} \tag{8}$$

and

$$(p_z)_{op} = -\iota \hbar \frac{\partial}{\partial z}. \tag{9}$$

Notice that we have switched to partial-derivative notation, as each of p_x, p_y, and p_z differentiate with respect to only one coordinate. These results can be summarized in a convenient vector form which makes no explicit mention of any particular coordinate system:

$$\boldsymbol{p}_{op} = -\iota \hbar \, \nabla, \tag{10}$$

where ∇ is the gradient operator. Some useful operators are summarized in Table 4.1.

Table 4.1   Useful Operators

Physical Quantity	Operator
Position	x
Linear momentum	$-\iota\hbar\nabla$
Kinetic Energy	$-\dfrac{\hbar^2}{2m}\nabla^2$
Potential Energy	$V(x)$
Any function $f(x)$ of x	$f(x)$

Just as one can multiply together a string of numbers, it is possible to successively treat a function by the action of a number of operators. There is, however, an important difference between ordinary algebra and operator algebra: in the latter, the order of operations can make a difference to the final outcome; that is, operator algebra is not necessarily commutative. An example utilizing the position, momentum, and kinetic energy operators will illustrate this point. Consider some arbitrary function $f(x)$ operated on first by the position operator and then by the momentum operator:

$$(p_x)_{op}[(x)_{op}f(x)] = (p_x)_{op}[xf(x)] = -\iota\hbar\frac{\partial}{\partial x}[xf(x)]$$

$$= -\iota\hbar\left[f(x) + x\frac{df}{dx}\right]. \qquad (11a)$$

On the other hand, if the order of the operators is reversed, we find

$$(x)_{op}[(p_x)_{op}f(x)] = (x)_{op}\left[-\iota\hbar\frac{\partial}{\partial x}f(x)\right] = -\iota\hbar\,x\frac{df}{dx}. \qquad (11b)$$

Only if $f(x) = 0$ will the operators for p and x commute, in which case we would be left with a null wavefunction. In other instances, however, the overall result is insensitive to the order of the operators:

$$(p_x)_{op}[(\mathrm{KE})_{op}f(x)] = (p_x)_{op}\left[-\frac{\hbar^2}{2m}\frac{d^2f}{dx^2}\right] = \frac{\iota\hbar^3}{2m}\frac{d^3f}{dx^3}, \qquad (12a)$$

and

$$(KE)_{op}[(p_x)_{op} f(x)] = (KE)_{op}\left[-\iota\hbar \frac{df}{dx}\right] = \frac{\iota\hbar^3}{2m}\frac{d^3f}{dx^3}. \tag{12b}$$

At present, the fact that the order of operations may or may not have an influence on the result of a calculation is academic. Later we will see that this feature is closely linked to Heisenberg's uncertainty principle.

Some comments on notation are appropriate here. Normally, bold type is reserved to denote vectors or vector operators such as that for linear momentum. An exception to this is to use H to designate the Hamiltonian operator, a scalar quantity (Equation 2). Also, we will henceforth often drop the superfluous "op" notation when there is little possibility of confusion arising.

■ 4.2   Expectation Values

We have already seen that some questions in quantum contexts will yield exact answers ("What is the energy of a particle in the $n = 3$ state of an infinite well?") whereas others can only be answered in terms of a probability distribution ("What is the position of the particle?"). In these latter cases, however, further information can be gleaned by rephrasing the question. Although it may be meaningless to ask where the particle is at any particular time, it is meaningful to ask what its *average* position is. Experimentally, one might answer such a question by preparing a large number of identical infinite wells containing electrons in the $n = 3$ state, somehow measure their positions simultaneously, and then average the results. The theoretically predicted value of this average is known as the **expectation value** of the position, designated by $\langle x \rangle$. Our goal in this section is to devise a procedure for expressing the expectation value of any function of x in terms of $\psi(x)$.

To establish the relationship between expectation values and probability distributions, it is helpful to start with the familiar concept of an arithmetic average. Suppose one takes a census of the heights of a number N individuals; if we designate the height of individual i to be x_i, then the average height will be given by

$$\langle x \rangle = \frac{1}{N}\sum_{i=1}^{N} x_i. \tag{1}$$

Now imagine binning the results; that is, counting up, histogram-style, the number of individuals in various height ranges. This is shown schematically in Figure 4.1.

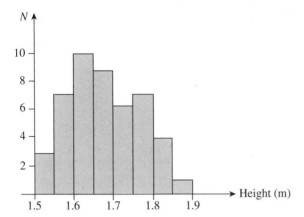

FIGURE 4.1   A hypothetical distribution of heights.

Designate bins by index j; if x_j designates the height corresponding to the middle of the range of bin j, and n_j the number of people falling in bin j, then the average height can be expressed as

$$\langle x \rangle = \frac{1}{N} \sum_{\text{bins } j} (\text{height corresponding to bin } j)(\text{number of people in bin } j)$$

or,

$$\langle x \rangle = \frac{1}{N} \sum_{\text{bins } j} x_j n_j = \sum_{\text{bins } j} x_j \left(\frac{n_j}{N} \right). \tag{2}$$

Now, n_j/N is just the ratio of the number of people falling in bin j to the total sample size. This is exactly the probability p_j of a randomly chosen individual falling in bin j:

$$\langle x \rangle = \sum_{\text{bins } j} x_j p_j. \tag{3}$$

Summing over all possible bins is equivalent to summing over all possible heights; Equation (3) can then be cast into a more suggestive form:

$$\langle x \rangle = \sum_{\text{all } x} x \, p(x). \tag{4}$$

In words, the average of some quantity x is just the sum (over all possible values of x) of x times the probability of a given member of the sample having as x its value for the quantity under consideration.

A simple example with a discretely valued variable can be used to illustrate Equation (4). Suppose that a census of a group of 30 students reveals 3 who are each enrolled in 3 courses, 18 who are each enrolled in 4 courses, 8 who are each enrolled in 5 courses, and 1 who is enrolled in 6 courses. The variable x is the number of courses that a student is enrolled in, and the index of summation j runs from 3 to 6. (Why?) The probability that a given student in the group is enrolled in {3, 4, 5, 6} courses is given by {3/30, 18/30, 8/30, 1/30} = {0.100, 0.600, 0.267, 0.033}; these numbers are the (n_j/N) of Equation (2). Note that the probabilities add up to unity. The average number of courses that any student is enrolled is then computed from Equation (4) as 3(0.l00) + 4(0.600) +5(0.267) + 6(0.033) = 4.233. (This could also be computed from the total number of student courses involved, 127, divided by the number of students.) Note that no student is actually enrolled in the average number of courses! This last feature is analogous to what happens in what are known as quantum mechanical *superposition states* (see Sections 4.8 and 9.2): a measurement of the number of courses that any one student is enrolled in will yield a discrete "eigenvalue" of 3, 4, 5, or 6, but the average is not (and in general will not be) one of the eigenvalues.

In the context of a quantum-mechanical average, we know that the probability of finding a particle between x and $x + dx$ is $\psi^*(x)\,\psi(x)\,dx$. On realizing that position is a continuous variable and not a discrete one, we can write the average or **expectation value** of position as

$$\langle x \rangle = \int x\psi^*(x)\psi(x)\,dx. \tag{5}$$

The limits of integration in any particular case correspond to the physical limits of space that the particle could occupy. Sometimes these are written purely formally as $\pm\infty$.

What if one wishes to compute the expectation value of a quantity that is a function of position or involves derivatives of position—momentum or energy, for example? The general rule for calculating expectation values is:

$$\langle \text{observable} \rangle = \int \psi^*(x)[(\text{Operator})\psi(x)]\,dx, \tag{6}$$

where (Operator) denotes the operator corresponding to the observable of interest. The order of computation is important here. First, [(Operator)$\psi(x)$] is computed. The result of this is then multiplied by ψ^*, and then the integral is carried out.

A formal proof of Equation (6) is rather involved. For the moment, it is sufficient to say that this form for computing expectation values is the only one consistent with the intuitive notion that the results of quantum calculations correspond to their Newtonian counterparts when one averages over the system. We discuss this point further in Section 4.5.

It is worth emphasizing that eigenvalues (for example, the possible "stationary energy states" of a system) and expectation values are very different quantities. As explained further in Section 4.8, a single measurement on a system will *always* yield one of the possible eigenvalues, but not necessarily the expectation value. Only if the system is in a time-independent stationary state will a measurement result in the expectation value. A time-dependent phenomenon such as the motion of a particle can only be modeled via what are known as *superposition* states (see Sections 4.7 and 4.8), in which case the expectation value of some quantity is a sort of average of its possible eigenvalues.

EXAMPLE 4.1

Use Equation (6) to compute $\langle x \rangle, \langle p \rangle, \langle E \rangle, \langle x^2 \rangle$, and $\langle p^2 \rangle$ for the infinite-well wavefunctions.

We have

$$\psi_n(x) = \sqrt{\frac{2}{L}} \sin\left(\frac{n\pi x}{L}\right),$$

According to Equation (6), and setting $a = n\pi/L$,

$$\langle x \rangle = \int_0^L \psi_n^*(x)\{x\psi_n(x)\}dx = \frac{2}{L}\int_0^L \sin(ax)\{x\sin(ax)\}dx$$

$$= \frac{2}{L}\int_0^L x\sin^2(ax)\,dx = \frac{2}{L}\left[\frac{x^2}{4} - \frac{x\sin(2ax)}{4a} - \frac{\cos(2ax)}{8a^2}\right]_0^L$$

$$= \frac{L}{2}.$$

This result means that the average of many measurements of the position of a particle in an infinite well would be $x = L/2$. Notice that this result is independent of the state number n. This is consistent with the fact that, because the well is symmetric, the particle should have no reason to prefer one side to the other no matter what state it is in.

When computing $\langle p \rangle$, care must be taken to respect the differential nature of $(p_x)_{op}$:

$$\langle p \rangle = \int_0^L \psi_n^*(x)\left[-\iota\hbar\frac{d}{dx}\psi_n(x)\right]dx = -\frac{2\iota\hbar}{L}\int_0^L \sin(ax)\left[\frac{d}{dx}\sin(ax)\right]dx$$

$$= -\frac{2\iota a\hbar}{L}\int_0^L \sin(ax)\cos(ax)dx = -\frac{\iota\hbar}{L}[\sin^2(ax)]_0^L = 0.$$

This result is also not surprising: the symmetry of the well is such that the particle should have no preference for traveling one way or the other.

The expectation value of the energy proceeds similarly:

$$\langle E \rangle = \int_0^L \psi_n^*(x)[H\psi_n(x)]dx = \frac{2}{L}\int_0^L \sin(ax)\left[-\frac{\hbar^2}{2m}\frac{d^2}{dx^2}\sin(ax)\right]dx$$

$$= \frac{\hbar^2 a^2}{mL}\int_0^L \sin^2(ax)\,dx = \frac{\hbar^2\pi^2 n^2}{mL^3}\left[\frac{x}{2} - \frac{\sin(2ax)}{4a}\right]_0^L$$

$$= \frac{\hbar^2\pi^2 n^2}{2mL^2} = E_n.$$

The expectation value of the energy for infinite well state n is just the energy eigenvalue of that state.

For $\langle x^2 \rangle$ we have

$$\langle x^2 \rangle = \int_0^L \psi_n^*(x)[x^2\psi_n(x)]dx = \frac{2}{L}\int_0^L x^2\sin^2(ax)dx$$

$$= \frac{2}{L}\left[\frac{x^3}{6} - \left(\frac{x^2}{4a} - \frac{1}{8a^3}\right)\sin(2ax) - \frac{x\cos(2ax)}{4a^2}\right]_0^L = \frac{2}{L}\left[\frac{L^3}{6} - \frac{L^3}{4\pi^2 n^2}\right]$$

$$= \frac{L^2}{3}\left[1 - \frac{3}{2\pi^2 n^2}\right].$$

Note that $\langle x \rangle^2$ is not equal to $\langle x^2 \rangle$; they are different quantities having different interpretations. $\langle x \rangle^2$ is the square of the mean value of the position, whereas $\langle x^2 \rangle$ is the mean value of (position squared).

The operator for any power of the linear momentum can be derived by operating $(p)_{op}$ successively on itself. Working in one dimension,

$$p_x^2 = (p_x)(p_x) = \left(-\iota\hbar\frac{\partial}{\partial x} \right)\left(-\iota\hbar\frac{\partial}{\partial x} \right) = -\hbar^2\frac{\partial^2}{\partial x^2} = 2m(KE).$$

Hence, for the infinite-well wavefunctions,

$$\langle p^2 \rangle = 2m < KE > \; = \frac{\pi^2\hbar^2 n^2}{L^2}.$$

Note that $\langle x^2 \rangle$ and $\langle p^2 \rangle$ have units of (length)^2 and (momentum)^2, respectively. These results will be used later (in Example 4.3) to establish measures of the spreads of p and x about their mean values.

EXAMPLE 4.2

In Chapter 7 we study the hydrogen atom, where we will often encounter wavefunctions of the form $\psi(x) = Ax^n e^{-kx/2}$, $0 \leq x \leq \infty$, with k positive and n being a positive integer. Such a function always exhibits a maximum at some value of x followed by an infinitely long exponential tail.

(a) If this function is to be normalized, what must be the value of A?

(b) At what value of x does ψ reach a maximum? What is $\langle x \rangle$, and how does it compare to the value of x at which ψ reaches a maximum?

Normalizing demands

$$A^2 \int_0^\infty x^{2n} e^{-kx} dx = 1.$$

This integral can be evaluated with the help of Appendix C, and emerges as $(2n)!/k^{2n+1}$. Hence

$$A^2 = \frac{k^{2n+1}}{(2n)!}.$$

To find where ψ reaches its maximum value, set $d\psi/dx = 0$:

$$\frac{d\psi}{dx} = A(nx^{n-1} - kx^n/2)e^{-kx/2} = 0$$

$$\Rightarrow x_{max} = \frac{2n}{k}.$$

Now, the expectation value of x is given by

$$\langle x \rangle = \int \psi x \psi \, dx = A^2 \int_0^\infty x^{2n+1} e^{-kx} dx.$$

Appendix C is again useful, giving

$$\langle x \rangle = A^2 \frac{(2n+1)!}{k^{2n+2}} = \frac{k^{2n+1}(2n+1)!}{(2n)!} \frac{}{k^{2n+2}} = \frac{2n+1}{k}.$$

For all n, the mean value of x exceeds the value of x at which ψ reaches its maximum value:

$$\frac{\langle x \rangle}{x_{max}} = \frac{2n+1}{2n}.$$

Integrals of the general form of Equation (6) arise frequently in quantum-mechanical calculations. To reduce the tedium of writing these out, it is convenient to adopt a shorthand known as **Dirac notation** (also known as Dirac **braket** notation). In this notation, the expectation value of $f(x)$ is written as $\langle \psi^*(x) | f(x) | \psi(x) \rangle$:

$$\langle \psi^*(x) | f(x) | \psi(x) \rangle = \int \psi^*(x) \{Op[f(x)]\} \psi(x) dx, \tag{7}$$

where $|f(x)|$ denotes $Op[f(x)]$, the operator corresponding to $f(x)$. A further simplification is to drop the wavefunctions and simply write $\langle f(x) \rangle$. In this system of notation, there need not even be an operator involved. For example, the **overlap integral** of two functions $\psi_1(x)$ and $\psi_2(x)$ (which are presumed to be valid over the same domain of x) can be written in Dirac notation as

$$\langle \psi_1 | \psi_2 \rangle = \int \psi_1(x) \psi_2(x) \, dx. \tag{8}$$

This is also known as the **inner product** of $\psi_1(x)$ and $\psi_2(x)$. These various forms of Dirac notation will often be invoked throughout the remainder of this book in order to simplify writing integrals.

Before closing this section, an interesting corollary can be made to the argument above that $\langle p \rangle = 0$ for the infinite-well wavefunctions is not surprising in view of the symmetry of the situation. One can in fact show that $\langle p \rangle = 0$ for any time-independent wavefunction. In general, the momentum operator is given in three dimensions by $\mathbf{p} = -\iota\hbar\nabla$. Hence

$$\langle \mathbf{p} \rangle = -\iota\hbar \int_V \psi(\nabla\psi) \, dV$$

where the integral extends over the volume domain of ψ; dV is an element of volume. Because $\psi(\nabla\psi) = \frac{1}{2}\nabla(\psi^2)$, we can write this as

$$\langle \mathbf{p} \rangle = -\frac{\iota\hbar}{2} \int_V \nabla(\psi^2) \, dV.$$

Now, the divergence theorem (also known as Gauss's theorem and Green's theorem) from vector calculus tells us that the volume integral of the gradient of a function can be replaced with the integral of the function over the surface that bounds that volume:

$$\langle \mathbf{p} \rangle = -\frac{\iota\hbar}{2} \int_S \psi^2 \, d\mathbf{S}, \tag{9}$$

where $d\mathbf{S}$ denotes an outwardly directed element of surface area bounding the volume V. Because the limits of any potential extend, in principle, to the edge of the universe, we are forced to conclude that ψ must always vanish asymptotically in order for it to be to be normalizable. That is, $[\psi^2]_{\text{boundaries}} = 0$ in general, and so we must have $\langle p \rangle = 0$ always.

That we have found $\langle p \rangle = 0$ here is not terribly surprising: intuitively, we would expect a time-independent wavefunction to have a time-independent expectation value for its position (that is, $\langle r \rangle = $ constant). This is because the position operator (r) has no time-dependence, from which it follows that $\langle p \rangle = 0$. Thus, a quantum particle with a time-independent ψ can be considered as analogous to a classical particle that is stationary. This result, although simple, points to a curious aspect of the quantum momentum operator. In classical mechanics, momentum is given by a time derivative: $\langle p \rangle = mv = m(dr/dt)$, but in quantum mechanics it is given by a spatial derivative: $p \equiv -\iota\hbar\nabla$. Classically, taking a spatial derivative to find momentum would be considered completely wrong, but, quantum mechanically, it works. Even if the spatial derivative is nonzero for a time-independent ψ, the boundary conditions guarantee $\langle p \rangle = 0$. This curious behavior of the p operator is yet another example of quantum counterintuitiveness.

■ 4.3 The Uncertainty Principle

Because particles possess a wave nature, it is impossible to specify their positions precisely. A quantitative statement of this uncertainty is embodied in the **Heisenberg uncertainty principle**. We begin with a qualitative argument to illustrate this important principle before moving on to a formal statement of it.

Figure 4.2 shows two hypothetical matter-waves. Pattern (a) is a segment of a sine curve of wavelength λ that otherwise extends from $-\infty$ to $+\infty$, whereas pattern (b) represents a matter-wave where the bulk of the particle is found within some spatial extent Δx. (Such a "wave packet" can be constructed using a technique known as superposition—see Sections 4.7 and 4.8.)

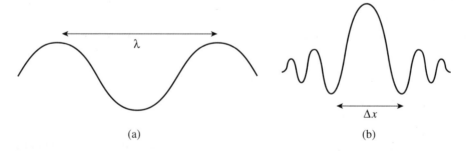

(a)   (b)

I FIGURE 4.2 Hypothetical matter-waves.

Pattern (a) can be described by a well-defined wavelength λ. Via the de Broglie wavelength we then have precise knowledge of the momentum of this matter-wave: $p = h/\lambda$. In case (b), however, the particle is essentially confined in a region of space of extent Δx. However, in localizing this wave packet we sacrifice precise knowledge of its momentum because the pattern is described by no unique wavelength. If you are familiar with Fourier analysis you will know that any wave pattern can be constructed by addition of a number of waves of appropriate amplitudes and frequencies. If the desired pattern is highly localized like pattern (b), then a great number of sine and cosine terms must be summed; that is, there will be a large number of contributing momenta. By adding more and more terms, Δx can be made arbitrarily small, but at the expense of the particle's momentum becoming less and less well-known. Nature thus imposes limits on how precisely we can know position and momentum simultaneously.

A formal statement of the uncertainty principle is as follows. If we define the uncertainty in x and p to be their variances

$$\Delta x = \sqrt{\langle x^2 \rangle - \langle x \rangle^2} \tag{1}$$

and

$$\Delta p = \sqrt{\langle p^2 \rangle - \langle p \rangle^2}, \tag{2}$$

then the product $\Delta x \, \Delta p$ must obey the restriction

$$\Delta x \, \Delta p \geq \hbar/2. \tag{3}$$

EXAMPLE 4.3

Use the results of Example 4.1 to calculate $\Delta x \, \Delta p$ for a particle moving in an infinite rectangular well.

From Example 4.1 we have

$$\langle x \rangle = L/2,$$

$$\langle p \rangle = 0,$$

$$\langle x^2 \rangle = \frac{L^2}{3}\left[1 - \frac{3}{2\pi^2 n^2}\right],$$

and

$$\langle p^2 \rangle = \frac{\pi^2 \hbar^2 n^2}{L^2}.$$

These give

$$\Delta x = L \sqrt{\frac{1}{12} - \frac{1}{2\pi^2 n^2}}$$

and

$$\Delta p = \frac{\pi \hbar n}{L}.$$

Therefore

$$\Delta x \, \Delta p = \sqrt{\frac{n^2 \pi^2}{12} - \frac{1}{2}} \, \hbar.$$

The minimum value of $(\Delta x \, \Delta p)$ obtains for $n = 1$, where

$$(\Delta x \, \Delta p)_{n=1} = 0.568 \, \hbar \quad (\geq 0.5 \, \hbar).$$

For large values of n, we find

$$(\Delta x \, \Delta p)_{n \to \infty} \approx \frac{n \pi \hbar}{\sqrt{12}} \approx 0.907 n \hbar.$$

Parenthetically, one might wonder if there is any potential having a wavefunction that realizes the minimum possible $\Delta x \Delta p$. There is: the ground-state of the simple harmonic oscillator (SHO) potential; the wavefunction in this case has a Gaussian form, $\psi \sim e^{-kx^2}$. We will study this potential and its solutions in Chapter 5.

An important practical aspect of the uncertainty principle lies in its use as a means to estimate ground state energies for a particle moving in a given potential. Consider again an infinite well of width L. Knowing that the particle must be confined within the well gives $\Delta x \leq L$. From symmetry we can argue that $\langle p \rangle = 0$, hence $\Delta p = \sqrt{\langle p^2 \rangle} = \sqrt{2m\langle E \rangle}$. As a result we have

$$L\sqrt{2m\langle E \rangle} \geq \hbar/2,$$

or

$$\langle E \rangle \geq \frac{\hbar^2}{8mL^2}.$$

Comparing this result with the exact value, Equation (3.2.11), shows that we are low by a factor of $4\pi^2$. Uncertainty-based arguments for ground state energies will not in general yield exact results, but are useful for establishing approximate estimates and for determining how the energy eigenvalues of a system depend on the parameters of the system. The following example demonstrates this.

EXAMPLE 4.4

The harmonic oscillator potential is given by $V(x) = kx^2/2$, $-\infty \leq x \leq \infty$. Use the uncertainty principle to estimate the ground-state energy for a particle of mass m moving in this potential.

This potential is symmetric about $x = 0$, so we must have $\langle x \rangle = \langle p \rangle = 0$. We can write the total energy of the system as

$$E = \frac{p^2}{2m} + V(x) = \frac{p^2}{2m} + \frac{kx^2}{2}.$$

We can write the average value of the total energy as the sum of the average values of the kinetic and potential energies:

$$\langle E \rangle = \frac{\langle p^2 \rangle}{2m} + \frac{k}{2}\langle x^2 \rangle.$$

Hence

$$\Delta x = \sqrt{\langle x^2 \rangle - \langle x \rangle^2} = \sqrt{\langle x^2 \rangle}$$

and

$$\Delta p = \sqrt{\langle p^2 \rangle - \langle p \rangle^2} = \sqrt{\langle p^2 \rangle}.$$

Hence

$$< E > \; = \frac{(\Delta p)^2}{2m} + \frac{k}{2}(\Delta x)^2.$$

The uncertainty relation demands

$$\Delta p \geq \frac{\hbar}{2(\Delta x)},$$

hence

$$\langle E \rangle = \frac{\hbar^2}{8m(\Delta x)^2} + \frac{k}{2}(\Delta x)^2.$$

The minimum possible value of E is found by minimizing this result with respect to Δx. Setting $d\langle E \rangle / d(\Delta x)$ to zero gives

$$\frac{d\langle E \rangle}{d(\Delta x)} = -\frac{\hbar^2}{4m(\Delta x)^3} + k(\Delta x) = 0,$$

or

$$(\Delta x)_{\min}^4 = \frac{\hbar^2}{4km}.$$

Substituting this result in the expression for $\langle E \rangle$ gives

$$\langle E \rangle \geq \hbar \omega / 2.$$

where ω is the classical angular frequency of the oscillator, $\sqrt{k/m}$. We will see in Chapter 5 that this ground-state energy is exactly what is predicted by a formal solution of Schrödinger's equation for this potential.

A proof of the uncertainty principle is somewhat lengthy, but worth looking at in view of its historical importance. So as not to disturb the flow of the text, the proof appears in Appendix A1. A website on Heisenberg's life and work prepared by the American Institute of Physics can be found at http://www.aip.org/history/heisenberg/.

■ 4.4   Commutators and Uncertainty Relations

How can one know *a priori* whether or not two observable quantities will obey an uncertainty relation? Equivalently, one might ask under what circumstances is it possible to measure simultaneous eigenvalues for two operators? We can answer this in terms of a generalized uncertainty relation. Consider any two operators A and B, and their corresponding variances ΔA and ΔB, defined as in Equation (1) in the previous section. It is possible to show [1] that these operators obey the general uncertainty relation

$$(\Delta A)(\Delta B) \geq \frac{1}{2}\sqrt{-[A,B]^2}, \tag{1}$$

where $[A, B]$ is itself an operator, known as the **commutator** of operators A and B, defined as

$$[A, B] = A_{op}B_{op} - B_{op}A_{op}. \tag{2}$$

If $[A, B]$ is nonzero, then there will be an uncertainty relation linking A and B. Pairs of physical variables that are linked by an uncertainty relation are known as **conjugate** or **complementary** variables. From the form of Equation (2), it is obvious that if a wavefunction is an eigenfunction of both A and B, then the order of operations does not matter and we will find $[A, B] = 0$; that is, the eigenvalues of A and B will be measurable simultaneously.

We can verify the uncertainty principle in one dimension for $(\Delta x \, \Delta p_x)$ via these general relations. Recall

$$x_{op} = x, \tag{3}$$

and

$$(p_x)_{op} = -\iota \hbar \frac{d}{dx}. \tag{4}$$

Using a dummy wavefunction ψ to keep the order of differentiations straight, we have (now dropping the "op" notation)

$$[x, p_x]\psi = (xp - px)\psi = \{x(p\psi) - p(x\psi)\}$$

$$= \left\{ x\left(-\iota\hbar\frac{d\psi}{dx}\right) + \iota\hbar\frac{d}{dx}(x\psi) \right\} = \iota\hbar \left\{ -x\frac{d\psi}{dx} + x\frac{d\psi}{dx} + \psi \right\}$$

$$= (\iota\hbar)\psi.$$

Hence,

$$[x, p_x] \equiv \iota\hbar,$$

and

$$(\Delta x)(\Delta p_x) \geq \frac{1}{2}\sqrt{-(\iota\hbar)^2},$$

or,

$$(\Delta x)(\Delta p_x) \geq \frac{\hbar}{2},$$

precisely the uncertainty principle.

A considerable amount of very muddy philosophy has been written around the uncertainty principle. Pais [2] summarizes the situation elegantly in the following quotation:

I have often felt that the expression uncertainty relation is unfortunate since it has all too often invoked imagery in popular writings utterly different from what Heisenberg very clearly had in mind, to wit, that the issue is not: what don't I know? but rather: what can't I know? In common language, "I am uncertain" does not exclude "I could be certain." It might therefore have been better had the term unknowability relations been used. Of course one neither can nor should do anything about that now.

Before closing this section, we establish a property of commutators that will be useful in Chapter 7. Suppose that we have three operators, A, B, and C, and that we wish to evaluate the commutator $[AB, C]\psi$. Tempting as it might be to factor the operator A outside of the square bracket and write $A[B, C]\psi$, this would not be a correct manipulation as it would change the order of the operations. A form of factoring can be achieved, however, by the following argument. The correct expansion of the commutator is

$$[AB,C]\psi = AB(C\psi) - C(AB\psi).$$

Now, it is quite legal to add to the right side of this expression the quantity $AC(B\psi) - AC(B\psi)$, because the net effect of such an addition is to add nothing:

$$[AB,C]\psi = AB(C\psi) - C(AB\psi) + AC(B\psi) - AC(B\psi).$$

Rearrange the right side of this expression to bring the first and fourth and second and third terms together:

$$[AB,C]\psi = A(BC - CB)\psi + (AC - CA)(B\psi).$$

Convince yourself that this is a legitimate rearrangement. The first bracketed term on the right side is just the commutator of B and C, and the second is the commutator of A and C:

$$[AB,C]\psi = A[B,C]\psi + [A,C](B\psi),$$

that is, we can factor the original commutator into the form

$$[AB,C] \equiv A[B,C] + [A,C]B. \tag{5}$$

EXAMPLE 4.5

A wavefunction ψ has an energy eigenvalue E given by $H\psi = E\psi$, where H is the Hamiltonian operator $H = -\epsilon(d^2/dx^2) + V(x)$, $\epsilon = (\hbar^2/2m)$. Taking $A \equiv x$, $B \equiv p_x$ and $C \equiv H$, evaluate $[xp_x, H]$ using Equation (5).
First compute $A[B, C]\psi$:

$$A[B,C]\psi = x(p_xH - Hp_x)\psi = x\{p_x(E\psi) - H(-\iota\hbar\psi')\},$$

where we use a prime to denote differentiation with respect to x. Applying the Hamiltonian operator gives

$$A[B,C]\psi = x\left\{(-\iota\hbar)(E\psi') - \left(-\epsilon\frac{d^2}{dx^2} + V\right)(-\iota\hbar\,\psi')\right\}$$

$$= x\{(-\iota\hbar)(E\psi') + (\iota\hbar)(-\epsilon\psi''' + V\psi')\}$$

$$= (\iota\hbar)\{xV\psi' - Ex\psi' - \epsilon x\psi'''\}.$$

The other term on the right side of Equation (5) is

$$[A, C](B\psi) = [x, H](p_x\psi) = (-\iota\hbar)[x, H]\psi'$$

$$= (-\iota\hbar)\{x(H\psi') - H(x\psi')\}$$

$$= (-\iota\hbar)\left\{x\left(-\epsilon\frac{d^2}{dx^2} + V\right)(\psi') - \left(-\epsilon\frac{d^2}{dx^2} + V\right)(x\psi')\right\}$$

$$= (-\iota\hbar)\{-\epsilon x\psi''' + xV\psi' - (-2\epsilon\psi'' - \epsilon x\psi''' + xV\psi')\}$$

$$= (\iota\hbar)\{-2\epsilon\psi''\}.$$

Hence

$$[xp_x, H] = (\iota\hbar)\{xV\psi' - Ex\psi' - \epsilon x\psi''' - 2\epsilon\psi''\}.$$

■ 4.5 Ehrenfest's Theorem

As alluded to in Section 4.2, it is possible to show that quantum-mechanical expectation values are in accord with the laws of classical physics if those expectation values are computed according to Equation (4.2.6). We now prove this assertion, which is known as Ehrenfest's theorem [3]. Our proof will be three-dimensional for sake of generality.

Consider a system with some wavefunction $\Psi(x, t)$. (We use an uppercase symbol for the wavefunction as a reminder that it is in general a function of position and time.) The expectation value of the linear momentum $\boldsymbol{p}$ is given by

$$\langle \boldsymbol{p} \rangle = -\iota\hbar \int \Psi^* \nabla \Psi \, dV, \tag{1}$$

where dV designates a three-dimensional volume element. Now, Newton's laws relate force to the rate of change of momentum. However, a force can always be expressed as the negative gradient of a potential:

$$\boldsymbol{F} = \frac{d\boldsymbol{p}}{dt} = -\nabla U, \tag{2}$$

where we use U to denote the potential function to avoid confusion with the volume element dV. If we can show that $\langle d\boldsymbol{p}/dt \rangle = -\langle \nabla U \rangle$, then we can conclude that, *on average*, a quantum system will behave in accord with classical mechanics. From Equation (1) we have

$$\frac{\partial}{\partial t}\langle \boldsymbol{p} \rangle = -\iota\hbar \frac{\partial}{\partial t} \int \Psi^* \nabla \Psi \, dV$$

$$= -\iota\hbar \int \left\{ \frac{\partial \Psi^*}{\partial t} \nabla \Psi + \Psi^* \frac{\partial}{\partial t}(\nabla \Psi) \right\} dV$$

$$= -\iota\hbar \int \left\{ \frac{\partial \Psi^*}{\partial t} \nabla \Psi + \Psi^* \nabla\left(\frac{\partial \Psi}{\partial t} \right) \right\} dV \tag{3}$$

In the last step the order of differentiation in the second term within the integral was exchanged. Equation (3) is an integral over the space coordinates, but derivatives with respect to time appear. We can eliminate these via the time-dependent Schrödinger equation from Chapter 2:

$$\nabla^2 \Psi - \epsilon U \Psi = \frac{2m}{\iota\hbar} \frac{\partial \Psi}{\partial t}, \tag{4}$$

and its complex conjugate,

$$\nabla^2 \Psi^* - \epsilon U \Psi^* = -\frac{2m}{\iota\hbar} \frac{\partial \Psi^*}{\partial t}, \tag{5}$$

where we have defined $\varepsilon = 2m/\hbar^2$. Solving Equations (4) and (5) for the time derivatives gives

$$\frac{\partial \Psi}{\partial t} = \frac{\iota\hbar}{2m}\{\nabla^2\Psi - \epsilon U \Psi\}, \tag{6}$$

and

$$\frac{\partial \Psi^*}{\partial t} = -\frac{\iota\hbar}{2m}\{\nabla^2\Psi^* - \epsilon U \Psi^*\}. \tag{7}$$

Substituting Equations (6) and (7) into Equation (3) gives

$$\frac{\partial <p>}{\partial t} = -\iota\hbar \int \left\{ -\frac{\iota\hbar}{2m}\{\nabla^2\Psi^* - \epsilon U \Psi^*\}(\nabla \Psi) + \frac{\iota\hbar}{2m}\Psi^*\nabla\{\nabla^2\Psi - \epsilon U \Psi\} \right\} dV. \tag{8}$$

On expanding out the gradient operation in the second term within the integral, some cancellations occur and one is left with

$$\frac{\partial <p>}{\partial t} = \frac{\hbar^2}{2m}\int \{-(\nabla \Psi)(\nabla^2\Psi^*) + \Psi^*(\nabla^3\Psi)\}dV + \int \Psi(-\nabla U)\Psi^*dV. \tag{9}$$

Consider the second integral in this expression. It has the physical interpretation

$$\int \Psi(-\nabla U)\Psi^*dV = \langle -\nabla U\rangle = \langle Force\rangle. \tag{10}$$

If we can show that the first integral in Equation (9) vanishes, we will have arrived at the desired result. To show this requires knowledge of a result from vector calculus.

For convenience, define $f = \Psi^*$ and $g = \nabla \Psi$. Then we have

$$\int \{-(\nabla \Psi)(\nabla^2\Psi^*) + \Psi^*(\nabla^3\Psi)\}dV = \int \{f(\nabla^2 g) - g(\nabla^2 f)\}dV. \tag{11}$$

According to Green's second identity, this integral is equivalent to an integral over the surface that bounds the volume V:

$$\int \{f(\nabla^2 g) - g(\nabla^2 f)\}dV = \int \{f(\nabla g) - g(\nabla f)\} \cdot d\mathbf{S}$$

$$= \int \{\Psi^*(\nabla^2 \Psi) - (\nabla \Psi)(\nabla \Psi^*)\} \cdot d\mathbf{S}. \qquad (12)$$

If we make the physically reasonable assumptions that ψ and its gradient vanishes asymptotically, the first integral on the right side of Equation (9) vanishes, and what remains proves Ehrenfest's theorem.

Ehrenfest's theorem shows that classical mechanics is the limiting case of quantum mechanics for suitably large averages over time and space. In the words of Max Born [4], "The motion of particles follows probability laws, but the probability itself propagates according to the law of causality."

■ 4.6   The Orthogonality Theorem

In this section we prove a theorem relating to solutions of Schrödinger's equation that will be of value in the development of perturbation theory in Chapter 9: the orthogonality theorem. Our proof will be one-dimensional; extension to three dimensions should be obvious.

Consider two wavefunctions, $\psi_n(x)$ and $\psi_k(x)$, both of which satisfy Schrödinger's equation for some potential $V(x)$. If their energy eigenvalues are E_n and E_k, respectively, then the orthogonality theorem states that

$$\int \psi_k^*(x)\psi_n(x)dx = 0 \quad (E_k \neq E_n), \qquad (1)$$

where the integral is over the limits of the system.

The wavefunctions must satisfy

$$-\frac{\hbar^2}{2m}\frac{d^2\psi_n}{dx^2} + V(x)\psi_n = E_n\psi_n \qquad (2)$$

and

$$-\frac{\hbar^2}{2m}\frac{d^2\psi_k}{dx^2} + V(x)\psi_k = E_k\psi_k. \tag{3}$$

Multiply Equation (2) and the complex conjugate of Equation (3) by ψ_k^* and ψ_n, respectively. Then subtract Equation (3) from Equation (2) to eliminate $V(x)$. This gives

$$-\frac{\hbar^2}{2m}\left[\psi_k^*\frac{d^2\psi_n}{dx^2} - \psi_n\frac{d^2\psi_k^*}{dx^2}\right] = (E_n - E_k)\psi_k^*\psi_n. \tag{4}$$

Now integrate Equation (4) over the domain relevant to the problem:

$$-\frac{\hbar^2}{2m}\int\left[\psi_k^*\frac{d^2\psi_n}{dx^2} - \psi_n\frac{d^2\psi_k^*}{dx^2}\right]dx = (E_n - E_k)\int\psi_k^*\psi_n dx. \tag{5}$$

Consider the integral on the left side. The integrand can be expressed as

$$\left[\psi_k^*\frac{d^2\psi_n}{dx^2} - \psi_n\frac{d^2\psi_k^*}{dx^2}\right] = \frac{d}{dx}\left[\psi_k^*\frac{d\psi_n}{dx} - \psi_n\frac{d\psi_k^*}{dx}\right].$$

With this, the left side of Equation (5) becomes

$$-\frac{\hbar^2}{2m}\int\frac{d}{dx}\left[\psi_k^*\frac{d\psi_n}{dx} - \psi_n\frac{d\psi_k^*}{dx}\right]dx = -\frac{\hbar^2}{2m}\left[\psi_k^*\frac{d\psi_n}{dx} - \psi_n\frac{d\psi_k^*}{dx}\right]_{\text{boundaries}} = 0.$$

The last step follows if we make the reasonable assumption that the wavefunctions vanish asymptotically. Equation (5) then reduces to

$$(E_n - E_k)\int\psi_k^*\psi_n dx = 0.$$

If $E_k \neq E_n$, then Equation (1) is proven.

Any set of functions $\psi_j(x)$ such that any two members of the set obey an integral constraint of this form is said to constitute an **orthogonal** set of functions. If in addition each individual member of the set is normalized, then they are said to constitute an **orthonormal** set of functions. In this case the mathematical expression of orthogonality can be written succinctly in Dirac notation as

$$\int \psi_k^* \psi_n \, dx = \langle \psi_k^* | \psi_n \rangle = \delta_k^n, \tag{6}$$

where δ_n^k denotes the **Kronecker delta**, defined as

$$\delta_k^n = \begin{cases} 1 & (k = n) \\ 0 & (\text{otherwise}). \end{cases} \tag{7}$$

■ 4.7 The Superposition Theorem

In this section we examine the superposition theorem, whose mathematical underpinnings will be useful in the development of the perturbation and variational approximation methods taken up in Chapter 9. This theorem is in fact much more generally useful than its application to just these areas; indeed, the entire mathematical development of time-dependent wavefunctions to describe real particles is critically dependent upon it, an issue we will touch upon briefly in the next section. If you go on to more advanced study or research in quantum mechanics you will undoubtedly frequently encounter this theorem.

Imagine that you have some potential $V(x)$ for which Schrödinger's equation has been solved, yielding a (potentially infinite) number of wavefunctions $\psi_i(x)$ and their corresponding eigenenergies E_i. Now imagine constructing a sort of "super wavefunction" Ψ via a linear sum of the individual solutions:

$$\Psi(x) = \sum_i a_i \psi_i(x), \tag{1}$$

where the a_i are expansion coefficients. If we demand in addition Ψ be normalized over the range over which the $\psi_i(x)$ apply, this leads to a constraint on the a_i:

$$\int \Psi \Psi^* dx = 1 \quad \Rightarrow \quad \int \left(\sum_i a_i \psi_i \right) \left(\sum_j a_j^* \psi_j^* \right) dx = 1. \tag{2}$$

You should be able to convince yourself that the order of integration and summation in this expression can be swapped without loss of generality. (If you are not sure, try writing out a Ψ of a few terms and doing the algebra directly.) That is, we can rewrite the normalization condition as

$$\sum_i \sum_j a_i a_j^* \langle \psi_i | \psi_j^* \rangle = 1, \tag{3}$$

where we have invoked Dirac notation for the integral. From the orthogonality theorem established in the preceding section, the integral must reduce to δ_i^j. Consequently, in the inner sum over j, only when $j = i$ will nonzero contributions arise. The normalization condition thus reduces to

$$\sum_i a_i^2 = 1, \tag{4}$$

where we have written $a_i a_i^* = a_i^2$. If Ψ is to be normalized, the sum of the squares of the expansion coefficients must be unity.

Now, suppose we wish to compute the expectation value of the energy of the superposition state represented by Ψ. From Section 4.2, we apply the Hamiltonian operator:

$$\langle E \rangle = \int \Psi (H \Psi^*) dx = \int \left(\sum_i a_i \psi_i \right) \left\{ H \sum_j a_j^* \psi_j^* \right\} dx. \tag{5}$$

Taking the operator within the sum, and recalling that $H(\psi_i) = E_i \psi_i$, we have

$$\langle E \rangle = \int \left\{ \left(\sum_i a_i \psi_i \right) \left(\sum_j a_j^* E_j \psi_j^* \right) \right\} dx = \sum_j \sum_j a_i a_j^* E_j \langle \psi_i | \psi_j^* \rangle. \tag{6}$$

Applying the orthogonality theorem (as in Equation 3) reduces this to

$$\langle E \rangle = \sum_i \sum_j a_i a_j^* E_j \delta_i^j = \sum_i a_i^2 E_i. \tag{7}$$

The expectation value of the energy for the superposition state is a weighted sum of the energies of the individual contributing states, with the weighting factors being the squares of the expansion coefficients.

It is a fundamental postulate of quantum mechanics that if a system can be in any one of the individual eigenstates ψ_i, then it can also be in a superposition state of the form of Equation (1); that is, *the system need not be in an eigenstate.* It is further postulated that when one proceeds to make a measurement to determine what state the system is actually in, then the superposition state Ψ "collapses" into one of the eigenstates ψ_i, with the probability that one will find the system to be in state ψ_i given by a_i^2. These postulates constitute the superposition theorem. Measurements of the energy of a number of identically prepared superposition-state systems will yield, on average, that predicted by Equation (7).

The superposition theorem will be of considerable use to us in Chapter 9 for exploring the idea of forming a function from a linear sum of eigenfunctions and invoking the orthogonality theorem in order to simplify integrals such as those appearing in Equations (3) and (6). In the following section, we illustrate an important application of the superposition theorem: constructing representations of *moving* probability distributions.

■ 4.8   Constructing a Time-Dependent Wave Packet

An important application of the superposition theorem in more advanced work is the construction of wavefunctions designed to represent particles that are time-dependently moving in some potential, or even freely. Such wavefunctions are inevitably developed via a superposition of stationary states for the potential at hand multiplied by exponential functions that incorporate the time-dependence. Although the emphasis in this book is on time-independent solutions of the SE, we devote this section to an example of how such a "wavepacket" can be constructed and interpreted. If you go on to further study of quantum mechanics you will encounter many such time-dependent superposition states.

Suppose that some wavefunction $\psi(x)$ with corresponding eigenenergy E is one of the solutions to the time-independent Schrödinger equation for some potential $V(x)$. From Equation (2.3.15), the corresponding solution $\Psi(x, t)$ to the time-*dependent* Schrödinger equation for this wavefunction and energy is given by

$$\Psi(x,t) = \psi(x)e^{-\iota\omega t} = \psi(x)e^{-\iota(E/\hbar)t}. \tag{1}$$

Even though this prescription transforms $\psi(x)$ into a time-dependent form $\Psi(x, t)$, no observable time-dependent consequence arises. This is because the physically observable manifestation of $\Psi(x, t)$, its corresponding probability distribution, retains no time-dependence:

$$\Psi^2 = \Psi^*\Psi = [\psi^*(x)e^{+\iota(E/\hbar)t}][\psi(x)e^{-\iota(E/\hbar)t}] = \psi^*(x)\psi(x). \tag{2}$$

This means that the particle's probability distribution would never be observed to alter in time. In other words, the particle would not move! Knowing full well that real particles do move, how can we model movement in the context of quantum-mechanical wavefunctions? The answer turns out to lie in formulating a *superposition* of wavefunctions of the form of Equation (1).

We can illustrate such a superposition by using only two wavefunctions. To keep the discussion general for the moment, imagine that $\psi_1(x)$ and $\psi_2(x)$ are two normalized wavefunctions that satisfy the same potential $V(x)$ with eigenenergies E_1 and E_2, respectively. For simplicity, we assume that both $\psi_1(x)$ and $\psi_2(x)$ are real functions, although this need not be the case in general. The subscripts should not be interpreted to mean that we are using the $n = 1$ and $n = 2$ states specifically (although such might be the case); they are intended to denote any two solutions of $V(x)$ in general. Now construct a time-dependent superposition state Ψ of the form

$$\Psi = \alpha\psi_1 e^{-\iota\omega_1 t} + \beta\psi_2 e^{-\iota\omega_2 t}, \tag{3}$$

where α and β are real-valued constants (again, this need not be the case) and where we drop the space-dependent-only nature of $\psi_1(x)$ and $\psi_2(x)$ for brevity. Now calculate the (observable) probability density of this superposition state:

$$\Psi^2 = \Psi^*\Psi = [\alpha\psi_1 e^{+\iota\omega_1 t} + \beta\psi_2 e^{+\iota\omega_2 t}][\alpha\psi_1 e^{-\iota\omega_1 t} + \beta\psi_2 e^{-\iota\omega_2 t}]$$

$$= \alpha^2\psi_1^2 + \beta^2\psi_2^2 + \alpha\beta(\psi_1\psi_1)[e^{+\iota(\omega_1-\omega_2)t} + e^{-\iota(\omega_1-\omega_2)t}]. \tag{4}$$

Using the Euler identity $e^{\pm\iota\theta} = \cos\theta \pm \iota\sin\theta$, we can cast this result in terms of purely real functions:

$$\Psi^2 = \alpha^2\psi_1^2 + \beta^2\psi_2^2 + 2\alpha\beta(\psi_1\psi_2)\cos[(\omega_1 - \omega_2)t]. \tag{5}$$

Ψ^2 is a real-valued space-and-*time* dependent function; repeated observations of the system would show a time-dependent probability distribution. The particle *moves*! Because a function of the form $\cos(\omega t)$ reproduces itself over a time period T such that $\omega T = 2\pi$, Ψ^2 will "oscillate" with a period that depends on the difference in energy of the two states involved:

$$T = \frac{2\pi}{(\omega_1 - \omega_2)} = \frac{2\pi}{(1/\hbar)(E_1 - E_2)} = \frac{h}{(E_1 - E_2)}. \tag{6}$$

It is easy to show that even if Ψ^2 oscillates in time, its normalization is time-independent. This follows from

$$\int \Psi^2 dx = 1 \quad \Rightarrow \quad \alpha^2 \int \psi_1^2 dx + \beta^2 \int \psi_2^2 dx + 2\alpha\beta \cos[(\omega_1 - \omega_2)t] \int \psi_1 \psi_2 dx = 1. \tag{7}$$

If E_1 and E_2 are different, then ψ_1 and ψ_2 must be orthogonal (Section 4.6). This means that the last integral will vanish, eliminating any time dependence. Because ψ_1 and ψ_2 can independently be normalized, Equation (7) reduces to

$$\alpha^2 + \beta^2 = 1, \tag{8}$$

in analogy to Equation (4.7.4) for a time-independent summation state. Likewise, the expectation value of the energy of such a superposition system looks like Equation (4.7.7):

$$\langle E \rangle = \alpha^2 E_1 + \beta^2 E_2. \tag{9}$$

It is worth emphasizing that these arguments will hold for *any* time-dependent superposition of the form of Equation (3): no assumptions were made as to the specific potential $V(x)$ that the ψ's satisfy. Equation (3) can be extended to a summation of any number of terms; if so, Equations (8) and (9) will be found to emerge similarly extended as well thanks to the orthogonality theorem.

We can calculate the time-dependence of the average position of a particle that finds itself in such a superposition state by the usual recipe for computing expectation values:

$$\langle x \rangle = \int (\Psi^* x \Psi) dx. \tag{10}$$

This integral proceeds much as Equation (7); the result emerges as

$$\langle x \rangle = \alpha^2 \int (x\psi_1^2) dx + \beta^2 \int (x\psi_2^2) dx + 2\alpha\beta \cos[(\omega_1 - \omega_2)t] \int (x\psi_1\psi_2) dx. \tag{11}$$

Note that even if ψ_1 and ψ_2 are orthogonal, the last integral in Equation (11) will not necessarily vanish.

We now apply these results to a specific case, a superposition state constructed from the sum of two infinite rectangular well wavefunctions:

$$\psi_1(x) = \sqrt{\frac{2}{L}} \sin\left(\frac{n_1 \pi x}{L}\right), \qquad E_1 = \left(\frac{\pi^2 \hbar^2}{2mL^2}\right) n_1^2,$$

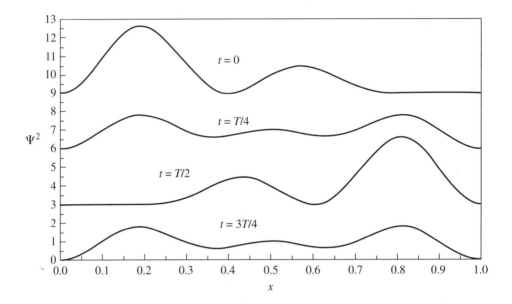

FIGURE 4.3 Time-varying probability-density distribution of a superposition state of the $n = 2$ and $n = 3$ infinite-rectangular well ($L = 1$) wavefunctions with $\alpha = 0.7$ and $\beta = \sqrt{0.51}$. (See Equations 4.8.3 and 4.8.8.) The curves are vertically offset from each other purely for clarity; they should all lie at $\Psi^2 = 0$ at $x = 0$ and 1.

and

$$\psi_2(x) = \sqrt{\frac{2}{L}} \sin\left(\frac{n_2 \pi x}{L}\right), \qquad E_2 = \left(\frac{\pi^2 \hbar^2}{2mL^2}\right) n_2^2.$$

Figure 4.3 shows plots of Ψ^2 for such a superposition with $n_1 = 2$, $n_2 = 3$, $\alpha = 0.7$, and $\beta = \sqrt{1 - \alpha^2} = \sqrt{0.51}$ at times $t = 0$, $T/4$, $T/2$, and $3T/4$. The curves are offset from each other in the vertical direction for clarity; $L = 1$ for simplicity. The particle begins at $t = 0$ with a dominant probability-distribution peak at $x \sim 0.2$ and a secondary peak at $x \sim 0.6$. By $t = T/4$ the distribution has spread out to become fairly uniform across the well. At $t = T/2$, half a cycle of the overall motion, the original probability peaks have reformed but in locations mirror-imaged from their original positions: the dominant peak has moved rightward and is about to reflect from the wall at $x = L$ while the secondary peak has moved leftward. At $t = 3T/4$ the distribution is the mirror-image of that at $T/4$, although this is not obvious as they are actually symmetric about $x = L/2$. At $t = T$, the pattern at $t = 0$ is recovered. The distribution sloshes back and forth in the well every T seconds.

Equation (11) shows that $\langle x \rangle$ will oscillate with the same period as Ψ^2 if the last integral in that equation does not vanish; if it does, then $\langle x \rangle$ will be independent of time. In the case of the present example, the results of Example 4.1 indicate the first two integrals in Equation (11) evaluate to $L/2$. The third integral is not particularly neat; the overall result is

$$\langle x \rangle = \frac{L}{2} + 2\alpha\beta\left(\frac{L}{\pi^2}\right)\cos\left[(\omega_1 - \omega_2)t\right]\left\{\left[\frac{(-1)^{n_1-n_2}-1}{(n_1-n_2)^2}\right] - \left[\frac{(-1)^{n_1+n_2}-1}{(n_1+n_2)^2}\right]\right\},$$

where the normalization $\alpha^2 + \beta^2 = 1$ has been used. If n_1 and n_2 are both even or both odd then the time-dependent term in this result vanishes, a consequence of the symmetry of the superposition state about $x = L/2$. If they are of opposite parity (as in the present example), then $\langle x \rangle$ oscillates with period T and an amplitude that depends on α, β, n_1, and n_2. For the values of the parameters chosen here, $\langle x \rangle$ oscillates between $0.3055L$ and $0.6945L$. For an electron in this particular superposition state moving in a well with $L = 1$ Å, the period of the motion is $T \sim 2.2 \times 10^{-17}$ sec. The full back-and-forth displacement of $\langle x \rangle$ over this time, $2(0.6945 - 0.3055)$ Å $= 0.778$ Å, then corresponds to a speed of about 3.5×10^6 m/s, or about $0.01c$, comfortably nonrelativistic. A speed computed in this way is known as a "group velocity."

After all of our mathematics and calculations, what does it *mean* to think of a particle as somehow being in a combination of two energy states at once? It is a fundamental postulate of quantum mechanics that the experimental answer to this question is that if one measured the energies of a large number of particles in such systems, any individual measurement would give only *either* E_1 or E_2 but that the *average* of the measurements would be as predicted by Equation (10). Wavefunctions predict only *statistical* results of the measurements of positions and energies of particles. It is now in fact experimentally possible to prepare and make measurements on quantum systems in superposition states. A brief article appearing in *Physics Today* 1997; 50(1):9 describes how observation of a superposition state "collapsing" to a definite single state has been achieved; see also *Physics Today* 1998;51(4):22, 2000;53(9):9, and 2003;56(8):43–49.

A more practical question is: "I have a particle in an infinite well (or any other potential) at some position "x" at $t = 0$. How can I turn this analysis around to express this condition as such a sum of wavefunctions for that potential? What does quantum mechanics then predict for the subsequent motion of the particle?" To deal with this you have to model the positional probability distribution of your particle at $t = 0$ as some function, say, a tall but narrow rectangularly-shaped function $\phi(x)$ whose width corresponds to the uncertainty in your knowledge of the particle's initial position.

Knowing the time-independent solutions $\psi_i(x)$ of Schrödinger's equation for the potential at hand, write $\phi(x)$ as an infinite-sum of the $\psi_i(x)$ with various coefficients a_i: $\phi(x) = \Sigma a_i \psi_i(x)$. Here, $\phi(x)$ is equivalent to $\Psi(x, t)$ at $t = 0$, and the coefficients a_i play the roles of α, β, ... in Equation (3). The point now, however, is that rather than being chosen arbitrarily, the a_i need to be chosen to reproduce $\phi(x)$ from the $\psi_i(x)$. An explicit recipe for determining the coefficients is developed in Section 9.2, a technique known as Fourier analysis. Once the coefficients have been determined, the fully time-dependent superposition state as in Equation (3) is then constructed by tacking on the time-dependent exponential factors to each of the $\psi_i(x)$. From this you can make predictions of observable quantities such as $\langle x \rangle$ and $\langle E \rangle$. In the end, it is only by constructing superposition states in this way that moving probability distributions can be obtained. This analysis can be extended as well to free particles; that is, ones not bound within a potential well. Further details on this extension can be found in Chapter 8 of French and Taylor, but one should first be familiar with the techniques of Section 9.2 of this text.

Finally, we can make a qualitative connection here back to Planck's blackbody radiation analysis in Chapter 1. Suppose that Figure 4.3 represents an electron oscillating back and forth in a potential well; the oscillation frequency is determined by the difference in energies of the superposition states. From electromagnetic theory we know that charges oscillating at some frequency emit electromagnetic radiation at that frequency. With quantized energy levels, it follows that the system will emit and absorb radiation only at certain discrete frequencies, as Planck hypothesized.

■ 4.9   The Virial Theorem

In this section we take up the virial theorem, an expression that relates the expectation values of the kinetic and potential energy operators for any potential.

To set the stage for this, suppose that we have some operator A that is known to be *time-independent*. Then operate the commutator of A and the Hamiltonian operator H on some wavefunction ψ:

$$[A, H]\psi = A(H\psi) - H(A\psi). \tag{1}$$

In general, it is assumed here that ψ may be both space- and time-dependent. From Equation (2.3.10) we can write the Hamiltonian operator as

$$H \equiv i\hbar \frac{\partial}{\partial t}, \tag{2}$$

so that Equation (1) becomes

$$[A, H]\psi = (\iota\hbar)\left\{ A\left(\frac{\partial\psi}{\partial t}\right) - \frac{\partial}{\partial t}(A\psi) \right\}. \tag{3}$$

Now, if A is independent of time (and only if it is so), it can be factored in the last term within the curly brackets of Equation (3):

$$[A, H]\psi = (\iota\hbar)\left\{ A\left(\frac{\partial\psi}{\partial t}\right) - A\left(\frac{\partial\psi}{\partial t}\right) \right\} = 0, \tag{4}$$

that is, we must have $[A, H]\psi = 0$ whenever A is time-independent.

The virial theorem involves using this identity in the case where A is defined as the vector dot product of the position and momentum operators:

$$A \equiv \mathbf{r}_{op} \cdot \mathbf{p}_{op} = -(\iota\hbar)\mathbf{r} \cdot \nabla, \tag{5}$$

where ∇ is the usual gradient operator. Since we are assuming that $A \equiv \mathbf{r}_{op} \cdot \mathbf{p}_{op}$ is time-independent, the following derivation applies only for stationary states, that is, ones for which $\langle \mathbf{rp} \rangle = 0$; it does *not* apply for superposition states such as those considered in Section 4.8. Applying the commutator of A and H to some wavefunction ψ that is a solution of Schrödinger's equation for some potential V gives:

$$[A, H]\psi = \iota\left(\frac{\hbar^3}{2m}\right)[\mathbf{r} \cdot \nabla(\nabla^2\psi) - \nabla^2(\mathbf{r} \cdot \nabla\psi)] + (\iota\hbar)[V(\mathbf{r} \cdot \nabla\psi) - \mathbf{r} \cdot \nabla(V\psi)], \tag{6}$$

where we have used the "spatial" form of the Hamiltonian in the usual Schrödinger equation, $H\psi = -(\hbar^2/2m)\nabla^2\psi + V\psi$.

Call the first square bracket appearing on the right side of Equation (6) "part 1" and the second one "part 2." We analyze each of them individually.

Consider first the first term within part 1. The gradient operations can be written as

$$\nabla(\nabla^2\psi) = \frac{\partial}{\partial x}(\nabla^2\psi)\mathbf{x} + \frac{\partial}{\partial y}(\nabla^2\psi)\mathbf{y} + \frac{\partial}{\partial z}(\nabla^2\psi)\mathbf{z},$$

where $\mathbf{x}$, $\mathbf{y}$, and $\mathbf{z}$ denote the usual Cartesian unit vectors. The Laplacian operator appears as

$$\nabla^2\psi = \frac{\partial^2\psi}{\partial x^2} + \frac{\partial^2\psi}{\partial y^2} + \frac{\partial^2\psi}{\partial z^2}.$$

In expanding this term, it is helpful to write derivatives in the more compact notation

$$\psi_{abc} = \frac{\partial^3 \psi}{\partial a\, \partial b\, \partial c}.$$

Hence we find

$$\nabla(\nabla^2 \psi) = (\psi_{xxx} + \psi_{xyy} + \psi_{xzz})\boldsymbol{x} + (\psi_{yxx} + \psi_{yyy} + \psi_{yzz})\boldsymbol{y} + (\psi_{zxx} + \psi_{zyy} + \psi_{zzz})\boldsymbol{z},$$

From the usual procedure for taking a dot product, this gives the first term in part 1 as

$$\boldsymbol{r} \cdot \nabla(\nabla^2 \psi) = x(\psi_{xxx} + \psi_{xyy} + \psi_{xzz}) + y(\psi_{yxx} + \psi_{yyy} + \psi_{yzz}) + z(\psi_{zxx} + \psi_{zyy} + \psi_{zzz}). \quad (7)$$

Now look at the second term of part 1. In similar notation for the derivatives, it evaluates to

$$\nabla^2(\boldsymbol{r} \cdot \nabla \psi) = 2(\psi_{xx} + \psi_{yy} + \psi_{zz})$$
$$+ x(\psi_{xxx} + \psi_{yyx} + \psi_{zzx}) + y(\psi_{xxy} + \psi_{yyy} + \psi_{zzy}) + z(\psi_{xxz} + \psi_{yyz} + \psi_{zzz}). \quad (8)$$

In combining Equations (7) and (8) to formulate part 1, all of the third-derivative terms cancel because the order of the derivatives is irrelevant. Also, $\psi_{xx} + \psi_{yy} + \psi_{zz} \equiv \nabla^2\psi$, so part 1 reduces to

$$\iota\left(\frac{\hbar^3}{2m}\right)[\boldsymbol{r} \cdot \nabla(\nabla^2 \psi) - \nabla^2(\boldsymbol{r} \cdot \nabla \psi)] = 2\iota\hbar\left(-\frac{\hbar^2}{2m}\nabla^2\psi\right) = 2\iota\hbar(KE_{op}\psi). \quad (9)$$

Part 2 is much more straightforward. Recalling that we can write $\nabla(V\psi) = \psi(\nabla V) + V(\nabla \psi)$, we have

$$V(\boldsymbol{r} \cdot \nabla \psi) - \boldsymbol{r} \cdot \nabla(V\psi) = V(\boldsymbol{r} \cdot \nabla \psi) - \boldsymbol{r} \cdot (\psi \nabla V) - \boldsymbol{r} \cdot (V \nabla \psi).$$

In the last term V is a purely scalar function, so it can be brought outside the brackets; the first and last terms on the right side then cancel. In the middle term on the right side, the scalar function ψ can likewise be brought outside the brackets, leaving

$$(\iota\hbar)[V(\boldsymbol{r} \cdot \nabla\psi) - \boldsymbol{r} \cdot \nabla(V\psi)] = -\iota\hbar\,(\boldsymbol{r} \cdot \nabla V)\psi. \tag{10}$$

Equations (6), (9), and (10) then give

$$[A, \boldsymbol{H}]\psi = 2\iota\hbar(KE_{op}\psi) - \iota\hbar\,(\boldsymbol{r} \cdot \nabla V)\psi. \tag{11}$$

Multiplying through by ψ^* and integrating over the domain of the wavefunction gives, in terms of expectation values,

$$\langle[A, \boldsymbol{H}]\rangle = \iota\hbar\,(2\langle KE \rangle - \langle \boldsymbol{r} \cdot \nabla V \rangle). \tag{12}$$

However, because $A \equiv \boldsymbol{r}_{op} \cdot \boldsymbol{p}_{op}$ is a time independent operator, Equation (4) tells us that $\langle[A, \boldsymbol{H}]\rangle = 0$, so we can conclude that, for any potential V,

$$2\langle KE \rangle = \langle \boldsymbol{r} \cdot \nabla V \rangle. \tag{13}$$

Equation (13) is the virial theorem (VT).

One of the more interesting conclusions resulting from the VT concerns a purely *radial* potential of the form

$$V(r) = kr^n, \tag{14}$$

where n is any power. In this case

$$\nabla V = \left(\frac{\partial V}{\partial r}\right)\boldsymbol{r}' = nkr^{n-1}\boldsymbol{r}',$$

where $\boldsymbol{r}'$ is the spherical-coordinate radial unit vector (see Section 6.2). Hence

$$\boldsymbol{r} \cdot \nabla V = (r\boldsymbol{r}') \cdot (nkr^{n-1}\boldsymbol{r}') = nkr^n = nV.$$

The VT then predicts

$$2\langle KE \rangle = n\langle V \rangle. \tag{15}$$

The Coulomb potential is of this form, with $n = -1$. This means that the VT predicts that, on average, the potential energy of a hydrogen atom will be negative twice its kinetic energy, a result consistent with the Bohr model. Because $\langle E \rangle = \langle KE \rangle + \langle V \rangle$ in general, this result also means that, for the Coulomb potential, $\langle E \rangle = -\langle KE \rangle$, and hence that the expectation value of the momentum, $\langle p^2 \rangle = 2m_e\langle KE \rangle$, can be expressed as $\langle p^2 \rangle = -2m_e\langle E_n \rangle = \hbar^2/(a_o^2 n^2)$.

EXAMPLE 4.6

The harmonic oscillator potential $V(x) = kx^2/2$, $-\infty \le x \le \infty$ leads to a ground-state wavefunction $\psi(x) = Ae^{-\alpha^2 x^2/2}$, where A is a normalization constant and $\alpha = (mk/\hbar^2)^{1/4}$ (this potential is analyzed in detail in Chapter 5). Verify that the virial theorem is satisfied by this potential and wavefunction.

We need to show that $2\langle KE \rangle = \langle \mathbf{r} \cdot \nabla V \rangle$. Deal with the left side first. The KE operator is $-(\hbar^2/2m)\partial^2/\partial x^2$, hence

$$2KE_{op}\psi = -\frac{\hbar^2 \partial^2 \psi}{m \partial x^2} = -\frac{A\hbar^2}{m}(-\alpha^2 e^{-\alpha^2 x^2/2} + \alpha^4 x^2 e^{-\alpha^2 x^2/2}).$$

The expectation value is

$$\langle 2KE_{op} \rangle = \int_{-\infty}^{\infty} \psi^*(KE_{op}\psi)\,dx = -\frac{A^2\hbar^2}{m}\left(-\alpha^2 \int_{-\infty}^{\infty} e^{-\alpha^2 x^2}\,dx + \alpha^4 \int_{-\infty}^{\infty} x^2 e^{-\alpha^2 x^2}\,dx\right).$$

The integrals are standard; the result is

$$\langle 2KE_{op} \rangle = \frac{A^2\hbar^2\alpha\sqrt{\pi}}{2m}.$$

On the right side of the VT we have

$$\mathbf{r} \cdot \nabla V = (x\mathbf{x}) \cdot (kx\mathbf{x}) = kx^2.$$

Hence

$$\langle r \cdot \nabla V \rangle = A^2 k \int_{-\infty}^{\infty} x^2 e^{-\alpha^2 x^2} dx = \frac{A^2 k \sqrt{\pi}}{2\alpha^3}.$$

Invoking the identity $\alpha = (mk/\hbar^2)^{1/4}$ shows that the VT is satisfied:

$$\langle 2KE_{op} \rangle = \frac{A^2 \hbar^2 \alpha \sqrt{\pi}}{2m} = \frac{A^2 \hbar^2 \sqrt{\pi}}{2m} \left(\frac{mk}{\hbar^2} \right)^{1/4} = \frac{A^2 \sqrt{\pi} \hbar^{3/2} k^{1/4}}{2m^{3/4}}$$

and

$$\langle r \cdot \nabla V \rangle = \frac{A^2 k \sqrt{\pi}}{2\alpha^3} = \frac{A^2 k \sqrt{\pi}}{2} \left(\frac{\hbar^2}{mk} \right)^{3/4} = \frac{A^2 \sqrt{\pi} \hbar^{3/2} k^{1/4}}{2m^{3/4}}.$$

Problem 5-18 in Chapter 5 investigates this question more fully.

EXAMPLE 4.7

Suppose that you are given the potential $V(x) = kx^n/2$, $-\infty \leq x \leq \infty$, with n being a positive, even-valued number. Hypothesizing that a solution of Schrödinger's equation to this potential is $\psi(x) = Ae^{-\alpha^2 x^2/2}$ for a particle of mass m, how must α depend on n, m, $\hbar$, and k such that the virial theorem is satisfied? Can this wavefunction in fact be made to be a solution of Schrödinger's equation of this potential for any n?

This is the same wavefunction as that used in Example 4.6, hence

$$\langle 2KE_{op} \rangle = \frac{A^2 \hbar^2 \alpha \sqrt{\pi}}{2m}.$$

Now,

$$r \cdot \nabla V = (xx) \cdot \left(\frac{nk}{2} x^{n-1} x \right) = \frac{nk}{2} x^n.$$

The right side of the VT is then

$$\langle r \cdot \nabla V \rangle = \frac{A^2 n k}{2} \int_{-\infty}^{\infty} x^n e^{-\alpha^2 x^2} dx = \frac{A^2 n k}{2\alpha^{n+1}} \Gamma\left(\frac{n+1}{2}\right).$$

The gamma function $\Gamma(x)$ is defined in Appendix C. Equating $\langle 2KE_{op}\rangle$ to $\langle r \cdot \nabla V \rangle$ and solving for α gives

$$\alpha^{n+2} = \frac{nmk}{\sqrt{\pi}\,\hbar^2} \Gamma\left(\frac{n+1}{2}\right).$$

We can check this result by setting $n = 2$. $\Gamma(3/2) = \sqrt{\pi}/2$, hence $\alpha^4 = mk/\hbar^2$, as claimed in Example 4.6.

Although we can make this trial wavefunction satisfy the VT for this potential, it does *not* in general satisfy Schrödinger's equation for this potential. To see this, substitute $\psi(x)$ and $V(x)$ into Schrödinger's equation; the result is

$$\frac{\hbar^2\alpha^2}{2m} - \frac{\hbar^2\alpha^4}{2m}x^2 + \frac{k}{2}x^n = E.$$

For this to be meaningful, the two terms with x-dependences must cancel each other; this demands $n = 2$ and $\alpha^4 = mk/\hbar^2$, as we found above. The remaining terms give $E = \hbar^2\alpha^2/2m$, which is known to be the ground state energy for this potential when $n = 2$. However, no solution is possible for $n \neq 2$.

This example appears to lead to a contradiction: we can apparently make a hypothetical wavefunction satisfy the VT for some potential just by including an adjustable parameter (α) in the wavefunction. However, the wavefunction is not guaranteed to be a solution of Schrödinger's equation for that potential. How can this be? The answer is that Schrödinger's equation was never used in the derivation of the VT. Our derivation of the VT depended on the definition of the Hamiltonian operator H [see just after Equation (6)] and the fact that any time-independent operator A must satisfy $[A, H] = 0$, but it was never demanded that ψ satisfy $H\psi = E\psi$. For practical purposes, the VT is not particularly helpful for establishing or even estimating solutions to Schrödinger's equation. We have developed it, however, as there is a corresponding theorem in classical dynamics, and it provides an interesting generalization of the relationship between kinetic and potential energies in central potentials of which the Coulomb potential is a specific example.

■ Summary

The *expectation value* $\langle \mathbf{Op} \rangle$ of some observable whose operator is $\mathbf{Op}$ is given by

$$\langle \mathbf{Op} \rangle \;=\; \int \psi^*(x)\,\{(\mathbf{Op})\psi(x)\}\,dx.$$

It is important to compute $\{(\mathbf{Op})\,\psi(x)\}$ first, then multiply by $\psi^*(x)$ before carrying out the integral. Some useful physical operators are given in Table 4.1. A powerful notational simplification can be had with Dirac notation:

$$\langle \psi^*(x)\,|\,f(x)\,|\,\psi(x) \rangle \;=\; \int \psi^*(x)\,\{\mathbf{Op}\,[f(x)]\}\,\psi(x)\,dx.$$

Heisenberg's uncertainty principle holds that the uncertainties Δx and Δp inherent in simultaneous measurements of the position and momentum of a particle obey the restriction

$$\Delta x\,\Delta p \;\geq\; \hbar/2,$$

with Δx defined as

$$\Delta x = \sqrt{\langle x^2 \rangle - \langle x \rangle^2},$$

where the angle brackets denote expectation values as defined in the Dirac notation; Δp is defined analogously. This relationship is most useful for establishing approximate ground-state energies for a given potential; see Section 4.3.

The commutator operator of two operators A_{op} and B_{op} corresponding to two physical quantities A and B is defined as

$$[A, B] = A_{op}B_{op} - B_{op}A_{op}.$$

If $[A, B]$ when operated on some wavefunction ψ yields a nonzero result, then there will be an uncertainty relation linking A and B of the form

$$(\Delta A)(\Delta B) \;\geq\; \frac{1}{2}\sqrt{-[A, B]^2}.$$

If $[A, B]\,\psi = 0$ then the eigenvalues of A and B can be measured simultaneously.

The orthogonality theorem states that for two wavefunctions $\psi_n(x)$ and $\psi_k(x)$ which satisfy the SE for some potential,

$$\langle \psi_k^* | \psi_n \rangle = \delta_k^n,$$

where δ_n^k is the Kronecker delta symbol, equal to 1 if $k = n$ and zero otherwise.

The superposition theorem states that if one forms a wavefunction from a linear sum of eigenstates,

$$\Psi(x) = \sum_i a_i \psi_i(x)$$

then the expectation value of the energy of such a superposition system is given by

$$\langle E \rangle = \sum_i a_i^2 E_i .$$

The virial theorem states that the expectation values of kinetic energy and the potential function V are related according as

$$2\langle KE \rangle = \langle r \cdot \nabla V \rangle$$

where r is the position vector.

■ Problems

4-1(E) For the data of Figure 4.1, compute $\langle \text{height} \rangle$, $\langle \text{height} \rangle^2$, $\langle \text{height}^2 \rangle$, and $\Delta(\text{height})$. The bins are 0.05 meters wide; take the effective height of each to be its midpoint (e.g., there are three people of height 1.525 meters, seven of height 1.575 meters, and so on).

4-2(I) Prove that for the infinite potential well wavefunctions, $\langle xp \rangle = -\langle px \rangle = \iota\hbar/2$.

4-3(I) A particle of mass m has the hypothetical wavefunction $\psi(x) = Ae^{-\alpha x}$, $(0 \le x \le \infty; \psi = 0,$ otherwise$)$. Determine the normalization constant A in terms of α. Determine $\langle x \rangle$ and $\langle p \rangle$ in terms of α and m.

4-4(E) The uncertainty principle tells us that $\Delta x \, \Delta p \ge \hbar/2$. Suppose that in some experiment the position of a proton at some initial time is known to an accuracy of $\Delta x = 10^{-15}$ meters. Using the classical definition of momentum, determine the uncertainty in the speed of the proton. Given that distance = vt, how much time must elapse before the uncertainty in the position of the proton has grown to 1 meter?

4-5(E) A brief radio-wave pulse of photons is of duration $\tau = 0.001$ seconds. The pulse must then have a length of $\tau c = 3 \times 10^5$ meters, and, because an individual photon might be anywhere in the pulse, the uncertainty in the position of that photon will be $\Delta x = 3 \times 10^5$ meters. What is the corresponding uncertainty in the momentum of the photon? If the momentum and frequency of a photon are related by $p = h\nu/c$, what is the uncertainty in the frequency of the photon?

4-6(I) The ground state wavefunction of the harmonic oscillator potential (see Chapter 5) is given by

$$\psi_0(x) = \frac{\sqrt{\alpha}}{\pi^{1/4}} e^{-\alpha^2 x^2/2},$$

where α is a constant. Verify that $(\Delta x \, \Delta p) = \hbar/2$ for this state.

4-7(I) Suppose that the hypothetical wavefunction $\psi(x) = A/(a^2 + x^2)$, $(-\infty \leq x \leq \infty)$ is a solution of Schrödinger's equation for some potential $V(x)$ with energy E.

(a) What must be the value of the normalization constant A in terms of a?

(b) What is the function $V(x)$?

(c) Evaluate $\Delta x \Delta p$ for this function; is the uncertainty principle satisfied?

4-8(I) A hypothetical wavefunction is given by $\psi(x) = Ax^2 e^{-\alpha x}$, $(0 \leq x \leq \infty)$. Normalize this wavefunction and compute $\Delta x \, \Delta p$ for it.

4-9(A) Generalize your calculations in the previous problem to a wavefunction of the form $\psi(x) = A x^{n/2} e^{(-\beta x^q/2)}$, $(0 \leq x \leq \infty; n, q > 0)$.
Plot $\Delta x \, \Delta p$ as a function of n and q. Can you discover any trends?

4-10(I) Use the uncertainty principle to estimate the ground state energy of a particle of mass m moving in the *linear potential*

$$V(x) = \begin{cases} \infty & (x \leq 0), \\ \alpha x & (x \geq 0). \end{cases}$$

Hint: Imagine some energy level E that cuts the potential at $x = 0$ and $x = E/\alpha$. Take $x \sim \Delta x$ and $p \sim \Delta p \sim \hbar/2(\Delta x)$.

4-11(E) Consider a nonrelativistic "free" particle (that is, one not subject to a potential) of mass m moving with speed v. The energy of this particle will be $mv^2/2 = p^2/2m$ where $p = mv$. Show that the uncertainty principle $\Delta x \Delta p \geq \hbar/2$ becomes $\Delta E \Delta t \geq \hbar/2$ in this case. According to Einstein, this mass has an energy equivalent given by $E = mc^2$; show also that the uncertainty principle can then be written in the form $\Delta m \Delta t \geq \hbar/2c^2$. A free neutron (one not bound within a nucleus) has a half-life against beta-decay of 10.25 minutes. Taking this time as an estimate of Δt, what is the corresponding uncertainty in the mass of the neutron?

4-12(I) Show that (a) $[x^n, p_x] \equiv \iota \hbar n x^{n-1}$ and (b) $[x, p_x^n] \equiv \iota \hbar n p_x^{n-1}$. In the latter case, it is helpful to know that the nth derivative of a product of two functions $u(x)$ and $v(x)$ is given by

$$\frac{d^n}{dx^n}(uv) = \sum_{j=0}^{n} \binom{n}{j} \frac{d^j v}{dx^j} \frac{d^{n-j} u}{dx^{n-j}}.$$

4-13(E) Show that for any function $k(x)$, $[k(x), p_x] \equiv \iota \hbar \dfrac{dk}{dx}$.

4-14(E) Show that for four operators A, B, C, and D,

$$[(A + D), (B + C)] = [A, B] + [A, C] + [D, B] + [D, C]$$

where the square brackets denote commutators.

4-15(E) Verify that the infinite potential well wavefunctions form an orthonormal set.

4-16(E) In Section 4.3 it was shown that if a particle of mass m is trapped within a linear distance $\Delta x \sim L$, then its energy must satisfy $E \geq \hbar^2/8mL^2$. Early in the history of nuclear physics (before the discovery of the neutron), it was speculated that the neutral mass that was known must reside in nuclei might be neutral particles composed of combinations of protons and electrons. However, the discovery of the uncertainty principle refuted this theory. What would be the minimum energy of an electron trapped in a nuclear potential of $L \sim 10^{-15}$ meter? Compare to the typical depth of nuclear wells for heavy elements computed in Section 3.9.

4-17(E) Current versions of *string theory* hold that the most fundamental structures in the Universe may be "strings" of length $L \sim 10^{-35}$ m vibrating in various energy states. The mass of these strings is taken to be the *Planck mass*, $m_p = \sqrt{\hbar c / G}$, where G is the Newtonian gravitational constant. Using the argument presented at the end of Section 4.3, estimate the lowest possible energy for a vibrating string. Express your answer in giga-electron-volts (GeV $= 10^9$ eV). Do you think such energies are obtainable with current particle accelerators?

4-18(I) Consider a superposition wavefunction formed from the lowest three states of an infinite potential well:

$$\Psi = \frac{1}{\sqrt{3}} \psi_1 + \frac{1}{\sqrt{4}} \psi_2 + \sqrt{\frac{5}{12}} \psi_3.$$

Verify that ψ is normalized. What is $\langle E \rangle$ for such a system? Put your answer in terms of the energy E_1 of the lowest infinite-well state.

4-19(E) Squares of wavefunctions must be normalized to unity. Express this in Dirac notation.

4-20(I) In Chapter 5 we will explore the simple harmonic oscillator potential. The wavefunctions for the two lowest energy states of this potential are of the form $\psi_0 = A_0 e^{-\gamma^2 x^2 / 2}$ and $\psi_1 = A_1 x e^{-\gamma^2 x^2 / 2}$ ($-\infty \le x \le +\infty$), where A_0 and A_1 are normalization constants given by $A_0 = \sqrt{\gamma / \sqrt{\pi}}$ and $A_1 = \sqrt{2\gamma^3 / \sqrt{\pi}}$ and where γ is a constant that depends upon the mass involved and the characteristics of the potential. (As explained in Chapter 5, there are good reasons why the quantum numbering for the states of this potential conventionally start at $n = 0$.) Construct a time-dependent superposition state from these two functions following the approach of Section 4.8. Show that the amplitude of the oscillations in $\langle x \rangle$ for your superposition state is given by $\langle x \rangle = \alpha \beta \sqrt{2}/\gamma$, where α and β are as in Equation (4.8.3). Do the units of this result make sense?

4-21(I) Suppose it is claimed that the function $\psi(x) = A x e^{-\beta x / 2}$ is a solution of Schrödinger's equation for a particle of mass m moving in the linear potential $V(x) = kx$. ($\beta, k > 0$; $0 \le x \le \infty$; $V(x) = \infty$ and $\psi = 0$ otherwise.) What is β in terms of k if the virial theorem is to be satisfied? Is this function actually a solution of Schrödinger's equation for this potential?

5 | The Harmonic Oscillator

In this chapter we take up the solution of Schrödinger's equation for the **harmonic oscillator potential**. This potential corresponds to any situation where a mass is subject to a **linear restoring force**:

$$F = -kx \quad (-\infty \leq x \leq \infty).$$

The classical model for such a system is a mass m attached to a spring of force constant k; if the spring is stretched (or compressed) a displacement x from its equilibrium position, it will pull (or push) back with a force proportional to x, and the result is a sinusoidal motion—a so-called simple harmonic motion—that repeats with period $T = 2\pi\sqrt{m/k}$ seconds. Diatomic molecules behave to a good approximation as two nuclei joined by a spring; by solving the SE for this potential we will see how the equally spaced spectral lines in Figure 1.2(d) arise.

The potential corresponding to the linear restoring force is obtained by integrating the force equation:

$$V(x) = -\int F\,dx = \int kx\,dx = kx^2/2 + c,$$

where c is a constant of integration. This is the **harmonic oscillator potential**. Normally, the constant c is dropped from further consideration as only *differences* in potential energy are physically meaningful; the effect of a nonzero value for c would be to raise or lower the permitted energy levels. The SE for the harmonic potential then appears as

$$-\frac{\hbar^2}{2m}\frac{d^2\psi(x)}{dx^2} + \frac{1}{2}kx^2\psi(x) = E\psi(x).$$

The solution of the SE for this potential is detailed in Sections 5.1–5.4. Because the simple harmonic oscillator is such a well-known system from Newtonian mechanics, it is instructive to compare results for the classical and quantum oscillators, an issue taken up in Section 5.5. An alternate solution to the harmonic oscillator potential is developed in Section 5.6, which can be considered optional.

■ 5.1   A Lesson in Dimensional Analysis

The harmonic potential is sketched in Figure 5.1. Classically, a system of total energy E moving in this potential cannot find itself beyond the turning points $\pm x_0$, given by $E = kx_0^2/2$. Quantum-mechanically, we can anticipate some finite probability of tunneling beyond these limits because ψ will not in general be zero for $|x| > x_0$. Because $V(x)$ is a function of x, the situation is more complex than the potential well/barrier problems previously encountered. However, because the expression for $V(x)$ is valid for all x, this complexity is mitigated somewhat in that there are no inside or outside regions to link via the continuity of ψ and $d\psi/dx$; that is, there will be but a single expression for $\psi(x)$ valid for all x. At the same time, with $V(x)$ extending to $\pm\infty$, we must ultimately force ψ to vanish as $x \rightarrow \pm\infty$. When $E > V$ (that is, within the well: $|x| \leq x_0$) we can expect some type of potential-well-sinusoidal behavior for ψ, while for $|x| > x_0$ we can expect to find an exponential-decay form for ψ. Also, because the harmonic potential is symmetric about $x = 0$, we can expect solutions of alternating parity.

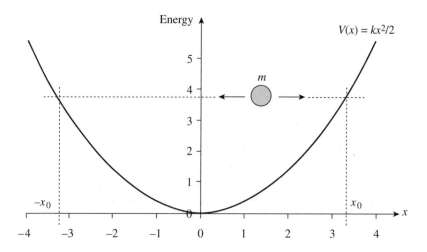

FIGURE 5.1   Harmonic potential $V(x) = kx^2/2$ with $k = 0.7$. The classical limits of motion for the energy level shown are $\pm x_0$.

Before plunging into the solution of Schrödinger's equation for the harmonic potential, we cast it into a dimensionless form (also along these lines, review Example 3.5). This is a valuable lesson in its own right, and will make subsequent algebra easier.

Almost any incarnation of Schrödinger's equation can be made dimensionless by finding two combinations of the mass of the particle involved (m), $\hbar$, and any constants that appear in the potential such that one combination has dimensions of reciprocal length and the other dimensions of reciprocal energy. Call these constants α and ϵ, respectively. Dimensionless variables $\xi = \alpha x$ and $\lambda = \epsilon E$ are then defined, and x and E in Schrödinger's equation are cast in terms of ξ and λ. The result is a dimensionless differential equation that is free of constants, consequently easier to manipulate than the original version. In particular, dimensionless formulations are particularly amenable to numerical computation because one is freed from concerns with units and quantities of exceptionally large or small magnitude. Once solutions to the dimensionless differential equation have been established, they can be put back in terms of the original variables by simple substitutions.

The harmonic oscillator potential involves only one constant, k. We begin by finding a combination of m, $\hbar$, and k that has units of reciprocal meters. This means that we seek values of the powers a, b, and c such that $m^a k^b \hbar^c$ has units of (meters)$^{-1}$. Recalling that mass has units of kg, k of Newton/meter ($=$ kg/sec^2), and $\hbar$ of Joule-sec ($=$ kg meter^2/sec), we have

$$\text{meter}^{-1} \equiv (\text{kg})^a \left(\frac{\text{kg}}{\text{sec}^2}\right)^b \left(\frac{\text{kg meter}^2}{\text{sec}}\right)^c \equiv \text{kg}^{a+b+c} \, \text{meter}^{2c} \, \text{sec}^{-(2b+c)}.$$

To balance units, we must have $c = -1/2$. Further, because $(2b + c)$ must equal zero, then $b = -c/2 = +1/4$. Finally, because $(a + b + c)$ must also equal zero, $a = +1/4$. Hence we define

$$\alpha = m^a k^b \hbar^c = m^{1/4} k^{1/4} \hbar^{-1/2} = \left(\frac{mk}{\hbar^2}\right)^{1/4}. \tag{1}$$

Second, we desire a combination $m^a k^b \hbar^c$ whose units are inverse Joules; that is,

$$\frac{\text{sec}^2}{\text{kg meter}^2} \equiv (\text{kg})^a \left(\frac{\text{kg}}{\text{sec}^2}\right)^b \left(\frac{\text{kg meter}^2}{\text{sec}}\right)^c \equiv \text{kg}^{a+b+c} \, \text{meter}^{2c} \, \text{sec}^{-(2b+c)}.$$

Here we must have $c = -1$, $b = -1/2$, and $a = +1/2$, so

$$\varepsilon = m^a k^b \hbar^c = m^{1/2} k^{-1/2} \hbar^{-1} = \frac{1}{\hbar}\sqrt{\frac{m}{k}} = \frac{1}{\hbar \omega},$$

where $\omega = \sqrt{k/m}$ is the **angular frequency** of a classical mass/spring system. For further algebraic convenience, ε is defined with an additional (dimensionless) factor of 2:

$$\varepsilon = \frac{2}{\hbar \omega}. \tag{2}$$

The reader should verify that α and ε do have units of reciprocal length and energy, respectively. The next step is to define dimensionless variables for position and energy

$$\xi = \alpha x \tag{3}$$

and

$$\lambda = \epsilon E. \tag{4}$$

On substituting Equations (3) and (4) into Schrödinger's equation for the harmonic oscillator, remember to make the substitution in the derivative as well; that is,

$$\frac{d^2}{dx^2} \equiv \alpha^2 \frac{d^2}{d\xi^2}.$$

These substitutions reduce Schrödinger's equation to

$$\frac{d^2\psi}{d\xi^2} + (\lambda - \xi^2)\psi = 0, \tag{5}$$

a considerably cleaner expression to work with than its ancestor (see Problem 1). Had ε not been defined with an additional factor of two as in Equation (2), such a factor would remain in the λ term in Equation (5). As λ involves the energy of the system, we can expect to see some boundary condition arise that restricts it to certain values.

EXAMPLE 5.1

In some cosmological theories, string theories, and grand-unified theories, the *Planck time* plays the role of a "quantum of time"; that is, a smallest possible time interval. This quantity is a combination of the constants G, c, and h that has units of time. Use dimensional analysis to derive an expression for the Planck time. What is its value?

We need to find powers (a, b, d) such that

$$s^1 \equiv c^a h^b G^d.$$

Note that we use d as the power of G as opposed to c to avoid confusion with the speed of light. Substituting the appropriate units (Appendix D) gives

$$s^1 \equiv \left(\frac{m}{s}\right)^a \left(\frac{kg\, m^2}{s}\right)^b \left(\frac{m^3}{kg\, s^2}\right)^d \equiv m^{a+2b+3d}\, kg^{b-d}\, s^{-a-b-2d}.$$

Matching powers shows that we have three constraints:

$$a + 2b + 3d = 0$$

$$b - d = 0$$

and

$$-a - b - 2d = 1.$$

The middle one of these shows that $d = b$. Substituting this into the first constraint gives $a = -5b$. The last constraint then gives $b = 1/2$. Hence we have $b = d = 1/2$ and $a = -5/2$. The Planck time is often abbreviated t_P:

$$t_P = c^{-5/2} h^{1/2} G^{1/2} = \sqrt{\frac{hG}{c^5}}.$$

Putting in the numbers gives

$$t_P = \sqrt{\frac{(6.626 \times 10^{-34})(6.674 \times 10^{-11})}{(2.998 \times 10^8)^5}} = 1.351 \times 10^{-43}\, s,$$

minute indeed.

■ 5.2   The Asymptotic Solution

Our task is to solve Equation (5.1.5) for $\psi(\xi)$, then revert the result back to x-space via the substitution $\xi = \alpha x$. Because of the form of the potential, the usual linear-equation-with-constant-coefficient recipes cannot be applied. One might then surmise that a brute-force series solution is called for, and indeed a series solution will figure prominently in what follows. There is, however, a more elegant approach available that exploits knowledge of the physics of the situation.

Recall the finite rectangular well (Sections 3.3–3.5). That situation, too, was characterized by turning points (the walls of the well) beyond which the wavefunction behaved in an asymptotically exponential fashion. Given the similarity of that situation to the present problem, we might infer that $\psi(\xi)$ approaches zero as ξ (or, equivalently, x) $\rightarrow \pm\infty$.

This inference proves to be correct, and leads to a technique of considerable power and generality: that of first establishing the **asymptotic form** of ψ. The problem then reduces to finding a solution valid for "small" values of ξ to be grafted onto the asymptotic solution in order to establish a solution valid for all ξ. The goal of the present section is to establish the asymptotic solution for the harmonic oscillator potential. The detailed general solution is then developed in Section 5.3, and some characteristics of the resulting wavefunctions are examined in Section 5.4.

To establish the asymptotic behavior of ψ, consider Equation (5.1.5) when ξ is large. In this case the ξ^2 term will dominate, rendering Schrödinger's equation as

$$\frac{d^2\psi}{d\xi^2} \sim \xi^2\psi \qquad (\xi \rightarrow \pm\infty). \tag{1}$$

Guided by the finite-well solution, we posit a trial solution to this asymptotic behavior of the form

$$\psi(\xi) \sim A \exp(\beta\xi^n), \qquad (\xi \rightarrow \pm\infty), \tag{2}$$

where A, β, and n are to be determined. Differentiating this trial solution gives

$$\frac{d^2\psi(\xi)}{d\xi^2} = \left[n^2\beta^2\xi^{2n-2} + n(n-1)\beta\xi^{n-2} \right] \psi(\xi), \tag{3}$$

which, upon back-substitution into Equation (1), gives

$$n^2\beta^2\xi^{2n-2} + n(n-1)\beta\xi^{n-2} \sim \xi^2, \tag{4}$$

Equation (4) is meaningless unless the various powers of ξ can be brought into accord. From the form of the trial solution, we can infer that n must be positive (why?). For large ξ, the first term will dominate the left side, leaving

$$n^2\beta^2\xi^{2n-2} \sim \xi^2. \tag{5}$$

Equality will hold for the powers of ξ only if $2n - 2 = 2$, or $n = 2$. For the multiplicative factors ($n^2\beta^2$ on the left; unity on the right) to agree, we must then have $4\beta^2 = 1$, or $\beta = \pm 1/2$. Choosing $\beta = +1/2$ would result in an asymptotic solution of the form $\psi(\xi) \propto \exp(+\xi^2/2)$, which would be impossible to normalize. On the other hand, choosing $\beta = -1/2$ would lead to a normalizable solution of the form

$$\psi(\xi) \sim A \exp(-\xi^2/2) \qquad (\xi \to \pm\infty). \tag{6}$$

This result tells us that the postulate of an exponential form for the asymptotic solution is valid if we pick the particular form $\psi(\xi) \propto \exp(-\xi^2/2)$: $n = 2$ is the only possibility if our postulated solution, Equation (2), is to satisfy Equation (1) as $\xi \to \infty$. At this point there is nothing to be gained in attempting to establish the normalization constant A as we have only a partial solution as yet; we can take care of normalization later. The important thing is that we have established the general form of ψ for large ξ.

◼ 5.3   The Series Solution

What of the general solution of the SE for the harmonic potential? In the absence of any recipe solution, we are reduced to a process of trial and error: postulate a trial solution (usually a polynomial series in the independent variable) and tinker with it until the differential equation is satisfied. This may seem a circuitous way of solving a problem, but it is legitimate: a solution is, after all, a solution, and can always be checked by back-substitution into the differential equation.

By whatever means we solve Schrödinger's equation for this problem, we wish to explicitly build in knowledge of the exponential asymptotic behavior of ψ that was established in the preceding section. One way to do this is by assuming that ψ can be expressed as the product of two functions, one of which embodies the asymptotic behavior of ψ and the other of which is an as-yet unknown function $H(\xi)$,

$$\psi(\xi) = H(\xi)e^{-\xi^2/2}, \tag{1}$$

with $H(\xi)$ to be determined.

How do we know if this is a valid assumption? The answer is that we don't, at least not yet. As in any trial-and-error circumstance, this can be known only after the fact by seeing if it can be made to work.

What of $H(\xi)$? From elementary calculus we know that any function of x (or ξ) can be represented as an infinite polynomial; that is, as a Taylor or MacLaurin series expansion. We will assume that $H(\xi)$ can be represented by such a series:

$$H(\xi) = a_0 + a_1\xi + a_2\xi^2 + \cdots = \sum_{n=0}^{\infty} a_n\xi^n, \tag{2}$$

where the a_n are numerical coefficients (expansion coefficients) to be manipulated until the series satisfies the differential equation at hand. Again, this is an assumption, the validity of which can be established only if we can force it to satisfy the differential equation.

Now, our task is to solve Schrödinger's equation for the harmonic oscillator,

$$\frac{d^2\psi}{d\xi^2} + (\lambda - \xi^2)\psi = 0. \tag{3}$$

The next step is to transform Schrödinger's equation into a differential equation for $H(\xi)$ by direct substitution of Equation (1). Differentiating Equation (1) twice gives

$$\frac{d^2\psi}{d\xi^2} = \left(\frac{d^2H}{d\xi^2} - 2\xi\frac{dH}{d\xi} + (\xi^2 - 1)H\right)e^{-\xi^2/2}, \tag{4}$$

where we have dropped the explicit dependence of H on ξ for sake of clarity. Substituting this result and Equation (1) into Equation (3) and canceling the common exponential factors gives the desired differential equation for H:

$$\frac{d^2H}{d\xi^2} - 2\xi\frac{dH}{d\xi} + (\lambda - 1)H = 0. \tag{5}$$

We now attempt a series solution for H of the form

$$H(\xi) = \sum_{n=0}^{\infty} a_n\xi^n. \tag{6}$$

Note that the index of summation n begins at zero; we cannot admit negative powers of ξ: because $\xi = 0$ is a legitimate point in the domain of the potential, negative powers would lead to infinities. (Actually, infinities do not automatically disqualify a ψ as being legitimate: so long as ψ is normalizable, it is fine. But the form of ψ being dealt with here does not admit this possibility.) Differentiating Equation (6) gives

$$\frac{dH}{d\xi} = \sum_{n=0}^{\infty} n a_n \xi^{n-1} \tag{7}$$

and

$$\frac{d^2H}{d\xi^2} = \sum_{n=0}^{\infty} n(n-1) a_n \xi^{n-2}. \tag{8}$$

Substituting Equations (6), (7), and (8) into Equation (5) and gathering terms with the same power of ξ gives

$$\sum_{n=0}^{\infty} n(n-1) a_n \xi^{n-2} + \sum_{n=0}^{\infty} [\lambda - 1 - 2n] a_n \xi^n = 0. \tag{9}$$

As it stands, Equation (9) is awkward: expanding out the sums would give contributions of the form ξ^j from both terms for $j \geq 2$. It would be convenient to have all terms involving the same power in ξ collected together. We can do this with a trick of notation. Consider the first sum in Equation (9). When $n = 0$ or 1, this sum makes no contribution due to the factor of $n(n-1)$:

$$\sum_{n=0}^{\infty} n(n-1) a_n \xi^{n-2} = 0 + 0 + \sum_{n=2}^{\infty} n(n-1) a_n \xi^{n-2}. \tag{10}$$

Now, the index of summation n is known as a *dummy* index. This means that because the sum runs over all possible integral values (≥ 0) up to infinity, it is irrelevant what label we assign the index of summation. This opens up the possibility of performing a transformation of index in exactly the same way as one does a transformation of variable to simplify an integral. Consider, for example, defining a new index j such that $j = n - 2$. We can then write Equation (10) as

$$\sum_{n=0}^{\infty} n(n-1) a_n \xi^{n-2} = \sum_{n=2}^{\infty} n(n-1) a_n \xi^{n-2} = \sum_{j=0}^{\infty} (j+2)(j+1) a_{j+2} \xi^j. \tag{11}$$

Note that in effecting this change of index, substitution is made everywhere the original index appears. Because the lowest value of n that makes a nonzero contribution to the sum is $n = 2$, then the lowest value of j making a nonzero contribution is $j = 0$ because $j = n - 2$.

Now, in Equation (11), both j and n are dummy indexes. We are at liberty to relabel j as n (in effect, define a new index $n = j$), and write

$$\sum_{n=0}^{\infty} n(n - 1)a_n\xi^{n-2} = \sum_{n=0}^{\infty} (n + 2)(n + 1)a_{n+2}\xi^n. \tag{12}$$

If you have doubts as to the veracity of Equation (12), simply expand out the sums on both sides: they are absolutely identical (Problem 2). The value of this manipulation is that it transforms the ξ^{n-2} term in Equation (9) into one involving ξ^n, which is exactly the form in which ξ appears in the other term. We can then combine the terms in Equation (9) to give

$$\sum_{n=0}^{\infty} [(n + 1)(n + 2)a_{n+2} + (\lambda - 1 - 2n)a_n]\xi^n = 0. \tag{13}$$

This transformation-of-index procedure is a useful artifice often employed in series solutions of differential equations.

Examine Equation (13) carefully. The terms within the square brackets are pure numbers; they have no dependence on ξ. In general, ξ is not equal to zero (indeed, $-\infty \le \xi \le \infty$), yet the sum evaluates to zero. The only way this can happen for all possible values of ξ is if the quantity in square brackets vanishes in general. This demands

$$a_{n+2} = \frac{(2n + 1 - \lambda)}{(n + 1)(n + 2)} a_n. \tag{14}$$

Equation (14) is a **recursion relation**: it specifies a given expansion coefficient **recursively** in terms of a preceding coefficient in the series. To complete the solution it is necessary to supply values for the first two coefficients, a_0 and a_1. All subsequent even-indexed coefficients can then be expressed in terms of a_0 and all subsequent odd-indexed coefficients in terms of a_1. The need to supply two coefficients can be understood on the basis that second-order differential equations always yield two constants of integration to be set by boundary conditions. In view of the fact that our recursion relation links pairs of successive coefficients, we can imagine splitting the solution for $H(\xi)$ into a sum of two subseries:

$$H(\xi) \sim (a_0 + a_2\xi^2 + a_4\xi^4 + \cdots) + (a_1\xi + a_3\xi^3 + a_5\xi^5 + \cdots), \tag{15}$$

with the coefficients in both subseries related by Equation (14).

In the present case there is only one boundary condition to satisfy: that $\psi(x)$ remains finite as $\xi \to \pm\infty$ (that is, as $x \to \pm\infty$). Now, from Equation (1), $\psi(\xi)$ is the product of two functions, $H(\xi)$ and $\exp(-\xi^2/2)$. The latter of these is clearly convergent; indeed, we deliberately chose the convergent case in Section 5.2. Thus, as long as $H(\xi)$ is convergent, or at worst if it diverges no more strongly than $\exp(+\xi^2/2)$, then the overall solution will remain convergent. The issue is then the asymptotic behavior of $H(\xi)$. Unfortunately, $H(\xi)$ proves to behave asymptotically as $\exp(2\xi^2)$. To see this, consider a general series expansion of the exponential function $\exp(\eta\xi^p)$:

$$\exp(\eta\xi^p) = 1 + \eta\xi^p + \frac{\eta^2\xi^{2p}}{2!} + \frac{\eta^3\xi^{3p}}{3!} + \cdots \tag{16}$$

$$+ \frac{\eta^n\xi^{np}}{n!} + \frac{\eta^{n+1}\xi^{(n+1)p}}{(n+1)!} + \frac{\eta^{n+2}\xi^{(n+2)p}}{(n+2)!} + \cdots.$$

Now, our assumed series solution resulted in an expression, Equation (14), that relates successive terms in even- and odd-indexed subseries, Equation (15). The ratio of successive terms in either subseries goes as, from Equations (2) and (14),

$$\left[\frac{\text{Term }(n+1)}{\text{Term }(n)}\right]_{\text{subseries}} = \frac{a_{n+2}}{a_n}\xi^2 = \frac{(2n+1-\lambda)}{(n+1)(n+2)}\xi^2.$$

The ratio of successive terms in the exponential function of Equation (16) behaves as

$$\left[\frac{\text{Term }(n+1)}{\text{Term }(n)}\right]_{\exp} = \frac{\eta\xi^p}{(n+1)}.$$

Now compare these expressions as $n \to \infty$:

$$\left[\frac{\text{Term}(n+1)}{\text{Term}(n)}\right]_{\substack{\text{subseries}\\ n\to\infty}} \sim \frac{2}{n}\xi^2 \tag{17}$$

and

$$\left[\frac{\text{Term}(n+1)}{\text{Term}(n)}\right]_{\substack{\exp\\ n\to\infty}} \sim \frac{\eta}{n}\xi^p. \tag{18}$$

The denominators of Equations (17) and (18) are identical; on identifying $p = 2$ and $\eta = 2$ we can conclude that the harmonic oscillator series solution behaves as an exponential of the form $\exp(\eta \xi^p) = \exp(2\xi^2)$. This means that $\psi(\xi)$ behaves as

$$\psi(\xi) = H(\xi)e^{-\xi^2/2} \sim e^{2\xi^2}e^{-\xi^2/2} \sim e^{3\xi^2/2}, \tag{19}$$

which is clearly divergent and hence nonnormalizable. The only way to prevent this catastrophe would be to somehow prevent the series for $H(\xi)$ from going on to an infinite number of terms in order to allow the convergent asymptotic solution $e^{-\xi^2/2}$ to dominate as $\xi \to \infty$. This means that the series for $H(\xi)$ must be forced to terminate after a finite number of terms. (A polynomial function with a finite number of terms multiplied by a convergent exponential function will always give a function whose overall behavior is convergent. Why?)

The demand that $H(\xi)$ so terminate has the physical consequence of quantizing the energy levels of the system. If the highest power of ξ appearing in $H(\xi)$ is n—that is, if all $a_j = 0$ for $j > n$—then the recursion relation demands

$$\lambda = 2n + 1. \tag{20}$$

One problem remains: because the recursion relation (Equation 14) links two coefficients that straddle another coefficient, we cannot simultaneously terminate both the even $(a_0, a_2, ...)$ and odd $(a_1, a_3, ...)$ sets of coefficients with this expedient. We must in addition arbitrarily demand that *either* a_0 *or* a_1 be zero.

The general result is a family of functions $H_n(\xi)$, with each member being a polynomial involving only even or odd powers of ξ (but not both) up to order ξ^n. The index n serves to label the different solutions.

From the preceding termination condition and the definition of λ (Equations 5.1.2 and 5.1.4), we can determine the energy corresponding to quantum number n:

$$\lambda = 2n + 1 = \frac{2E}{\hbar \omega}$$

or,

$$E = \left(n + \frac{1}{2} \right)\hbar\omega = \left(n + \frac{1}{2} \right)\hbar\sqrt{\frac{k}{m}}, \quad n = 0, 1, 2, 3, \dots . \tag{21}$$

Notice that E is proportional to n; that is, harmonic-potential energy levels are equally spaced. This is the reason for the equal spacing of molecular spectral lines illustrated in Chapter 1 in Figure 1.2(d). The **zero-point energy** of the harmonic oscillator is $\hbar\omega/2$; from Example 4.4 we can regard this as an aspect of Heisenberg's uncertainty principle.

These equally spaced energy levels are known as **vibrational levels** because the harmonic potential mimics the attractive forces between molecules. In Problem 5–7, it is shown that for real molecules the force constants involved are on the order of a few hundred Newton/meter.

In reality, molecules are three-dimensional entities, so we cannot expect our one-dimensional analysis to reveal the entire story. Indeed, it is clear from Figure 1.2(d) that molecular spectra exhibit lines between the equally spaced vibrational transitions. These so-called **rotational levels** are due to the quantization of the rotational angular momentum of the molecule about its center of mass in accordance with the wave mechanics of angular momentum, as discussed further in Chapters 6, 7, and 8; the energetics of diatomic molecules is treated briefly in Chapter 8. The situation is further complicated by the fact that diatomic-bond potentials are more complex than $V = kx^2/2$. In more advanced treatments, the Morse potential [1]

$$V(r) = D\{1 - \exp[-a(r - r_o)]\}^2$$

is found to give a better fit to observed spectra. To a first order expansion, the Morse and simple harmonic oscillator potentials are identical. The structure and spectra of molecules is a vast, active area of research.

EXAMPLE 5.2

In Problem 5–7 you will show that diatomic molecules act like harmonic oscillators with force constants $k \sim 500\ N/m$. Consider a hydrogen atom ($m \sim m_{\text{proton}} = 1.673 \times 10^{-27}$ kg) subject to such a potential. What is the value of the zero-point energy?

A force constant of 500 *N/m* is surprisingly strong, corresponding to a spring of strength ~ 3.5 pounds per inch. Despite this very macroscopic strength, however, the zero-point energy (E_{ZP}) energy is distinctly atomic in scale:

$$E_{ZP} = \frac{\hbar}{2}\sqrt{\frac{k}{m}} = \frac{(1.055 \times 10^{-34}\ J\ sec)}{2}\sqrt{\frac{500\ N/m}{1.673 \times 10^{-27}\ kg}} = 2.88 \times 10^{-20}\ J,$$

or about 0.18 eV. This is a tiny amount of energy; however, when one considers how many atoms there would be in a lengthy molecular chain the sum could be appreciable. This energy is, however, inaccessible.

Parenthetically, the value of $k \sim 500 \; N/m$ can be understood with a simple estimate. If you compute the Coulomb force between two electrons separated by 1Å, you will find a magnitude $F \sim 2.3 \times 10^{-8} \; N$. The force per unit distance is then $\sim (2.3 \times 10^{-8} \; N)/(10^{-10} \; m) \sim 230 \; N/m$, of the same order of magnitude claimed here for k. The details will depend on the molecule at hand, but we can expect atomic-scale situations to be characterized by charges and physical sizes of these sorts of magnitudes.

■ 5.4   Hermite Polynomials and Harmonic Oscillator Wavefunctions

The family of solutions $H_n(\xi)$ to Equation (5.3.5) are known as **Hermite polynomials**. Full details on their properties and normalization can be found in Chapter 13 of Weber and Arfken. The first few Hermite polynomials are listed in Table 5.1. Note that in each case the highest power of ξ appearing in the series for $H_n(\xi)$ is ξ^n. To get the polynomials in terms of real (x) space, substitute $\xi = \alpha x$.

The normalized harmonic-oscillator wavefunctions are given by

$$\psi_n(x) = A_n H_n(\xi) e^{-\xi^2/2} = A_n H_n(\alpha x) e^{-\alpha^2 x^2/2}, \tag{1}$$

where A_n is a normalization factor:

$$A_n = \sqrt{\frac{\alpha}{\sqrt{\pi} 2^n n!}}, \tag{2}$$

and where

$$\alpha = (mk/\hbar^2)^{1/4}. \tag{3}$$

Table 5.1   Hermite Polynomials

$H_0(\xi) = 1$	$H_4(\xi) = 16\xi^4 - 48\xi^2 + 12$
$H_1(\xi) = 2\xi$	$H_5(\xi) = 32\xi^5 - 160\xi^3 + 120\xi$
$H_2(\xi) = 4\xi^2 - 2$	$H_6(\xi) = 64\xi^6 - 480\xi^4 + 720\xi^2 - 120$
$H_3(\xi) = 8\xi^3 - 12\xi$	$H_7(\xi) = 128\xi^7 - 1344\xi^5 + 3360\xi^3 - 1680\xi$

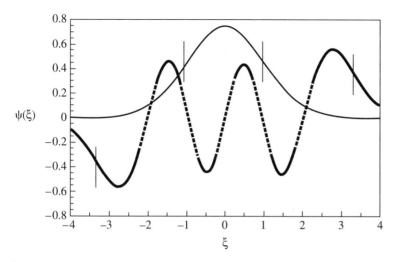

$\psi(\xi)$

FIGURE 5.2 Harmonic oscillator wavefunctions for $n = 0$ (solid line) and $n = 5$ (dashed line). The vertical lines designate the classical turning points for each curve; $\xi_{turn} = \pm 1$ and $\pm\sqrt{11}$ for $n = 0$ and 5, respectively. See Problem 5–8.

Hermite polynomials of order $n \geq 2$ can be generated from $H_0(x)$ and $H_1(x)$ from the recursion relation

$$H_{n+1}(x) = 2xH_n(x) - 2nH_{n-1}(x).$$

Figure 5.2 shows the $n = 0$ and $n = 5$ harmonic-oscillator wavefunctions (assuming $\alpha = 1$). $\psi_n(\xi)$ is symmetric for even n and antisymmetric for odd n; for a given n, there are $n + 1$ maxima. As n increases, the value(s) of ξ at which ψ reaches its maximum values move closer to the classical turning points (the vertical lines in the figure). The probability of finding the oscillator outside the well is greatest for $n = 0$.

EXAMPLE 5.3

Determine the probability that a harmonic oscillator in the ground state $(n = 0)$ will be found beyond the classical turning points.

The normalized wavefunction for the ground-state harmonic oscillator is

$$\psi_0(x) = \frac{\sqrt{\alpha}}{\pi^{1/4}} e^{-\alpha^2 x^2/2},$$

with

$$E_0 = \hbar\omega/2.$$

The classically forbidden region corresponds to $V(x) > E_0$, or

$$kx^2/2 > \hbar\omega/2,$$

that is,

$$|x| > \beta, \text{ where } \beta = \sqrt{\frac{\hbar\omega}{k}}.$$

It is easier to calculate the desired probability by determining the probability that the oscillator will be found *inside* the well and subtracting the result from unity:

$$P(\text{outside}) = 1 - P(\text{inside}).$$

Hence

$$P(\text{inside}) = 2\int_0^\beta \psi_0^* \psi_0 dx = \frac{2\alpha}{\sqrt{\pi}} \int_0^\beta e^{-\alpha^2 x^2} dx.$$

The factor of 2 comes from the symmetry of $\psi^*\psi$ about $x = 0$. Defining $\xi = \alpha x$ gives

$$P(\text{inside}) = \frac{2}{\sqrt{\pi}} \int_0^{\alpha\beta} e^{-\xi^2} d\xi.$$

This integral cannot be solved analytically; it has to be evaluated numerically. Integrals of this form turn up in a number of problems in mathematical physics (in particular, statistics), and are known as **error functions**:

$$erf(z) = \frac{2}{\sqrt{\pi}} \int_0^z e^{-\xi^2} d\xi.$$

Values of $erf(z)$ are tabulated in a number of mathematical handbooks; some of the asymptotic properties of this function are discussed in Section 5.10 of Weber and Arfken, and methods for computing error functions are discussed in Section 6.2 of Press et al. In the present case we have $erf(1)$ because

$$z = \alpha\beta = \left(\frac{mk}{\hbar^2}\right)^{1/4}\left(\frac{\hbar\omega}{k}\right)^{1/2} = \left(\frac{m\omega^2}{k}\right)^{1/4} = 1,$$

given that $\omega^2 = k/m$. Since $erf(1) = 0.843$, we find $P(\text{outside}) = 0.157$, a distinctly nonnegligible result. This is another manifestation of the phenomena of quantum tunneling that we first explored in Chapter 3.

EXAMPLE 5.4

Determine the root-mean-square position $\sqrt{\langle x^2 \rangle}$ for a ground-state harmonic oscillator, and compare the result to the classical turning point.

Here we have

$$\langle x^2 \rangle = \int_{-\infty}^{\infty} \psi_0^* x^2 \psi_0 \, dx = \frac{\alpha}{\sqrt{\pi}} \int_{-\infty}^{\infty} x^2 e^{-\alpha^2 x^2} \, dx = \frac{2\alpha}{\sqrt{\pi}} \int_0^{\infty} x^2 e^{-\alpha^2 x^2} \, dx$$

$$= \frac{2\alpha}{\sqrt{\pi}}\left(\frac{\sqrt{\pi}}{4\alpha^3}\right) = \frac{1}{2\alpha^2} = \frac{\hbar}{2\sqrt{mk}}.$$

Because $x_{turn} = \sqrt{\hbar\omega/k}$,

$$\frac{\langle x^2 \rangle}{x_{turn}^2} = \frac{\hbar}{2\sqrt{mk}}\frac{k}{\hbar\omega} = \frac{k}{2\omega\sqrt{mk}} = \frac{k}{2\sqrt{k/m}\sqrt{mk}} = \frac{1}{2}.$$

Hence

$$\sqrt{\langle x^2 \rangle} = \frac{x_{turn}}{\sqrt{2}}.$$

The RMS displacement of the oscillator from the origin is less that the turning-point position, an intuitively sensible result.

■ **5.5   Comparing the Classical and Quantum Simple Harmonic Oscillators**

Our analysis of the quantum harmonic oscillator has resulted in wavefunctions which, for a given quantum state n, are products of an nth order polynomial and an exponential function. These wavefunctions look nothing like what one sees as the *time-dependent* functions used to describe a mass-spring system in Newtonian physics. In the latter analysis, if a mass m is attached to a spring of force constant k, displaced (stretched or compressed) a distance D from the spring's equilibrium position ($x = 0$) and then released, the resulting motion is described by

$$x = D \cos(\omega t), \tag{1}$$

where the angular frequency ω is identical to that appearing in the quantum analysis, $\omega = \sqrt{k/m}$ (Section 5.1). The total energy of the classical oscillator is given by $E = kD^2/2$, an apparently continuous function of total displacement.

Because the simple harmonic oscillator is such a well-known Newtonian system, it is instructive to compare the quantum and classical solutions for it and to try to reconcile their apparently very different descriptions. Quantum-mechanical predictions are invariably given as probabilities, so we effect our comparison via probabilistic predictions. Quantum-mechanically, the probability of finding the oscillator between x and $x + dx$ is given by $P_{\text{quant}}(x, x + dx) = |\psi|^2 dx$; our task is to derive an analogous expression for a classical oscillator and hence to compare expressions for quantized and classical oscillators of the same energy. Equation (1) tells us *where* the classical oscillator will be as a function of time. We can turn it into an expression for the *velocity* of the oscillator at any time by taking a derivative:

$$v = \frac{dx}{dt} = -\omega D \sin(\omega t). \tag{2}$$

For a reason that will become clear momentarily, it is helpful to rewrite this expression so that the right side is in terms of $x(t)$. From the identity $\sin^2\theta + \cos^2\theta = 1$, we can write $D \sin(\omega t) = \sqrt{D^2 - D^2 \cos^2(\omega t)}$, hence

$$v = -\omega D \sin(\omega t) = -\omega\sqrt{D^2 - D^2 \cos^2(\omega t)} = -\omega\sqrt{D^2 - x^2}. \tag{3}$$

Now, imagine that you observe a classical mass-spring system by taking a large number of superimposed stop-action photographs of it at random times over many periods of the motion. As you examine the resulting image, you could tabulate a census of how many exposures out of the total number taken show the mass to be between positions x and $x + dx$. Because all oscillations of the system are identical, this number would be given simply by the amount of time that the oscillator spends between those limits over the course of each full oscillation divided by the period $T = 2\pi/\omega$ for one oscillation. For a small spatial slice of width dx, the passage time would be $dx/v(x)$, where $v(x)$ is the velocity of the oscillator at position x; this is why we cast the velocity of Equation (2) into the position-specific form of Equation (3). On recalling that a full back-and-forth motion of the oscillator will bring it through the relevant region of space twice during each cycle, we can write

$$P_{class}(x, x + dx) = 2\frac{[dx/v(x)]}{T} = \left[\frac{2}{T\omega\sqrt{D^2 - x^2}}\right]dx = \left[\frac{1}{\pi\sqrt{D^2 - x^2}}\right]dx, \quad (4)$$

where we have dropped the negative sign in Equation (3) because we are interested only in the magnitude of the time that the oscillator spends in the relevant region.

For a meaningful comparison, we need to have our quantum and classical oscillators to be of the same energy:

$$\left(n + \frac{1}{2}\right)\hbar\omega = \frac{1}{2}kD^2 \quad \Rightarrow \quad D^2 = (2n + 1)\frac{\hbar\omega}{k}. \quad (5)$$

It is convenient to cast Equation (4) into a form involving the dimensionless variable $\xi = \alpha x$ that was introduced in Section 5.1 (Equations 5.1.1 and 5.1.3). Using Equation (5) to eliminate D, the reader should verify that this transformation brings Equation (4) to the form

$$P_{class}(\xi, \xi + d\xi) = \left[\frac{1}{\pi\sqrt{2n + 1 - \xi^2}}\right]d\xi. \quad (6)$$

The square bracket is the *classical probability density*.

For the quantum oscillator we have

$$P_{quant}(x, x + dx) = \psi^2(x)dx = [A_n H_n(\alpha x)e^{-\alpha^2 x^2/2}]^2 dx,$$

where the normalization coefficients are given in Equation (5.4.2) and the $H_n(\alpha x)$ are the Hermite polynomials. On converting to ξ-space, this becomes

$$P_{quant}(\xi, \xi + d\xi) = \left[\frac{1}{\sqrt{\pi 2^n n!}}H_n^2(\xi)e^{-\xi^2}\right]d\xi. \quad (7)$$

For quantum state n, the turning points of the motion—that is, the classical limits of the motion—are given by (Problem 5–8) $\xi = \pm\sqrt{2n+1}$. Note that P_{class} diverges at these points; this corresponds to the fact that the oscillator is momentarily at rest at those points and hence has a high probability of being found at one or the other of them in a series of short-exposure photographs of the system.

Equations (6) and (7) are difficult to compare analytically, so we content ourselves with a numerical example. If we desired a macroscopic-scale energy we might set $m = 1$ kg, $k = 500$ N/m, and $D = 1$ meter, in which case $n \sim 10^{35}$. Given the oscillatory nature of the Hermite polynomials, however, it would be impossible to plot P_{quant} and still resolve the individual probability peaks. We will have to settle for a much smaller value of n.

Figure 5.3 shows the probability densities [square-bracketed quantities in Equations (6) and (7)] for the case of $n = 15$. The wiggly line shows P_{quant}; the upward-opening smooth curve is P_{class}. Eyeball inspection of the graph shows that P_{class} tracks closely to the average run of P_{quant}. Indeed, on considering that this energy would be of distinctly microscopic scale, the agreement is striking (for our 1 kg oscillator with $k = 500$ N/m and $n = 15$, Equation (5) gives $D \sim 10^{-17}$ m; the energy would be about 10^{-13} eV). If n is increased, the wiggles in the P_{quant} curve would come closer and closer together because the spatial density of peaks is $\xi_{turn}/n \propto 1/\sqrt{n}$ (Equation 5), which grows as n increases. (P_{class} always has the upward-opening form shown in the figure.) For practical purposes, measurements of the position of the oscillator would necessarily sample a finite range of distance incorporating many such wiggles; the derived quantum probability distribution would then agree with the classical one to an

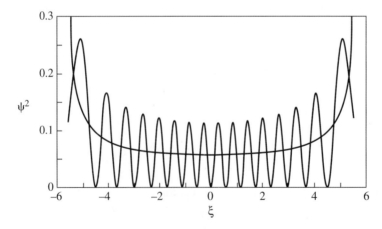

FIGURE 5.3 Probablilty densities for $n = 15$ classical (smooth upward-opening curve) and quantum (wiggly curve) oscillators. The classical turning points of the motion are $\xi \sim \pm 5.57$.

incredible degree of accuracy. (If the agreement is good for $n = 15$, try to imagine what it would be like for $n = 10^{35}$!) It is in this way that we say that the predictions of quantum mechanics merge into their classical counterparts when the quantum number of the system is large. Real mass and spring systems have quantized energies, but the energy levels and spatial probability distributions are, for all practical purposes, continuous.

■   5.6   Raising and Lowering Operators (Optional)

In this section we explore an ingenious operator-based alternate solution to the harmonic oscillator potential originally developed by Dirac. The advantage of this approach is that it allows one to completely circumvent the lengthy solution of Schrödinger's equation as laid out in Sections 5.1–5.3. Although this technique can be extended to other potentials, the disadvantage is that is can be difficult to establish the appropriate form for the relevant operators.

Dirac's approach is predicated on defining two operators:

$$A^+ = \frac{\iota}{\alpha\sqrt{2}}\left(-\frac{d}{dx} + \alpha^2 x \right) \tag{1}$$

and

$$A^- = \frac{\iota}{\alpha\sqrt{2}}\left(-\frac{d}{dx} - \alpha^2 x \right), \tag{2}$$

where α is as defined in Equation (5.1.1),

$$\alpha = \left(\frac{mk}{\hbar^2} \right)^{1/4}. \tag{5.1.1}$$

For reasons that will soon become clear, these operators are respectively known as the *raising* and *lowering* operators.

In order to see how defining A^+ and A^- lead to solutions for the harmonic-oscillator potential, it is necessary to first establish some of their properties. Let ψ be some wavefunction on which these operators can act. Although α here is defined as that for the harmonic oscillator states, this dummy wavefunction can in fact be *any* wave-function; it need *not* be one of the harmonic oscillator wavefunctions. First consider what happens if A^- is allowed to operate on the result of $(A^+\psi)$:

$$A^-\,(A^+\psi) = \frac{\iota}{\alpha\sqrt{2}}\left(-\frac{d}{dx} - \alpha^2x\right)\left[\frac{\iota}{\alpha\sqrt{2}}\left(-\frac{d\psi}{dx} + \alpha^2x\psi\right)\right]$$

$$= \frac{\iota^2}{2\alpha^2}\left(\frac{d^2\psi}{dx^2} - \alpha^2\psi - \alpha^2x\frac{d\psi}{dx} + \alpha^2x\frac{d\psi}{dx} - \alpha^4x^2\psi\right)$$

$$= -\frac{1}{2\alpha^2}\left(\frac{d^2\psi}{dx^2} - \alpha^2\psi - \alpha^4x^2\psi\right). \tag{3}$$

Similarly,

$$A^+(A^-\psi) = -\frac{1}{2\alpha^2}\left(\frac{d^2\psi}{dx^2} + \alpha^2\psi - \alpha^4x^2\psi\right). \tag{4}$$

The commutator of A^+ and A^- operating on ψ is then

$$[A^-, A^+]\psi = (A^-A^+ - A^+A^-)\psi$$

$$= -\frac{1}{2\alpha^2}\left(\frac{d^2\psi}{dx^2} - \alpha^2\psi - \alpha^4x^2\psi\right) + \frac{1}{2\alpha^2}\left(\frac{d^2\psi}{dx^2} + \alpha^2\psi - \alpha^4x^2\psi\right)$$

$$= \psi. \tag{5}$$

Equation (5) indicates that we can regard $[A^-, A^+]$ as being a sort of "unity" operator:

$$[A^-, A^+] \equiv (A^-A^+ - A^+A^-) \equiv 1. \tag{6}$$

This result is entirely independent of the particular wavefunction that $[A^+, A^-]$ should happen to be operating on. Now consider the result of operating $(A^-A^+ + A^+A^-)$ on ψ:

$$(A^-A^+ + A^+A^-)\psi = -\frac{1}{2\alpha^2}\left(\frac{d^2\psi}{dx^2} - \alpha^2\psi - \alpha^4x^2\psi\right) - \frac{1}{2\alpha^2}\left(\frac{d^2\psi}{dx^2} + \alpha^2\psi - \alpha^4x^2\psi\right)$$

$$= \left(-\frac{1}{\alpha^2}\frac{d^2}{dx^2} + \alpha^2x^2\right)\psi. \tag{7}$$

But for a multiplicative factor, the bracketed quantity on the right side of Equation (7) is precisely the Hamiltonian operator for the harmonic-oscillator potential:

$$-\frac{1}{\alpha^2}\frac{d^2\psi}{dx^2} + \alpha^2x^2\psi = -\frac{\hbar}{\sqrt{mk}}\frac{d^2\psi}{dx^2} + \frac{\sqrt{mk}}{\hbar}x^2\psi$$

$$= \frac{2\sqrt{m/k}}{\hbar}\left(-\frac{\hbar^2}{2m}\frac{d^2}{dx^2} + \frac{k}{2}x^2\right)\psi. \tag{8}$$

Defining $\omega = \sqrt{k/m}$, Equations (7) and (8) give

$$\boldsymbol{H} \equiv \frac{\hbar\omega}{2}(A^-A^+ + A^+A^-). \tag{9}$$

Now, from Equation (6) we can write

$$(A^-A^+ - A^+A^-) \equiv 1 \;\Rightarrow\; A^-A^+ \equiv 1 + A^+A^-. \tag{10}$$

This result, when substituted into Equation (9) gives

$$\boldsymbol{H} \equiv \hbar\omega(A^+A^- + 1/2). \tag{11}$$

With this result, form the commutator of $\boldsymbol{H}$ and A^+ acting on ψ:

$$[\boldsymbol{H}, A^+]\psi = (\boldsymbol{H}A^+ - A^+\boldsymbol{H})\psi$$

$$= \hbar\omega(A^+A^- + 1/2)(A^+\psi) - \hbar\omega A^+(A^+A^- + 1/2)\psi$$

$$= \hbar\omega(A^+A^-A^+ - A^+A^+A^-)\psi$$

$$= \hbar\omega A^+(A^-A^+ - A^+A^-)\psi$$

$$= (\hbar\omega A^+)\psi, \tag{12}$$

where Equation (6) was used to simplify $(A^- A^+ - A^+ A^-)$ in the second-to-last line. Equation (12) gives us the identity

$$[\boldsymbol{H}, A^+] \equiv \hbar \omega A^+. \tag{13}$$

Similarly, it is easy to show that

$$[\boldsymbol{H}, A^-] \equiv -\hbar \omega A^-. \tag{14}$$

Circular as it may seem, now redo the calculation of Equation (12), but using Equation (13). This will reveal a remarkable conclusion.

$$(\boldsymbol{H}A^+ - A^+\boldsymbol{H})\psi = \hbar \omega (A^+ \psi)$$

$$\Rightarrow \boldsymbol{H}(A^+\psi) - A^+(\boldsymbol{H}\psi) = \hbar \omega (A^+ \psi).$$

Now, the action of $\boldsymbol{H}$ on ψ must be to return $E\psi$ where E is the energy corresponding to ψ, that is, we must have

$$\boldsymbol{H}(A^+\psi) - A^+(E\psi) = \hbar \omega (A^+ \psi),$$

or

$$\boldsymbol{H}(A^+\psi) = (E + \hbar \omega)(A^+ \psi). \tag{15}$$

Look at the structure of Equation (15): it is an eigenvalue equation. *The remarkable conclusion here is that when* A^+ *acts on* ψ *it gives rise to a new function,* $(A^+\psi)$, *whose energy eigenvalue is just that of* ψ, *plus* $\hbar \omega$. By a similar approach, it is easy to show that

$$\boldsymbol{H}(A^-\psi) = (E - \hbar \omega)(A^- \psi), \tag{16}$$

that is, *when* A^- *acts on* ψ *it gives rise to a new function,* $(A^-\psi)$, *whose energy eigenvalue is just that of* ψ, *less* $\hbar \omega$. It is worth reiterating that these results are quite independent of the details of the wavefunctions that A^+ and A^- are operating on; nowhere in the derivation have we assumed that the ψ's are harmonic oscillator wavefunctions.

The reason why A^+ and A^- are known as *raising* and *lowering* operators should now be clear: when applied to any wavefunction they give rise to new wavefunctions whose energies are raised (in the case of A^+) or lowered (in the case of A^-) from that of the original ones by an amount $\hbar \omega$. A^+ and A^- are also sometimes known as **ladder operators**.

To establish the harmonic-oscillator wavefunctions and energies by this approach requires an inference. The potential is

$$V(x) = \frac{k}{2}x^2. \tag{17}$$

Because $V > 0$ everywhere, we can infer that the energy eigenvalues must be positively valued. Suppose, then, that ψ is some solution of this potential with energy $E > 0$. Successive applications of the lowering operator A^- would yield functions whose energies are decremented by $\hbar\omega$ at each application. If this process continued indefinitely, we would arrive at negative energies, in contradiction to the conclusion that all eigenenergies of this potential must be positive. We infer, then, that there must exist some state of lowest positive energy, say (ψ_0, E_0), which cannot be allowed to generate a yet lower state when acted upon by A^-; that is, ψ_0 must be such that

$$A^-\psi_0 = 0. \tag{18}$$

ψ_0 can be explicitly determined by demanding the veracity of Equation (18):

$$\frac{\iota}{\alpha\sqrt{2}}\left(-\frac{d\psi_0}{dx} - \alpha^2 x\psi_0\right) = 0. \tag{19}$$

The solution of this simple differential equation is $\psi_0 = Ke^{-\alpha^2 x^2/2}$ where K is a constant of integration; normalizing yields the ground-state harmonic-oscillator wavefunction. E_0 can be determined by substituting ψ_0 back into Schrödinger's equation or by applying Equation (11):

$$\mathbf{H}\psi_0 = E_0\psi_0 \implies \hbar\omega(A^+A^- + 1/2)\psi_0 = \left(\frac{1}{2}\hbar\omega\right)\psi_0 = E_0\psi_0, \tag{20}$$

where we have used the fact that $A^-\psi_0 = 0$.

Do not think that because A^+ and A^- act to raise and lower the energy of a wavefunction that they operate on by $\pm\hbar\omega$ that it follows that they must give rise exactly to other harmonic oscillator wavefunctions. In fact, they act as

$$A^+\psi_n = \iota\sqrt{n+1}\,\psi_{n+1} \tag{21}$$

and

$$A^-\psi_n = -\iota\sqrt{n}\,\psi_{n-1}. \tag{22}$$

To prove these, it is crucial to have on hand two recursion relationships satisfied by Hermite polynomials (see Weber and Arfken, Section 13.1):

$$-\frac{dH_n}{d\xi} + 2\xi H_n = H_{n+1} \tag{23}$$

and

$$\frac{dH_n}{d\xi} = 2n H_{n-1}. \tag{24}$$

Equation (21), for example, can be proven as follows: In terms of $\xi = \alpha x$, A^+ appears as

$$A^+ = \frac{\iota}{\sqrt{2}}\left(-\frac{d}{d\xi} + \xi\right).$$

Hence, from Equation (5.4.1),

$$A^+\psi_n = \frac{\iota}{\sqrt{2}}\left(-\frac{d}{d\xi} + \xi\right)(A_n H_n e^{-\xi^2/2}) = \frac{\iota A_n}{\sqrt{2}}\left(-\frac{dH_n}{d\xi} + 2\xi H_n\right)e^{-\xi^2/2}. \tag{25}$$

From Equation (5.4.2), the normalization factors satisfy

$$A_n = \sqrt{2(n+1)}\, A_{n+1}. \tag{26}$$

Equations (23) and (26) in Equation (25) give

$$A^+\psi_n = \frac{\iota\sqrt{2(n+1)}\, A_{n+1}}{\sqrt{2}}(H_{n+1})e^{-\xi^2/2} = \iota\sqrt{n+1}\, A_{n+1} H_{n+1} e^{-\xi^2/2} = \iota\sqrt{n+1}\,\psi_{n+1}. \tag{27}$$

Equation (22) follows similarly, using Equation (24).

This operator approach to the harmonic potential has other advantages. Because the momentum operator is $p_{op} = -(\iota\hbar)(d/dx)$, Equations (1) and (2) can be rearranged to give

$$p_{op} = \frac{\alpha\hbar}{\sqrt{2}}(A^+ + A^-) \tag{28}$$

and

$$x_{op} = -\frac{\iota}{\sqrt{2}\alpha}(A^+ - A^-). \tag{29}$$

Suppose we wish to compute the expectation value of x^2 for any harmonic-oscillator state, say ψ_n, with $E_n = (n + 1/2)\hbar\omega$. This demands calculating

$$\langle x^2 \rangle = \int \psi_n(x_{op}^2 \psi_n)\,dx$$

$$= \frac{\iota^2}{2\alpha^2} \int \psi_n[(A^+ - A^-)(A^+\psi_n - A^-\psi_n)]\,dx$$

$$= -\frac{1}{2\alpha^2} \int \psi_n(A^+A^+\psi_n - A^+A^-\psi_n - A^-A^+\psi_n + A^-A^-\psi_n)\,dx.$$

Look at the first term within the bracket in the integrand. $A^+A^+\psi_n$ will give rise to ψ_{n+2}, which will be orthogonal to ψ_n (review the development of the orthogonality theorem in Chapter 4); the integral of the product of this result and ψ_n must consequently be zero. A similar argument applies for the last term within the brackets. Only the second and third terms will make any contribution to the integral:

$$\langle x^2 \rangle = \frac{1}{2\alpha^2} \int \psi_n(A^+A^- + A^-A^+)\psi_n\,dx.$$

The bracketed term in the integrand is just the Hamiltonian operator of Equation (9):

$$\langle x^2 \rangle = \frac{1}{2\alpha^2}\frac{2}{\hbar\omega} \int \psi_n(H\psi_n)\,dx = \frac{1}{\alpha^2\hbar\omega} \int \psi_n(E_n\psi_n)\,dx$$

$$= \frac{E_n}{\alpha^2\hbar\omega} = \frac{1}{\alpha^2}(n + 1/2). \tag{30}$$

$\langle p^2 \rangle$ follows similarly. Doing these calculations directly from the wavefunctions and properties of Hermite polynomials is considerably more involved (see Problem 5–10).

The power of this operator approach derives from but is limited by the fact that the harmonic-oscillator Hamiltonian has a sort of "sum of squares" form (Equation 8) and can so be "factored" as in Equation (9). Although this sort of manipulation will not in general be possible for any arbitrary potential, there are situations where defining similar raising and lowering operators can be valuable in more advanced work; we will explore such a situation concerning angular momentum in Chapter 8.

■ Summary

The solution of the harmonic oscillator (*HO*) potential $V(x) = kx^2/2$ is one of the classic triumphs of quantum mechanics, and can be found in virtually any text on the subject. Variants of this potential are central to our understanding of molecular spectra.

Almost as important as obtaining the wavefunctions and energies of the harmonic-oscillator potential is that its solution illustrates three techniques of considerable generality and power: (i) casting Schrödinger's equation into dimensionless form, (ii) establishing and factoring out an asymptotic solution valid for extreme values of x, and (iii) establishing a series solution to be grafted onto the asymptotic solution to yield an overall solution valid for all x. Forcing the convergence of the series solution leads to the energy eigenvalues of the system.

The normalized *HO* wavefunctions are given by

$$\psi_n(x) = A_n H_n(\xi)e^{-\xi^2/2} = A_n H_n(\alpha x)e^{-\alpha^2 x^2/2},$$

where A_n is a normalization factor:

$$A_n = \sqrt{\frac{\alpha}{\sqrt{\pi}\,2^n n!}},$$

with

$$\alpha = (mk/\hbar^2)^{1/4}.$$

$H_n(x)$ denotes a Hermite polynomial of order n, with n being the quantum number ($n = 0, 1, 2, 3, ...$). Explicit expressions for the first few $H_n(x)$ are given in Table 5.1; expressions for any others can be produced from the recursion relation

$$H_{n+1}(x) = 2xH_n(x) - 2nH_{n-1}(x),$$

or, if you are ambitious, directly from the generating function

$$H_n(x) = (-1)^n e^{x^2} \frac{d^n}{dx^n}(e^{-x^2}).$$

The energy of a *HO* in state n is given by

$$E = \left(n + \frac{1}{2}\right)\hbar\sqrt{\frac{k}{m}}, \quad n = 0,1,2,3,\ldots.$$

The raising and lowering operators are given by

$$A^+ = \frac{\iota}{\alpha\sqrt{2}}\left(-\frac{d}{dx} + \alpha^2 x\right)$$

and

$$A^- = \frac{\iota}{\alpha\sqrt{2}}\left(-\frac{d}{dx} - \alpha^2 x\right).$$

In terms of these, the harmonic oscillator Hamiltonian can be written as

$$\boldsymbol{H} \equiv \hbar\omega(A^+ A^- + 1/2).$$

These operators act on the harmonic oscillator states according as

$$A^+\psi_n = \iota\sqrt{n+1}\,\psi_{n+1}$$

and

$$A^-\psi_n = -\iota\sqrt{n}\,\psi_{n-1}.$$

In terms of these operators, the position and momentum operators appear as

$$x_{op} = -\frac{\iota}{\sqrt{2}\alpha}(A^+ - A^-)$$

and

$$p_{op} = \frac{\alpha\hbar}{\sqrt{2}}(A^+ + A^-).$$

■ Problems

5-1(I) Verify that Equation (5.1.5) results upon substitution of Equations (5.1.2), (5.1.3), and (5.1.4) into Schrödinger's equation for the harmonic oscillator potential.

5-2(E) Convince yourself that Equation (5.3.12) is valid by expanding out the first few terms on both sides.

5-3(A) Working from Equations (5.3.1), (5.3.6), (5.3.14), and the normalization condition, develop explicitly the expression for the $n = 2$ harmonic oscillator wavefunction. Compare to Table 5.1.

5-4(I) From Table 5.1 and Equations (5.4.1), (5.4.2), and (5.4.3), write out an explicit expression for the wavefunction for the third excited state ($n = 3$) of the harmonic oscillator. Verify that it satisfies Schrödinger's equation for the *HO* potential.

5-5(I) Verify by explicit calculation that the $n = 0$ and $n = 2$ harmonic oscillator wavefunctions are orthonormal.

5-6(I) Consider a particle of mass m in the first excited state ($n = 1$) of a harmonic oscillator potential. Compute the probability of finding the particle outside the classically allowed region.

5-7(E) In the case of a diatomic molecule, the analysis of the harmonic potential proceeds as above but with the mass m replaced by the reduced mass of the molecule, $m_1 m_2/(m_1 + m_2)$, where m_1 and m_2 are the masses of the individual atoms. In the case of molecular hydrogen, H_2, the equal spacing between the vibrational levels corresponds to a linear frequency ν of 12.48×10^{13} sec^{-1}. Determine the effective force constant k for H_2.

5-8(E) Show that the classical turning points for a harmonic oscillator in energy state n are given by $\xi_{turn} = \pm \sqrt{2(n + 1/2)}$.

5-9(A) In Chapter 9 we will study the so-called linear potential

$$V(x) = \begin{cases} \infty, & x \leq 0 \\ \alpha x, & x > 0. \end{cases}$$

Following the development in Sections 5.1 and 5.2, cast Schrödinger's equation for this potential into a dimensionless form and derive an asymptotically valid solution to it. Then hypothesize a series solution and attempt to establish a recursion relation. Is this potential soluble analytically?

5-10(A) Prove that $\Delta x \Delta p = (n + 1/2)\hbar$ for the harmonic oscillator wavefunctions. *HINTS:*

(i) What can you say of $\langle x \rangle$ and $\langle p \rangle$?

(ii) It is helpful to know that Hermite polynomials satisfy

$$\int_{-\infty}^{\infty} \xi^2 H_n^2(\xi) e^{-\xi^2} d\xi = \sqrt{\pi}\, 2^n n!\, (n + 1/2).$$

(iii) When computing $\langle p^2 \rangle$, Equation (5.1.5) may be helpful; convert from ξ to x.

5-11(I) A form of the *Morse potential* is

$$V(x) = V_o \{e^{-2x/b} - 2e^{-x/b}\},$$

where b is a constant. Show by appropriate expansions that for small values of (x/b) this potential is equivalent to a harmonic-oscillator potential with $k = 2V_o/b^2$, and which is offset by an additive energy $-V_o$, that is,

$$V(x) \sim -V_o + \left(\frac{V_o}{b^2}\right) x^2.$$

5-12(A) In Section 5.1, we rendered Schrödinger's equation for the harmonic oscillator dimensionless by establishing quantities α and ε with units of inverse meters and inverse Joules, respectively, and then replacing x and E with the dimensionless proxies ξ and λ. Consider a more general potential of the form $V(x) = A\,|x|^p$. Generalize the expressions for α and ε to be in terms of the power p. Include with each quantity a purely numerical multiplicative constant $(K_\alpha, K_\varepsilon)$ and determine these as functions of p such that Schrödinger's equation can be reduced to the form

$$\left(\frac{d^2\psi}{d\xi^2}\right) + (\lambda - |\xi|^p)\psi = 0.$$

Check your results against the harmonic oscillator case. Are there any values of p for which this scheme will not work?

5-13(I) As in Problem 5–12, consider a potential of the form $V(x) = Ax^p$ $(-\infty \le x \le \infty)$; presume that p is even so that no absolute values are involved. Generalize the asymptotic solution of Section 5.2 to this case; put $\psi \sim \exp(-\beta\xi^n)$. How do n and β depend on p? Then generalize the series solution of Section 5.3 to this case by setting $\psi = F(\xi)\exp(-\beta\xi^n)$. Show that the differential equation for $F(\xi)$ analogous to Equation (5.3.5) is

$$\frac{d^2F}{d\xi^2} - 2\xi^{p/2}\frac{dF}{d\xi} + \left[\lambda - (p/2)\xi^{p/2-1}\right]F = 0.$$

5-14(I) In setting up the series solution for $H(\xi)$, we assumed a summation of the form $H(\xi) = \Sigma a_n\xi^n$. To accommodate the possibility that the solution might not be a series in integral powers of ξ, we should be more careful and include an "indicial" power "c" in ξ: $H(\xi) = \Sigma a_n\xi^{n+c}$. Rework the solution with this assumption, and show that we must have $c = 0$.

5-15(E) Show that Equations (5.6.28) and (5.6.29) follow from Equations (5.6.1) and (5.6.2).

5-16(E) Show that application of the lowering operator A^- to the $n = 3$ harmonic-oscillator wavefunction leads to the result predicted by Equation (5.6.22).

5-17(E) Following the approach that led to Equation (5.6.30), use the raising and lowering operators to show that $\langle p^2 \rangle = \alpha^2\hbar^2(n + 1/2)$ for the nth harmonic-oscillator state, and hence verify that $\Delta x\Delta p$ is as given in Problem 5–10.

5-18(I) Show that the virial theorem holds for all harmonic-oscillator states. The identity given in Problem 5–10 is helpful.

5-19(I) Use dimensional analysis to construct a quantity whose units are that of time from the physical constants ϵ_o, m_e, e, and c.

6 Schrödinger's Equation in Three Dimensions and an Introduction to the Quantum Theory of Angular Momentum

In Chapters 3 and 5 we examined solutions of Schrödinger's equation for various examples of one-dimensional potentials. Those examples yielded a number of uniquely quantum-mechanical effects such as discrete energy states, alternating parity wavefunctions, barrier penetration, and resonance scattering. Although these examples are instructive in that they make clear the differences between classical and quantum mechanics, it is evident that if we seek to examine truly realistic problems it will be necessary to consider fully three-dimensional solutions of the SE. This is the purpose of both this chapter and Chapter 7.

Examining three-dimensional solutions to Schrödinger's equation even for relatively simple potentials will prove to be an involved task. Culminating as it does with a study of the hydrogen-atom Coulomb potential in Chapter 7, however, this work very much comprises the heart of this book. The purpose of this introduction is to lay out the plan of attack for these two chapters. Ultimately, we will see that the addition of extra dimensions leads to two physical phenomena not present in purely one-dimensional problems: **energy degeneracy** and **quantization of angular momentum**.

The three-dimensional Schrödinger equation was given in Chapter 2:

$$-\frac{\hbar^2}{2m}\nabla^2\psi(\mathbf{r}) + V(\mathbf{r})\psi(\mathbf{r}) = E\psi(\mathbf{r}),$$

where $\mathbf{r}$ denotes a three-dimensional vector position. In Section 6.1 we examine a quite powerful method, known as separation of variables, for solving this equation in multidimensional Cartesian coordinates. Application of this technique to a three-dimensional analog of the infinite square well will allow us to develop an approximate treatment of the number of photon states lying within a narrow band of frequencies (Equation 1.2.4), one of the great problems in the history of quantum mechanics. Since our ultimate goal is to study solutions of the SE for the Coulomb potential, Section 6.2 is devoted to a review of some of the properties of spherical coordinates, the coordinate system in which that potential proves most easily separable. An important aspect of solutions of the SE for potentials such as the Coulomb potential is quantization of angular momentum, so Section 6.3 is devoted to establishing some properties of so-called angular momentum operators that will prove extremely useful throughout the remainder of this chapter and in Chapter 7. The Coulomb potential is an example of what is known as a **central potential** or **radial potential**, one that depends only on the magnitude of the separation between two particles and not on their orientation in space. Any central potential is thus normally symbolized in the form $V(r)$, as opposed to $V(\mathbf{r})$. (In the case of the Coulomb potential, r is the electron/nucleus separation as in the treatment of the Bohr model in Chapter 1.) Section 6.4 is devoted to separating the SE for central potentials in spherical coordinates. We will see that an important result of this separation is that the SE naturally breaks into a "radial equation" and an "angular equation," with the potential $V(r)$ being involved only in the radial part. As a consequence, the solution to the angular part is quite general for *any* central potential, and turns out to intimately involve the angular momentum operators developed in Section 6.3. Section 6.5 is devoted to the general solution of this angular part of the SE; this will lead to some rather complicated functions known as **spherical harmonics**. Anticipating things somewhat, we might expect to see no suggestion of energy levels in the angular solution inasmuch as the energy eigenstates of a system depend exclusively on the potential and the boundary conditions. This proves to be the case: for central potentials, energy levels are the purview of only the radial equation. Chapter 7 opens with a general introduction to the radial equation for central potentials (Section 7.1), and then takes up the solution of this radial equation for three specific central potentials: the infinite and finite spherical potential wells (Sections 7.2 and 7.3; these are analogs of the one-dimensional wells of Chapter 3), and then, in Sections 7.4 and 7.5, the all-important Coulomb potential. Chapter 8, which is optional, explores some advanced aspects of the angular momentum operators introduced in this chapter.

This is a lengthy, heavily mathematical, somewhat abstract chapter. The best advice is to go through it step by step, convincing yourself of the manipulations and arguments at each point, and then being sure (as always) to do the end-of-chapter problems.

■ 6.1   Separation of Variables: Cartesian Coordinates

If the potential energy function $V(\mathbf{r})$ is a function of all three coordinates, solving the Schrödinger equation could be a daunting task. Fortunately, there is a technique available that often simplifies the job considerably. We illustrate this technique, known as **separation of variables**, by example.

Our example is the three-dimensional analog of a particle of mass m in an infinite potential well, a so-called infinite potential box. In analogy to the one-dimensional potential well, this is a container of dimensions (a, b, c) with impenetrable walls, as shown in Figure 6.1.

Formally, the infinite potential box is defined by

$$V(x, y, z) = \begin{cases} 0, & (0 \le x \le a, 0 \le y \le b, 0 \le z \le c) \\ \infty, & otherwise. \end{cases} \tag{1}$$

Outside the box we must have $\psi = 0$ for the same reasons as were elucidated in the one-dimensional case.

Inside the box the SE becomes

$$-\frac{\hbar^2}{2m}\left(\frac{\partial^2 \psi}{\partial x^2} + \frac{\partial^2 \psi}{\partial y^2} + \frac{\partial^2 \psi}{\partial z^2}\right) = E\psi. \tag{2}$$

Equation (2) is a partial differential equation—much more difficult to solve, in general, than the ordinary differential equations we have heretofore encountered.

The essence of the separation of variables technique is to assume that ψ can be written as the product of three separate functions, each depending on only one of the coordinates. That is, we assume that we can write

$$\psi(x, y, z) = X(x)Y(y)Z(z). \tag{3}$$

Note that uppercase letters denote functions of the coordinates represented by lowercase letters. We have no rigorous justification for this assumption; its validity can only be known in retrospect, after attempting to solve the differential equation. If

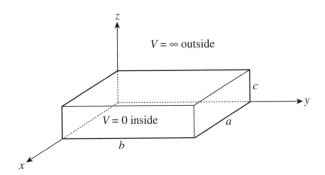

I FIGURE 6.1 Infinite potential box.

it is a valid assumption, then we will be able to obtain a solution; if not, we will have to try some other approach.

On substituting Equation (3) into Equation (2), two of the three functions X, Y, and Z come through each of the partial derivatives as would constants because they do not depend on the coordinate involved in the derivative:

$$-\frac{\hbar^2}{2m}\left(YZ\frac{\partial^2 X}{\partial x^2} + XZ\frac{\partial^2 Y}{\partial y^2} + XY\frac{\partial^2 Z}{\partial z^2}\right) = E(XYZ). \tag{4}$$

Since each partial derivative operates on a function of only one variable, they can be replaced with ordinary derivatives:

$$-\frac{\hbar^2}{2m}\left(YZ\frac{d^2 X}{dx^2} + XZ\frac{d^2 Y}{dy^2} + XY\frac{d^2 Z}{dz^2}\right) = E(XYZ). \tag{5}$$

Dividing through Equation (5) by (XYZ) gives

$$-\frac{\hbar^2}{2m}\left(\frac{1}{X}\frac{d^2 X}{dx^2} + \frac{1}{Y}\frac{d^2 Y}{dy^2} + \frac{1}{Z}\frac{d^2 Z}{dz^2}\right) = E. \tag{6}$$

Study Equation (6) carefully. Each term within the brackets is a function of only one coordinate. Inasmuch as the coordinates are independent, these terms can be varied independently of one another. The right-hand side, however, is a constant. The result of our assumption is that three independently variable functions add up to a constant. This can only be so if each function is itself equal to a constant. Labeling these constants E_x, E_y, and E_z, we can split Equation (6) into three simultaneous ordinary differential equations:

$$-\frac{\hbar^2}{2m}\left(\frac{1}{X}\frac{d^2 X}{dx^2}\right) = E_x, \tag{7}$$

$$-\frac{\hbar^2}{2m}\left(\frac{1}{Y}\frac{d^2 Y}{dy^2}\right) = E_y, \tag{8}$$

$$-\frac{\hbar^2}{2m}\left(\frac{1}{Z}\frac{d^2 Z}{dz^2}\right) = E_z, \tag{9}$$

with

$$E = E_x + E_y + E_z. \tag{10}$$

E_x, E_y, and E_z are known as **separation constants**; in any successful application of this method, one will always end up with as many separation constants as there are dimensions.

The essential result here is that we have reduced the original partial differential equation to three ordinary differential equations, one for each dimension. Equations (7)–(9) are of exactly the same form as the SE for the one-dimensional infinite well. From Chapter 3, we can now write the normalized solutions for X, Y, and Z as

$$X(x) = \sqrt{\frac{2}{a}} \sin\left(\frac{n_x \pi x}{a}\right), \quad E_x = \frac{h^2 n_x^2}{8ma^2}, \tag{11}$$

$$Y(y) = \sqrt{\frac{2}{b}} \sin\left(\frac{n_y \pi y}{b}\right), \quad E_y = \frac{h^2 n_y^2}{8mb^2}, \tag{12}$$

$$Z(z) = \sqrt{\frac{2}{c}} \sin\left(\frac{n_z \pi z}{c}\right), \quad E_z = \frac{h^2 n_z^2}{8mc^2}. \tag{13}$$

Note that each dimension acquires its own quantum number and that the (x, y, z) dimensions of the box appear in their corresponding wavefunctions. This is so because Equations (7)–(9) must be solved independently of each other.

Recognizing that the volume of the box is given by $V = abc$, we can write the total wavefunction as

$$\psi(x,y,z) = \sqrt{\frac{8}{V}} \sin\left(\frac{n_x \pi x}{a}\right) \sin\left(\frac{n_y \pi y}{b}\right) \sin\left(\frac{n_z \pi z}{c}\right), \tag{14}$$

and the total energy as

$$E = \frac{h^2}{8m}\left(\frac{n_x^2}{a^2} + \frac{n_y^2}{b^2} + \frac{n_z^2}{c^2}\right), \quad (n_x, n_y, n_z) = 1, 2, 3, \dots . \tag{15}$$

The infinite potential box wavefunction can thus be regarded as the product of three one-dimensional infinite-well wavefunctions, with a total energy equal to that given by summing contributions from each dimension. Since each of X, Y, and Z are independently normalized, ψ will be normalized as well. That we have found a solution to the problem means that our initial assumption of separation of variables was valid.

To plot such three-dimensional wavefunctions on a two-dimensional piece of paper is a challenge: Equation (14) associates a value (ψ) with each point in (x, y, z)

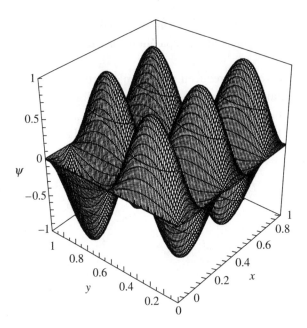

| FIGURE 6.2 Two-dimensional infinite-well wavefunction with $(n_x, n_y) = (5, 2)$.

space, and so we have the problem of trying to represent four numbers on a two-dimensional surface. Wavefunctions for a two-dimensional infinite well are easier to deal with. Figure 6.2 shows $\psi(x, y)$ for the case $(a, b) = (1, 1)$ and $(n_x, n_y) = (5, 2)$; in creating the plot, the two-dimensional amplitude factor $\sqrt{4/ab}$ has been set equal to unity for convenience. Notice that there are five and two maxima in the x and y directions, respectively. It is left as a mental exercise to the reader to extrapolate to a three-dimensional situation.

An important facet of such multidimensional solutions of Schrödinger's equation is **energy degeneracy**. For simplicity, consider an infinite potential box with sides all of the same length L; that is, $a = b = c = L$. The possible energy states are then

$$E = \frac{h^2}{8mL^2}(n_x^2 + n_y^2 + n_z^2), \quad (n_x, n_y, n_z) = 1, 2, 3, \dots . \tag{16}$$

Since each of the quantum numbers can independently take on the values 1, 2, 3, ... , it follows that different combinations of (n_x, n_y, n_z) can yield the same total energy. For example, $E = 6h^2/8mL^2$ can be realized in three different ways: $(n_x, n_y, n_z) = (2, 1, 1)$ or $(1, 2, 1)$ or $(1, 1, 2)$. This energy level is said to be triply degenerate.

Degeneracy means a condition in which different individual quantum *states* (n_x, n_y, n_z) result in the same *level* of total energy E. Clearly, the degree of degeneracy of a given energy level rises rapidly with the energy. But this does not mean that any infinite potential box will exhibit degeneracy: from Equation (15) it can be seen that only when the ratio of side lengths $a:b:c$ is as a ratio of squares of integers will degeneracy arise. The possibility of degeneracy is inherent in multidimensional problems; its presence in any particular case depends on the boundary conditions.

The concept of degeneracy can be tricky to get hold of if it is new to you. A simple analogy might help. Consider rolling two regular dice. There is one, and only one, way in which a total of 12 can appear: both dice must show 6. On the other hand, there are four distinct ways ("states") in which a total of 5 can arise: $(1, 4)$, $(2, 3)$, $(3, 2)$, and $(4, 1)$. We can say that the level wherein the total is 12 has a degeneracy of one, whereas that in which the total is 5 has a degeneracy of 4.

How can one know, a priori, if the separation of variables technique will work in any particular case? The answer to this depends on what coordinate system is being used, and on the form of the potential function. Eisenhart has shown [1] that Schrödinger's equation is separable in no less than 11 coordinate systems (including the familiar Cartesian, cylindrical, and spherical systems), provided that the potential is of the form

$$V = A\,X_1(x_1) + B\,X_2(x_2) + C\,X_3(x_3),$$

where the uppercase letters X_i designate functions of the coordinates x_i.

To close this section we take up a problem with connections to the development of Planck's theory of blackbody radiation discussed in Chapter 1: a derivation of the number of individual quantum states available to a particle of mass m trapped within an infinite three-dimensional potential box. This problem is analogous to the derivation in Section 3.5 of an expression for the number of energy states available to a particle of mass m moving in a finite one-dimensional rectangular well.

From Equation (15), the energy corresponding to quantum state (n_x, n_y, n_z) is given by

$$E = \frac{h^2}{8m}\left(\frac{n_x^2}{a^2} + \frac{n_y^2}{b^2} + \frac{n_z^2}{c^2}\right), \quad (n_x, n_y, n_z) = 1, 2, 3, \ldots . \tag{17}$$

The question of the number of available quantum states can be more precisely phrased as, "How many individual quantum states with energies $\leq E$ are available to the particle?" A derivation of this is an interesting exercise in geometry.

First, rearrange Equation (17) by dividing through by E:

$$1 = \left(\frac{n_x^2}{\alpha^2}\right) + \left(\frac{n_y^2}{\beta^2}\right) + \left(\frac{n_z^2}{\gamma^2}\right), \tag{18}$$

where we have defined

$$\{\alpha, \beta, \gamma\} = \left\{ \sqrt{\frac{8mEa^2}{h^2}}, \sqrt{\frac{8mEb^2}{h^2}}, \sqrt{\frac{8mEc^2}{h^2}} \right\}. \tag{19}$$

Consult a textbook on three-dimensional geometry: you will find that Equation (18) describes the surface of a three-dimensional ellipsoid of semi-axes (α, β, γ) along the (n_x, n_y, n_z) axes. This is sketched in Figure 6.3, where only the positive octant of the ellipsoid is shown. The volume of the entire ellipsoid (all eight octants) is $(4\pi/3)\,\alpha\beta\gamma$.

In our case, the dimensionless axes (n_x, n_y, n_z) do not correspond to continuous variables, but rather to discrete integer quantum numbers. Imagine the space represented in Figure 6.3 to be divided up into a large number of tiny cubes of volume Δn_x $\Delta n_y \, \Delta n_z$ centered at integral values of (n_x, n_y, n_z), each with $\Delta n_x = \Delta n_y = \Delta n_z = 1$. Each such tiny volume (one is shown in Figure 6.3) would then correspond to a single quantum state (n_x, n_y, n_z). The total volume within the ellipsoid then represents the number of individual quantum states lying below energy E, a quantity usually designated as

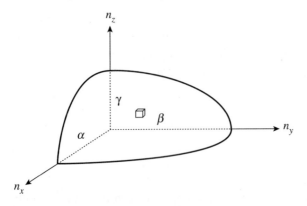

I FIGURE 6.3 Positive octant of an ellipsoid of semi-axes (α, β, γ).

$N(E)$. This is given by the volume of only the positive octant of the ellipsoid since (n_x, n_y, n_z) are restricted to positive integers:

$$N(E) = \frac{1}{8}\left(\frac{4\pi}{3}\right)\alpha\beta\gamma = \frac{\pi}{6}\sqrt{\frac{8mEa^2}{h^2}}\sqrt{\frac{8mEb^2}{h^2}}\sqrt{\frac{8mEc^2}{h^2}},$$

or

$$N(E) = \frac{8^{3/2}\pi}{6}\frac{Vm^{3/2}}{h^3}E^{3/2}, \tag{20}$$

where we have again put $V = abc$ for the volume of the box.

Equation (20) represents the number of individual quantum states of energy $\leq E$ available to a particle of mass m trapped in a box of volume V with impenetrable walls. It is true that if $N(E)$ is small (that is, if E is small), then $N(E)$ will not be accurately predicted by Equation (20) because the ellipsoidal surface in Figure 6.3 will cut through a relatively large number of the individual unit volumes and we will not get an accurate count. But if E is large, the approximation made by representing the volume enclosed within the ellipsoid as little cubes will be quite accurate.

Another quantity of interest to Planck was the number of quantum states lying between energies E and $E + dE$. We can get an expression for this by evaluating Equation (20) at $E + dE$ and taking the difference between $N(E + dE)$ and $N(E)$:

$$N(E + dE) = \frac{8^{3/2}\pi}{6}\frac{Vm^{3/2}}{h^3}(E + dE)^{3/2} = \frac{8^{3/2}\pi}{6}\frac{Vm^{3/2}}{h^3}E^{3/2}(1 + dE/E)^{3/2}.$$

If $dE \ll E$, then we can perform a Taylor series expansion:

$$N(E + dE) \sim \frac{8^{3/2}\pi}{6}\frac{Vm^{3/2}}{h^3}E^{3/2}\left[1 + \frac{3}{2}\frac{dE}{E} + \ldots\right].$$

Thus, the number of energy states lying between energies E and $E + dE$ must be

$$N(E + dE) - N(E) \sim \frac{8^{3/2}\pi}{4}\frac{Vm^{3/2}}{h^3}E^{1/2}dE, \tag{21}$$

which is often designated as $N(E)dE$.

The connection between this result and Planck's radiation formula can now be made as follows. First, for a reason that will become clear momentarily, we transform Equation (21) to an equivalent momentum form $N(p)dp$ by writing $E = p^2/2m$ and $dE = (p/m)dp$. This gives

$$N(p)dp \sim \frac{4\pi V}{h^3} p^2 dp. \tag{22}$$

Equation (22) gives the number of quantum states where a particle's momentum would lie between p and $p + dp$. Now suppose that the particles are photons. In Chapter 1 we saw how Einstein's energy-momentum-rest mass relationship $E^2 = p^2 c^2 + m_0^2 c^4$ can be used to derive the wavelength-momentum relationship for photons, $\lambda = h/p$, by setting the rest mass m_0 to be zero. Setting $\lambda = c/\nu$ we can put this into the form $p = h\nu/c$, hence $dp = (h/c)d\nu$. In frequency form, then, Equation (22) becomes

$$N(\nu)d\nu \sim \frac{4\pi V}{c^3} \nu^2 d\nu, \tag{23}$$

But for a factor of two, this is Planck's Equation (1.2.4) for the number of photon "normal modes" in a chamber of volume V; note how Planck's constant cancelled out. The reason for first transforming to a momentum distribution is that putting $m = 0$ in Equation (21) directly would give a zero result. The missing factor of two can be attributed to different photon polarizations. It is in fact somewhat surprising that this derivation gives a result that even looks correct: Schrödinger's equation is not relativistic and was not designed to deal with massless particles! A rigorous derivation involves computing the number of normal modes directly from Maxwell's equations [2]. The present derivation should consequently not be regarded as rigorous; it is included here only to give a sense of the situation.

EXAMPLE 6.1

Estimate the volume of space necessary to support a single quantum state of energy $E \leq 1$ eV to be occupied by an electron.

Rearranging Equation (20) to solve for the volume gives

$$V = \frac{6Nh^3}{8^{3/2}\pi m^{3/2} E^{3/2}}.$$

Now, setting $N = 1$ and with $E = 1$ eV $= 1.602 \times 10^{-19}$ Joule, we have, in *MKS* units,

$$V = \frac{6 N h^3}{8^{3/2} \pi m^{3/2} E^{3/2}} = \frac{(1.745 \times 10^{-99})}{8^{3/2} \pi (8.694 \times 10^{-46})(6.412 \times 10^{-29})}$$

$$= 4.403 \times 10^{-28} \, m^3.$$

If this volume were in the shape of a sphere, the radius would be about 4.7 Å: atomic-scale.

■ 6.2   Spherical Coordinates

Problems wherein the quantity of interest is a function only of the distance from some point (the origin, say), and not of the direction are said to possess spherical symmetry. For example, the magnitude of the electric field due to a point charge Q is given by

$$E = \frac{Q}{4 \pi \epsilon_o r^2},\tag{1}$$

where r is the distance between the charge and the field point. As long as one remains at distance r from the charge, the magnitude of E will not change, irrespective of how you are oriented with respect to the charge. To describe such situations it is convenient to develop a coordinate system wherein one of the coordinates is simply r itself. Specifying r indicates only that you are somewhere on the surface of a sphere; to completely specify your location in space requires two other coordinates, analogous to latitude and longitude. The spherical polar system, with coordinates designated by (r, θ, ϕ), has been defined with such situations in mind.

The relationship between spherical and Cartesian coordinates is illustrated in Figure 6.4. Cartesian coordinates corresponding to a point $P(r, \theta, \phi)$ are defined by

$$\left. \begin{array}{l} x = r \sin\theta \cos\phi \\ y = r \sin\theta \sin\phi \\ z = r \cos\theta \end{array} \right\},\tag{2}$$

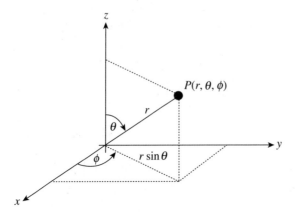

I FIGURE 6.4 Spherical coordinates.

or equivalently by the inverse relations

$$\left. \begin{aligned} r &= \sqrt{x^2 + y^2 + z^2} \\ \theta &= \cos^{-1}(z/r) \\ \phi &= \tan^{-1}(y/x) \end{aligned} \right\}. \tag{3}$$

The volume of space enclosed between (r, θ, ϕ) and $(r + dr, \theta + d\theta, \phi + d\phi)$ is given by

$$dV = r^2 \sin\theta \, dr \, d\theta \, d\phi. \tag{4}$$

The drawback of spherical coordinates is that the unit vectors are functions of the coordinates themselves. This is due to the fact that the coordinates are defined in terms of combinations of Cartesian coordinates (Equation 3). In terms of the usual Cartesian units vectors $(\boldsymbol{x}, \boldsymbol{y}, \boldsymbol{z})$, the spherical units vectors $(\boldsymbol{r}, \boldsymbol{\theta}, \boldsymbol{\phi})$ are given by

$$\left. \begin{aligned} \boldsymbol{r} &= \sin\theta\cos\phi\,\boldsymbol{x} + \sin\theta\,\sin\phi\,\boldsymbol{y} + \cos\theta\,\boldsymbol{z} \\ \boldsymbol{\theta} &= \cos\theta\cos\phi\,\boldsymbol{x} + \cos\theta\,\sin\phi\,\boldsymbol{y} - \sin\theta\,\boldsymbol{z} \\ \boldsymbol{\phi} &= -\sin\phi\,\boldsymbol{x} + \cos\phi\,\boldsymbol{y} \end{aligned} \right\}. \tag{5}$$

Conversely, Cartesian unit vectors can be expressed in terms of the spherical unit vectors as

$$\left. \begin{aligned} \boldsymbol{x} &= \sin\theta\cos\phi\,\boldsymbol{r} + \cos\theta\cos\phi\,\boldsymbol{\theta} - \sin\phi\,\boldsymbol{\phi} \\ \boldsymbol{y} &= \sin\theta\sin\phi\,\boldsymbol{r} + \cos\theta\sin\phi\,\boldsymbol{\theta} + \cos\phi\,\boldsymbol{\phi} \\ \boldsymbol{z} &= \cos\theta\,\boldsymbol{r} - \sin\theta\,\boldsymbol{\theta} \end{aligned} \right\}. \tag{6}$$

In the following section, it will prove useful to have available derivatives of the spherical unit vectors with respect to θ and ϕ, in terms of themselves:

$$\left. \begin{array}{ll} \dfrac{\partial \boldsymbol{r}}{\partial \theta} = \boldsymbol{\theta} & \dfrac{\partial \boldsymbol{r}}{\partial \phi} = \sin\theta\, \boldsymbol{\phi} \\[2ex] \dfrac{\partial \boldsymbol{\theta}}{\partial \theta} = -\boldsymbol{r} & \dfrac{\partial \boldsymbol{\theta}}{\partial \phi} = \cos\theta\, \boldsymbol{\phi} \\[2ex] \dfrac{\partial \boldsymbol{\phi}}{\partial \theta} = 0 & \dfrac{\partial \boldsymbol{\phi}}{\partial \phi} = -\sin\theta\, \boldsymbol{r} - \cos\theta\, \boldsymbol{\theta} \end{array} \right\}. \tag{7}$$

These expressions were derived by differentiating Equations (5) (remembering that (x, y, z) are constants), and then substituting Equations (6) into the results. It will also prove helpful to have expressions for gradient and Laplacian operators in spherical coordinates:

$$\nabla \equiv \boldsymbol{r}\frac{\partial}{\partial r} + \boldsymbol{\theta}\frac{1}{r}\frac{\partial}{\partial \theta} + \boldsymbol{\phi}\frac{1}{r\sin\theta}\frac{\partial}{\partial \phi}, \tag{8}$$

and

$$\nabla^2 \equiv \frac{1}{r^2}\frac{\partial}{\partial r}\left(r^2\frac{\partial}{\partial r}\right) + \frac{1}{r^2\sin\theta}\frac{\partial}{\partial \theta}\left(\sin\theta\frac{\partial}{\partial \theta}\right) + \frac{1}{r^2\sin^2\theta}\frac{\partial^2}{\partial \phi^2}. \tag{9}$$

Complicated as these expressions are, we will find that they greatly facilitate application of the SE to naturally spherical systems such as the hydrogen atom.

One can imagine an "infinite spherical potential" analogous to the infinite box potential taken up in Section 6.1. Such a construct is considered to be a central potential and is examined in Chapter 7.

■ 6.3   Angular Momentum Operators

The concept of angular momentum will prove central to the analysis of Schrödinger's equation for the hydrogen atom. In classical mechanics, the angular momentum of a particle is a vector quantity given by $\mathbf{L} = \mathbf{r} \times \mathbf{p}$, where $\mathbf{r}$ and $\mathbf{p}$ are, respectively, the position and linear momentum of the particle and where $\times$ denotes a vector cross-product. The purpose of this section is to develop general expressions for quantum-mechanical operators for the components of angular momentum and for the square of the magnitude of angular momentum. Our derivation of the latter follows that developed by P. T. Leung [3].

We saw in Chapter 4 that the operator for linear momentum is given by

$$\mathbf{p}_{op} = -\iota\hbar\nabla, \tag{1}$$

where ∇ is the gradient operator. The quantum-mechanical operator for **L** is then defined as:

$$\mathbf{L}_{op} = \mathbf{r}_{op} \times \mathbf{p}_{op} = -ih \, (\mathbf{r} \times \nabla). \tag{2}$$

We reintroduce temporarily here the "*op*" notation of Chapter 4 to make clear which quantities are operators.

In Cartesian coordinates, $\mathbf{L}_{op}$ appears as

$$\mathbf{L}_{op} \equiv \mathbf{r} \times \mathbf{p}_{op} \equiv (x\mathbf{x} + y\mathbf{y} + z\mathbf{z}) \times (-\iota\hbar)\left(\mathbf{x}\frac{\partial}{\partial x} + \mathbf{y}\frac{\partial}{\partial y} + \mathbf{z}\frac{\partial}{\partial z}\right)$$

$$\equiv -\iota\hbar \left[x\mathbf{z}\frac{\partial}{\partial y} - x\mathbf{y}\frac{\partial}{\partial z} - y\mathbf{z}\frac{\partial}{\partial x} + y\mathbf{x}\frac{\partial}{\partial z} + z\mathbf{y}\frac{\partial}{\partial x} - z\mathbf{x}\frac{\partial}{\partial y} \right]$$

$$\equiv -\iota\hbar \left[\mathbf{x}\left(y\frac{\partial}{\partial z} - z\frac{\partial}{\partial y}\right) + \mathbf{y}\left(z\frac{\partial}{\partial x} - x\frac{\partial}{\partial z}\right) + \mathbf{z}\left(x\frac{\partial}{\partial y} - y\frac{\partial}{\partial x}\right) \right],$$

where (x, y, z) again represent the usual Cartesian-coordinate units vectors. We can then write operators for the components of **L** as

$$L_x \equiv -\iota\hbar\left(y\frac{\partial}{\partial z} - z\frac{\partial}{\partial y}\right), \tag{3}$$

$$L_y \equiv -\iota\hbar\left(z\frac{\partial}{\partial x} - x\frac{\partial}{\partial z}\right), \tag{4}$$

and

$$L_z \equiv -\iota\hbar\left(x\frac{\partial}{\partial y} - y\frac{\partial}{\partial x}\right). \tag{5}$$

Notice the way in which the various coordinates enter these operators: no "x" appears in the operator for L_x; similarly, no "y" appears in L_y, nor a "z" in L_z. In fact, L_y and L_z can be derived from L_x by performing what is called a "cyclical permutation" of the coordinates: everywhere a "y" appears, replace it by "z"; similarly, replace "z" with "x" (think of the order $x \to y \to z \to x \to$ and so on). L_x and L_z can similarly be derived from L_y, or L_x and L_y from L_z.

EXAMPLE 6.2

Prove that $[L_x, L_y]\psi = (\iota\hbar L_z)\psi$.
The operators are

$$L_x \equiv -\iota\hbar\left(y\frac{\partial}{\partial z} - z\frac{\partial}{\partial y}\right),$$

$$L_y \equiv -\iota\hbar\left(z\frac{\partial}{\partial x} - x\frac{\partial}{\partial z}\right),$$

and

$$L_z \equiv -\iota\hbar\left(x\frac{\partial}{\partial y} - y\frac{\partial}{\partial x}\right).$$

Apply $[L_x, L_y]$ to some dummy wavefunction ψ:

$$[L_x, L_y]\psi = (L_xL_y - L_yL_x)\psi$$

$$= -\hbar^2\left\{\left(y\frac{\partial}{\partial z} - z\frac{\partial}{\partial y}\right)\left(z\frac{\partial\psi}{\partial x} - x\frac{\partial\psi}{\partial z}\right) - \left(z\frac{\partial}{\partial x} - x\frac{\partial}{\partial z}\right)\left(y\frac{\partial\psi}{\partial z} - z\frac{\partial\psi}{\partial y}\right)\right\}.$$

For convenience, denote derivative by subscripts; for example, $\psi_{xy} = \dfrac{\partial^2\psi}{\partial x\partial y}$. Expanding
out the commutator then gives

$$[L_x, L_y]\psi = -\hbar^2\{(y\psi_x + yz\psi_{zx} - xy\psi_{zz} - z^2\psi_{yx} + xz\psi_{yz})$$
$$- (zy\psi_{xz} - z^2\psi_{xy} - xy\psi_{zz} + x\psi_y + xz\psi_{zy})\}.$$

On recalling the order of derivatives is irrelevant—that is, that $\psi_{xy} = \psi_{yx}$—a number of
terms cancel. What remains is

$$[L_x, L_y]\psi = -\hbar^2(y\psi_x - x\psi_y) = -\hbar^2\left(y\frac{\partial}{\partial x} - x\frac{\partial}{\partial y}\right)\psi$$

$$= -\hbar^2\left(\frac{L_z}{\iota\hbar}\right)\psi = (\iota\hbar L_z)\psi.$$

Problem 6-10 elaborates on this example to show as well that $[L_y, L_z] \equiv (\iota\hbar)L_x$ and $[L_z, L_x] \equiv (\iota\hbar)L_y$. The physical meaning of these results is that it is not possible to measure simultaneous eigenvalues for the various components of **L**; they will be connected by uncertainty relations.

Since our ultimate purpose is to apply $\mathbf{L}_{op}$ to the Coulomb (hydrogen) potential, it is actually more convenient to have some of these results expressed purely in terms of spherical coordinates. Working from the expression for the gradient in spherical coordinates, Equation (8) in the previous section, we have, for $\mathbf{L}_{op}$,

$$\mathbf{L}_{op} = -\iota\hbar(\mathbf{r} \times \nabla) = -\iota\hbar\left\{ \mathbf{rr} \times \left(\mathbf{r}\frac{\partial}{\partial r} + \boldsymbol{\theta}\frac{1}{r}\frac{\partial}{\partial \theta} + \boldsymbol{\phi}\frac{1}{r\sin\theta}\frac{\partial}{\partial \phi} \right) \right\}$$

$$= -\iota\hbar\left\{ \boldsymbol{\phi}\frac{\partial}{\partial \theta} - \boldsymbol{\theta}\frac{1}{\sin\theta}\frac{\partial}{\partial \phi} \right\}, \tag{6}$$

where we used the identities $\mathbf{r} \times \mathbf{r} = 0, \mathbf{r} \times \boldsymbol{\theta} = \boldsymbol{\phi}$, and $\mathbf{r} \times \boldsymbol{\phi} = -\boldsymbol{\theta}$.

A physically important quantity is the square of the magnitude of **L**. An operator for computing this quantity, usually designated L_{op}^2 or just L^2, can be derived by operating $\mathbf{L}_{op}$ on itself. Since the vector equivalent of multiplication is to take a dot product, we have

$$\mathbf{L}_{op} \cdot \mathbf{L}_{op} = \left[-\iota\hbar\left\{ \boldsymbol{\phi}\frac{\partial}{\partial \theta} - \boldsymbol{\theta}\frac{1}{\sin\theta}\frac{\partial}{\partial \phi} \right\} \right] \cdot \left[-\iota\hbar\left\{ \boldsymbol{\phi}\frac{\partial}{\partial \theta} - \boldsymbol{\theta}\frac{1}{\sin\theta}\frac{\partial}{\partial \phi} \right\} \right]. \tag{7}$$

In expanding out this expression, we must be careful to respect the order of dot products and derivatives. Expanding from left to right gives

$$L_{op}^2 = -\hbar^2\left[\left(\boldsymbol{\phi}\frac{\partial}{\partial \theta} \right) \cdot \left(\boldsymbol{\phi}\frac{\partial}{\partial \theta} \right) - \left(\boldsymbol{\phi}\frac{\partial}{\partial \theta} \right) \cdot \left(\boldsymbol{\theta}\frac{1}{\sin\theta}\frac{\partial}{\partial \phi} \right) \right.$$

$$\left. - \left(\boldsymbol{\theta}\frac{1}{\sin\theta}\frac{\partial}{\partial \phi} \right) \cdot \left(\boldsymbol{\phi}\frac{\partial}{\partial \theta} \right) + \left(\boldsymbol{\theta}\frac{1}{\sin\theta}\frac{\partial}{\partial \phi} \right) \cdot \left(\boldsymbol{\theta}\frac{1}{\sin\theta}\frac{\partial}{\partial \phi} \right) \right]. \tag{8}$$

When evaluating the four terms in this expression, care must be taken to first compute the partial derivatives, including those of the unit vectors, and then to do the dot products. The third term is worked through the following example:

$$\left(\boldsymbol{\theta}\frac{1}{\sin\theta}\frac{\partial}{\partial\phi}\right)\cdot\left(\boldsymbol{\phi}\frac{\partial}{\partial\theta}\right)=\boldsymbol{\theta}\frac{1}{\sin\theta}\cdot\left\{\frac{\partial\boldsymbol{\phi}}{\partial\phi}\frac{\partial}{\partial\theta}+\boldsymbol{\phi}\frac{\partial^2}{\partial\phi\,\partial\theta}\right\}=\frac{1}{\sin\theta}\boldsymbol{\theta}\cdot\left(\frac{\partial\boldsymbol{\phi}}{\partial\phi}\frac{\partial}{\partial\theta}\right)$$

$$=\frac{1}{\sin\theta}\boldsymbol{\theta}\cdot\left(-\sin\theta\,\boldsymbol{r}-\cos\theta\,\boldsymbol{\theta}\right)\frac{\partial}{\partial\theta}=-\cot\theta\frac{\partial}{\partial\theta}. \quad (9)$$

In the first line of Equation (9), the second term inside the curly brackets vanished because $\boldsymbol{\theta}\cdot\boldsymbol{\phi}=0$; in the second line, Equation (7) in the preceding section was used to simplify $\partial\boldsymbol{\phi}/\partial\phi$, and we have written $\cos\theta/\sin\theta=\cot\theta$. The other three terms in Equation (8) similarly simplify, leaving

$$L_{op}^2=-\hbar^2\left[\frac{\partial^2}{\partial\theta^2}+\cot\theta\frac{\partial}{\partial\theta}+\frac{1}{\sin^2\theta}\frac{\partial^2}{\partial\phi^2}\right] \quad (10)$$

which, upon combining the first two terms, can be expressed more compactly as

$$L_{op}^2=-\hbar^2\left[\frac{1}{\sin\theta}\frac{\partial}{\partial\theta}\left(\sin\theta\frac{\partial}{\partial\theta}\right)+\frac{1}{\sin^2\theta}\frac{\partial^2}{\partial\phi^2}\right]. \quad (11)$$

This is our desired expression for the operator for the squared magnitude of angular momentum expressed in spherical coordinates. Now compare Equation (11) with Equation (9) in the preceding section, which is the equation for the Laplacian operator in spherical coordinates. But for a factor of $-\hbar^2/r^2$, the angular parts are identical. We can thus write the Laplacian in terms of L_{op}^2 as

$$\nabla^2\equiv\frac{1}{r^2}\frac{\partial}{\partial r}\left(r^2\frac{\partial}{\partial r}\right)-\frac{L_{op}^2}{\hbar^2 r^2}. \quad (12)$$

The Hamiltonian operator $H\equiv-(\hbar^2/2m)\nabla^2+V(r,\theta,\phi)$ then appears in spherical coordinates as

$$H\equiv-\frac{\hbar^2}{2mr^2}\frac{\partial}{\partial r}\left(r^2\frac{\partial}{\partial r}\right)+\frac{L_{op}^2}{2mr^2}+V(r,\theta,\phi), \quad (13)$$

where $V(r,\theta,\phi)$ is the potential function.

One further expression that will prove useful in the following section is an operator for the magnitude of the z-component of angular momentum, $(L_z)_{op}$. The component of any vector in any desired direction can always be found by taking the dot product of the unit vector representing the desired direction with the vector at hand. From Equation (6) in this section and Equation (6) in the preceding one, we have

$$(L_z)_{op} \equiv \mathbf{z} \cdot \mathbf{L}_{op} = (\cos\theta\, \mathbf{r} - \sin\theta\, \boldsymbol{\theta}) \cdot \left\{ -\iota\hbar \left(\boldsymbol{\phi} \frac{\partial}{\partial\theta} - \boldsymbol{\theta} \frac{1}{\sin\theta} \frac{\partial}{\partial\phi} \right) \right\},$$

or

$$(L_z)_{op} \equiv -\iota\hbar \left\{ (\cos\theta\, \mathbf{r}) \cdot \left(\boldsymbol{\phi} \frac{\partial}{\partial\theta} \right) - (\cos\theta\, \mathbf{r}) \cdot \left(\boldsymbol{\theta} \frac{1}{\sin\theta} \frac{\partial}{\partial\phi} \right) \right.$$

$$\left. - (\sin\theta\, \boldsymbol{\theta}) \cdot \left(\boldsymbol{\phi} \frac{\partial}{\partial\theta} \right) + (\sin\theta\, \boldsymbol{\theta}) \cdot \left(\boldsymbol{\theta} \frac{1}{\sin\theta} \frac{\partial}{\partial\phi} \right) \right\}.$$

In this expression, the first three terms vanish because the dot product of orthogonal unit vectors always vanishes, no matter what coordinate system one is working in. What remains from the last term is

$$(L_z)_{op} \equiv -\iota\hbar \frac{\partial}{\partial\phi}. \qquad (14)$$

This result can also be derived by substituting the expressions for the spherical-coordinate unit vectors in terms of their Cartesian counterparts (Equation 5 in the preceding section) into Equation (6) and then taking the dot product with z.

A number of important points regarding angular momentum are worth emphasizing here. In Example 6.2, we concluded that since the operators for L_x, L_y, and L_z do not commute with each other, any pair of them will be linked by an uncertainty relation; that is, a measurement of any one component of $\mathbf{L}$ will introduce uncertainty into our knowledge of the other two components. A measurement of L_y, for example, will force a system into an eigenstate of L_y, which cannot simultaneously be an eigenstate of L_x or L_z. In Problem 6–18 and in Chapter 8, however, we will see that $[L_{op}^2, (L_x)_{op}]\psi = [L_{op}^2, (L_y)_{op}]\psi = [L_{op}^2, (L_z)_{op}]\psi = 0$ for any wavefunction that is a product of separable functions of θ and ϕ. This means that eigenvalues for L^2 and any component of $\mathbf{L}$ can be found. The overall result is that simultaneous eigenvalues for L^2 and *one* of the components of $\mathbf{L}$ can be found, but, once a measurement has been made, knowledge of the other two components is irretrievably lost. The measured component is conventionally taken to be L_z; the corresponding eigenfunctions of L^2 and L_z are the spherical harmonics developed in Section 6.5. Further, we will see in Section 6.4 that for a potential that is a function of r only, the wavefunction can be separated into the form

$\psi(r, \theta, \phi) = R(r)\, g(\theta, \phi)$, and that it will satisfy $[\boldsymbol{H}, L^2_{op}]\, \psi = 0$ (Problem 6–19). This means that both energy and L^2_{op} will possess simultaneous eigenvalues; the hydrogen-atom Coulomb potential satisfies this criterion. In such cases we can ultimately expect three quantum numbers to arise: one for energy, one for L^2_{op}, and one for one of the components of $\mathbf{L}$, conventionally taken to be L_z. Solutions for the L^2_{op} and L_z pieces are developed in Section 6.5.

Finally, we remark that it is possible to define raising and lowering operators for angular momentum in analogy to the harmonic oscillator raising and lowering operators introduced in Chapter 5 (see Problem 6–8). These operators do not play a role in our solution of the Coulomb potential, however, so we do not discuss them here. Readers interested in learning more about these operators are directed to Chapter 8.

■ 6.4   Separation of Variables in Spherical Coordinates: Central Potentials

In this section we apply the separation of variables technique to Schrödinger's equation written in spherical coordinates for central potentials; that is, ones that can be written in the form $V(r)$. As emphasized in the introduction to this chapter, these are potentials that depend only on the magnitude of the separation between two particles and not on their orientation in space. Spherical coordinates are the natural system within which to examine this type of potential; the usual x-y-z Cartesian coordinates are not used because any function of $r = \sqrt{x^2 + y^2 + z^2}$ is not suitable for separation. It is worth emphasizing that the results that are developed in this section are very general for any central potential, irrespective of the precise dependence of $V(r)$ on r. In anticipation of applying these results to the Coulomb potential, one might wonder how the fact that the hydrogen atom is really a two-body system with both the proton and electron "orbiting" their mutual center of mass is built into the SE. For the moment, suffice it to say that the situation can be reduced to an equivalent one-body problem in a way that has no effect on the radial/angular separation that is the concern of this section; this two-body issue is taken up in Section 7.4.

Using the expression for ∇^2 in spherical coordinates, the SE for a particle of mass μ moving in a central potential $V(r)$ is

$$-\frac{\hbar^2}{2\mu}\left\{\frac{1}{r^2}\frac{\partial}{\partial r}\left(r^2\frac{\partial}{\partial r}\right) + \frac{1}{r^2\sin\theta}\frac{\partial}{\partial\theta}\left(\sin\theta\frac{\partial}{\partial\theta}\right) + \frac{1}{r^2\sin^2\theta}\left(\frac{\partial^2}{\partial\phi^2}\right)\right\}\psi(r,\theta,\phi)$$

$$+ V(r)\psi(r,\theta,\phi) = E\psi(r,\theta,\phi). \qquad (1)$$

We use μ to designate mass here and in Chapter 7 because the symbol m will soon be adopted to designate a quantity known as the magnetic quantum number. We now attempt a separation of variables into radial and angular terms by assuming that $\psi(r, \theta, \phi)$ can be expressed as the product of a "radial wavefunction" $R(r)$ and an "angular wavefunction" $Y(\theta, \phi)$:

$$\psi(r, \theta, \phi) = R(r) Y(\theta, \phi). \tag{2}$$

As in Section 6.1, uppercase letters represent functions of variables represented by lowercase letters. For convenience we shall often refer to these functions simply as R and Y, dropping the implicitly understood arguments. Substituting Equation (2) into Equation (1) gives

$$-\frac{\hbar^2}{2\mu}\left\{\frac{Y}{r^2}\frac{\partial}{\partial r}\left(r^2\frac{\partial R}{\partial r}\right) + \frac{R}{r^2}\left[\frac{1}{\sin\theta}\frac{\partial}{\partial\theta}\left(\sin\theta\frac{\partial Y}{\partial\theta}\right) + \frac{1}{\sin^2\theta}\left(\frac{\partial^2 Y}{\partial\phi^2}\right)\right]\right\}$$

$$+ V(r)(RY) = E(RY). \tag{3}$$

Multiplying through by r^2/RY and rearranging gives

$$-\frac{\hbar^2}{2\mu}\left\{\frac{1}{R}\frac{\partial}{\partial r}\left(r^2\frac{\partial R}{\partial r}\right)\right\} + [V(r) - E]r^2$$

$$= \frac{\hbar^2}{2\mu}\left[\frac{1}{Y\sin\theta}\frac{\partial}{\partial\theta}\left(\sin\theta\frac{\partial Y}{\partial\theta}\right) + \frac{1}{Y\sin^2\theta}\left(\frac{\partial^2 Y}{\partial\phi^2}\right)\right]. \tag{4}$$

Equation (4) expresses the desired separation of variables: the left-hand side is a function of r only [$f(r)$, say], whereas the right-hand side is a function of θ and ϕ [say, $g(\theta, \phi)$]. The equality can only hold if both sides are equal to some constant:

$$f(r) = g(\theta, \phi) = \text{constant}. \tag{5}$$

Equation (5) can also be expressed in terms of the operator for squared total angular momentum derived in the preceding section:

$$-\frac{\hbar^2}{2\mu}\left\{\frac{1}{R}\frac{\partial}{\partial r}\left(r^2\frac{\partial R}{\partial r}\right)\right\} + [V(r) - E]r^2 = -\frac{1}{2\mu Y}[L_{op}^2 Y] = \text{constant}. \tag{6}$$

Equation (6) is quite general for any central potential.

A remark concerning normalization of the eventual solution is worthwhile here. Normalization demands that the square of ψ integrated over the entire space available to the electron must evaluate to unity. We can express this as

$$\int_0^{2\pi} \int_0^{\pi} \int_0^{\infty} \psi^2(r, \theta, \phi)\, r^2 \sin\theta\, dr\, d\theta\, d\phi = 1$$

$$\Rightarrow \left\{ \int_0^{\infty} R^2(r)\, r^2 dr \right\} \left\{ \int_0^{2\pi} \int_0^{\pi} Y^2(\theta, \phi)\, \sin\theta\, d\theta\, d\phi \right\} = 1.$$

If R and Y are separately normalized, then ψ will be as well; it is conventional to separately normalize each function in such a product wavefunction. Anticipating things somewhat, we remark that Y will itself eventually be broken into individual functions of θ and ϕ; hence we will have three functions to be individually normalized.

We now turn to the solution of the right side of Equation (4) [or (6)], the angular equation for any central potential.

■ 6.5 Angular Wavefunctions and Spherical Harmonics

We seek functions $Y(\theta, \phi)$ such that the right side of Equation (4) is a constant. It is convenient to define this constant in such a way that there are no factors of μ or $\hbar$ to carry along in the manipulations. To this end, if we define the constant appearing in the right-hand side of Equation (5) to be

$$\text{constant} = -\frac{\alpha \hbar^2}{2\mu}, \tag{1}$$

where α is a constant, then the angular equation can be written as

$$-\left[\frac{1}{\sin\theta} \frac{\partial}{\partial\theta} \left(\sin\theta \frac{\partial Y}{\partial\theta} \right) + \frac{1}{\sin^2\theta} \left(\frac{\partial^2 Y}{\partial\phi^2} \right) \right] = \alpha Y. \tag{2}$$

We can simplify this equation by another application of separation of variables. Assume that $Y(\theta, \phi)$ can be expressed as the product of a function of θ and a function of ϕ:

$$Y(\theta, \phi) = \Theta(\theta)\, \Phi(\phi). \tag{3}$$

With this assumption, Equation (2) becomes

$$-\frac{\Phi}{\sin\theta}\frac{d}{d\theta}\left(\sin\theta\frac{d\Theta}{d\theta}\right) - \frac{\Theta}{\sin^2\theta}\left(\frac{d^2\Phi}{d\phi^2}\right) = \alpha\Theta\Phi, \tag{4}$$

where partial derivatives have been converted to ordinary derivatives as they operate on functions of only one variable. Multiplying through by $\sin^2\theta/\Theta\Phi$ and rearranging gives

$$-\frac{\sin\theta}{\Theta}\frac{d}{d\theta}\left(\sin\theta\frac{d\Theta}{d\theta}\right) - \alpha\sin^2\theta = \frac{1}{\Phi}\frac{d^2\Phi}{d\phi^2}. \tag{5}$$

A further separation of variables has been effected: the angular equation reduces to a function of θ equal to a function of ϕ, both of which must equal some constant.

6.5.1   Solution of the Φ Equation

We arbitrarily define the constant to which both sides of Equation (5) are equal to be $-m^2$. The m is known as the magnetic quantum number, a designation whose meaning will be made clear later.

With this definition we have

$$\frac{d^2\Phi}{d\phi^2} = -m^2\Phi, \tag{1}$$

with m to be determined by appropriate boundary conditions. This differential equation is identical in form to that for the infinite potential well of Section 3.2. The solution is

$$\Phi(\phi) = Ae^{\iota m\phi} + Be^{-\iota m\phi}. \tag{2}$$

To normalize Φ, we must demand

$$\int_0^{2\pi} \Phi^*\Phi d\phi = 1.$$

Carrying out the integral results in a constraint involving A, B, and m:

$$2\pi(A^*A + B^*B) - \frac{A^*B}{2\iota m}(e^{-4\iota m\pi} - 1) + \frac{AB^*}{2\iota m}(e^{4\iota m\pi} - 1) = 1. \tag{3}$$

Now, $\Phi(\phi)$ must satisfy one very important additional condition: ϕ is a **cyclic coordinate**; that is, if the value of ϕ is changed by adding any integral multiple (positive, negative, or zero) of 2π radians, then it must describe the same direction in space as it did initially. Mathematically, this can be expressed as

$$\Phi(\phi) = \Phi(\phi + 2\pi),$$

or,

$$\Phi(\phi) = Ae^{\iota m\phi} + Be^{-\iota m\phi} = Ae^{\iota m(\phi + 2\pi)} + Be^{-\iota m(\phi + 2\pi)}. \tag{4}$$

We can rewrite this constraint as

$$Ae^{\iota m\phi} + Be^{-\iota m\phi} = Ae^{\iota m\phi}(e^{2\pi\iota m}) + Be^{-\iota m\phi}(e^{-2\pi\iota m}). \tag{5}$$

Equation (5) can only be satisfied if $e^{\pm 2\pi\iota m} = 1$; that is, if

$$\cos(2\pi m) \pm \iota\sin(2\pi m) = 1,$$

which can only be satisfied if

$$m = 0, \pm 1, \pm 2, \pm 3, \ldots. \tag{6}$$

Once again, imposition of a boundary condition has led to a quantization condition on a separation constant. On back-substituting this constraint into Equation (3), we have

$$2\pi\left(A^*A + B^*B\right) = 1. \tag{7}$$

Having accounted for both the normalization of Φ and the cyclic nature of ϕ, we are at this point at liberty to choose A and B as we please, provided that Equation (7) is satisfied in the bargain. Tradition is to take $B = 0$, giving

$$A = 1/\sqrt{2\pi}, \tag{8}$$

and hence

$$\Phi(\phi) = \frac{1}{\sqrt{2\pi}} e^{\iota m\phi}, \quad m = 0, \pm 1, \pm 2, \pm 3, \ldots. \tag{9}$$

Another way of looking at this choice is that since m is allowed to be both positive and negative, either the A or B term in Equation (2) is redundant and can be dropped. We choose to drop the B term. Note that $|\Phi|^2$ is independent of ϕ; this feature will be useful when we come to constructing and interpreting plots of hydrogen-atom probability densities in Chapter 7.

The integral restriction on m implies that something physical is being quantized. But what? To elucidate this, consider the operator for the z-component of angular momentum, Equation (6.3.14):

$$L_z = -\iota\hbar\frac{\partial}{\partial\phi}.$$

Applying L_z to $\Phi(\phi)$ gives

$$L_z\Phi(\phi) = -\iota\hbar\frac{\partial}{\partial\phi}(Ae^{\iota m\phi}) = -\iota^2 m\hbar(Ae^{\iota m\phi}) = (m\hbar)\Phi(\phi), \tag{10}$$

an eigenvalue equation. *This result indicates that for a particle moving in a central potential, the z-component of its angular momentum is quantized in integral multiples of ℏ.* In the case of the Coulomb potential, this angular momentum is that of the proton/electron system "orbiting" about their mutual center of mass.

The form of Equations (6.3.3)–(6.3.5) should convince you that none of the x, y, or z components of **L** are any more "special" than either of the others. Consequently, as discussed following Equation (6.3.14), *all* components of **L** are quantized in this way, not just the z-component. The compact form of Equation (10) is a result of the way that the angle ϕ is defined in spherical coordinates; it has become conventional (if misleading) to consider the z-component as the "one" that is so quantized. Ultimately, **L** will be quantized along a direction defined by an experimental arrangement; see Chapter 8. Also, bear in mind that Equation (10) is a statement regarding *eigenvalues*, not *expectation* values: a system might well find itself in a superposition of angular momentum states.

EXAMPLE 6.3

Equation (9) clearly satisfies Equation (1) at the beginning of this subsection. However, if $m = 0$, the normalization condition, Equation (3), would appear to involve infinities. Without invoking this form of normalization, show that Equation (9) is valid for $m = 0$.

With $m = 0$, Equation (1) becomes

$$\frac{d^2\Phi}{d\phi^2} = 0,$$

which has the solution $\Phi = A\phi + B$. Normalization then demands

$$\int_0^{2\pi} \Phi^2 d\phi = 1 \quad \Rightarrow \quad \frac{(2\pi)^3}{3}A^2 + (2\pi)^2 AB + (2\pi)B^2 = 1.$$

Now, the cyclic nature of ϕ demands $\Phi(\phi) = \Phi(\phi + 2\pi)$, or

$$A(\phi + 2\pi) + B = A\phi + B.$$

This can only be satisfied if $A = 0$. The normalization condition then gives $B = 1/\sqrt{2\pi}$, leading to an identical solution for Φ as Equation (9) when $m = 0$. As a further exercise, you should be able to show that Equation (3) does not in fact diverge as $m \rightarrow 0$.

6.5.2   Solution of the Θ Equation

From Equation (6.5.5) in combination with the result for Φ derived in the preceding subsection, we have

$$-\frac{\sin\theta}{\Theta}\frac{d}{d\theta}\left(\sin\theta\frac{d\Theta}{d\theta}\right) - \alpha\sin^2\theta = -m^2. \tag{1}$$

Recall that m is the magnetic quantum number, *not* a mass. Multiplying through by $-\Theta/\sin^2\theta$ casts this equation into a somewhat neater form:

$$\frac{1}{\sin\theta}\frac{d}{d\theta}\left(\sin\theta\frac{d\Theta}{d\theta}\right) + \left(\alpha - \frac{m^2}{\sin^2\theta}\right)\Theta = 0. \tag{2}$$

The presence of $\sin\theta$ and $\sin^2\theta$ in this differential equation hint that the solution likely involves a polynomial series in sines and cosines of θ. Because the algebra involved in handling infinite series of trigonometric functions is awkward, it is convenient to introduce an independent variable that transforms the differential equation into a linear form. Define

$$\chi = \cos\theta. \tag{3}$$

With this definition we have

$$d\chi = -\sin\theta\, d\theta = -\sqrt{1-\chi^2}\, d\theta$$

or

$$\frac{d}{d\theta} = -\sqrt{1 - \chi^2}\frac{d}{d\chi}. \tag{4}$$

Substituting Equations (3) and (4) into Equation (2) gives

$$\frac{d}{d\chi}\left[(1 - \chi^2)\frac{d\Theta}{d\chi}\right] + \left[\alpha - \frac{m^2}{(1 - \chi^2)}\right]\Theta = 0. \tag{5}$$

where Θ is now regarded as a function of χ.

At this point it would seem reasonable to attempt a series expansion of Θ in terms of powers of χ. Such an attempt leads to a problem, however: the recursion relation involves more than two coefficients, making it impossible to terminate the series by the sort of artifice employed in the solution of the harmonic oscillator. However, it is possible to transform Equation (5) into a form wherein a series solution yields a more tractable recursion relation. Define $\Theta(\chi)$ in terms of another function $G(\chi)$ according as

$$\Theta(\chi) = (1 - \chi^2)^{|m|/2}G(\chi). \tag{6}$$

With this definition [4], Equation (5) transforms into a differential equation for G:

$$(1 - \chi^2)\frac{d^2G}{d\chi^2} - 2\chi(|m| + 1)\frac{dG}{d\chi} + [\alpha - |m|(|m| + 1)]G(\chi) = 0. \tag{7}$$

We now attempt a series solution of the form

$$G(\chi) = \sum_{n=0}^{\infty}a_n\chi^n. \tag{8}$$

Substituting this trial solution into Equation (7) gives

$$\sum_{n=0}^{\infty}n(n - 1)a_n\chi^{n-2} + \sum_{n=0}^{\infty}[\beta - 2(|m| + 1)n - n(n - 1)]a_n\chi^n = 0, \tag{9}$$

where

$$\beta = [\alpha - |m|(|m| + 1)]. \tag{10}$$

The first term of Equation (9) vanishes for $n = 0$ and $n = 1$. Now

$$\sum_{n=0}^{\infty} n(n-1)a_n \chi^{n-2} = \sum_{n=2}^{\infty} n(n-1)a_n \chi^{n-2} = \sum_{j=0}^{\infty} (j+1)(j+2)a_{j+2}\chi^j,$$

where $j = n - 2$. Since j is a dummy index, we are at liberty to relabel it as n, just as we did in the case of the harmonic oscillator. The result of this is to reduce Equation (9) to the form

$$\sum_{n=0}^{\infty} \{[\beta - 2(|m| + 1)n - n(n-1)]a_n + (n+1)(n+2)a_{n+2}\}\chi^n = 0. \quad (11)$$

Since $\chi \, (= \cos\theta)$ is not in general equal to zero, we are forced to establish the recursion relation

$$a_{n+2} = -\frac{[\beta - 2(|m| + 1)n - n(n-1)]}{(n+1)(n+2)}a_n, \quad (12)$$

or, on substituting for β,

$$a_{n+2} = \frac{[(n+|m|)(n+|m|+1) - \alpha]}{(n+1)(n+2)}a_n. \quad (13)$$

Again we have a recursion relation in which there are two arbitrary constants, a_0 and a_1, corresponding to even and odd series, respectively.

Now, refer back to Equation (6). Since χ was defined as $\chi = \cos\theta$ and since $0 \le \theta \le \pi$, then $-1 \le \chi \le 1$; that is, χ itself can never diverge. Hence, $(1 - \chi^2)$ will never diverge. What about the convergence of $G(\chi)$? We will not investigate this rigorously, but we will give an informal argument to show that $G(\chi)$ does diverge for certain values of χ.

First we note that, for large n, the recursion relation gives

$$a_{n+2} \sim a_n, \quad (14)$$

that is, in either the even or the odd series, all of the high-n coefficients are of the same sign and approximately the same value. Hence, $G(\chi)$ would appear to converge, since χ^n diminishes rapidly for large n. A problem occurs, however, when $\chi = \pm 1$ ($\theta = 0$ or π), for which the high-order terms in the series for $G(\chi)$ behave as

$\pm$ constant $(\ldots + 1 + 1 + 1 + 1 \ldots),$

which is clearly divergent. [Strictly, as $\chi \to \pm 1$, $\Theta(\chi) \to (0)(\infty)$, which is indeterminate. But it is possible to show that $\Theta(\chi)$ diverges as $\chi \to \pm 1$: see Problem 6–15.] To avoid this catastrophe, it is necessary to terminate the solution for $G(\chi)$ at some maximum value of n; that is, it is necessary to demand that

$$a_n = 0, \quad n > n_{\text{max}}. \tag{15}$$

Since the recursion relation involves every second coefficient, either the even or the odd series will also have to be suppressed by assuming in addition that either a_0 or a_1 vanishes.

For Equation (15) to be satisfied, the recursion relation demands

$$\alpha = [(n_{\text{max}} + |m|)(n_{\text{max}} + |m| + 1)]. \tag{16}$$

The choice of n_{max} is as yet arbitrary, except that it must be an integer ≥ 0: as long as the series for $G(\chi)$ contains a finite (even if very large) number of terms, it can never diverge. Since $|m| = 0, 1, 2, \ldots$, then $(n_{\text{max}} + |m|) = 0, 1, 2, \ldots$. Defining $\ell = (n_{\text{max}} + |m|)$, we can write

$$\alpha = \ell(\ell + 1), \quad \ell = 0, 1, 2, \ldots. \tag{17}$$

ℓ is known as the **orbital angular momentum quantum number**. To understand its physical significance, recall Equation (6.4.6):

$$-\frac{1}{2\mu Y}[L_{op}^2 Y] = \text{constant}. \tag{6.4.6}$$

Recalling the definition of the constant from Equation (6.5.1) casts this into the form

$$L_{op}^2 Y(\theta, \phi) = \hbar^2 \alpha Y(\theta, \phi) = [\hbar^2 \ell(\ell + 1)]Y(\theta, \phi). \tag{18}$$

Once again we have an eigenvalue equation. The interpretation of this result is that the square of the magnitude of the angular momentum of the system (in the Coulomb case, essentially the electron's orbital angular momentum) is quantized in units of $\hbar^2$, or

$$L = \sqrt{\ell(\ell + 1)}\hbar, \quad \ell = 0, 1, 2, 3, \ldots. \tag{19}$$

We can combine this result with our previous conclusion that $L_z = m\hbar$. Since we must obviously have $L_z \leq |L|$, the possible values that m can take are restricted once ℓ is chosen: $m \leq \sqrt{\ell(\ell + 1)}$. Since m and ℓ are integers, this corresponds to $|m| \leq \ell$, hence

$$L_z = m\hbar, \quad (|m| \leq \ell). \tag{20}$$

The essential physical conclusion here is that the lengths of both L and L_z are quantized according as Equations (19) and (20).

As an example, consider the case of $\ell = 2$; that is, $L = \sqrt{6}\hbar$, for which $L_z = m\hbar$, $-2 \leq m \leq 2$. In the convention where the z-component of L is taken to be quantized as $m\hbar$, the **L** vector can lie on any one of five cones concentric with the z-axis consistent with its z-component being an integral multiple of $\hbar$ lying between -2 and $+2$, inclusive. This is illustrated in Figures 6.5 and 6.6.

Quantization of angular momentum components is another purely quantum-mechanical effect; there is no analog in classical mechanics. Experimental proof of this effect is powerful evidence in support of Schrödinger's wave mechanics. Ironically, the experimental verification, due to Stern and Gerlach, was in hand before the arrival of Schrödinger's equation. (So as not to disturb the flow of the present chapter, a discussion of this important experiment and its interpretation appears in Chapter 8.) An excellent article on the history of the Stern-Gerlach experiment is given in the article "Stern and Gerlach: How a bad cigar helped re-orient atomic physics," by Freidrich, B., and Hershbach, D., *Physics Today* 2003; 56(12):53–59.

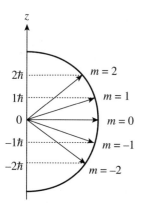

I FIGURE 6.5 Possible orientations of **L** for $\ell = 2$, $|L| = \sqrt{6}\hbar$.

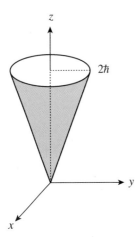

FIGURE 6.6   For $\ell = 2$, $m = 2$, L lies anywhere on the cone.

6.5.3   Spherical Harmonics

What of the detailed solutions for $G(\chi)$? The series solution gave

$$\Theta_{\ell,\,m}(\theta) = (1 - \chi^2)^{|m|/2} G(\chi) = (\sin\theta)^{|m|} G(\cos\theta), \tag{6.5.2.6}$$

where

$$G(\cos\theta) = \sum_{n=0}^{\ell-|m|} a_n (\cos\theta)^n, \tag{6.5.2.8}$$

with coefficients a_n satisfying the recursion relation (Equation 6.5.2.13). The solution for $\Theta(\theta)$ now contains two indices, ℓ and m, designating a particular (L, L_z) state; the upper limit of the sum for $G(\chi)$ in Equation (6.5.2.8) is consequently written as $n_{max} = \ell - |m|$.

With a view to the fact that we will eventually wish to compute probabilities, it is useful to choose a_0 or a_1 (as applicable) for a given (ℓ, m) to be such that $\Theta_{\ell,\,m}(\theta)$ is normalized; that is, such that

$$\int_0^\pi |\Theta_{\ell,\,m}(\theta)|^2 \sin\theta\, d\theta = 1.$$

The details of this normalization are rather involved (see Appendix VI of Pauling and Wilson); we omit them in favor of quoting the final results:

$$\Theta_{\ell,\,m}(\theta) = \sqrt{\frac{2\ell+1}{2}\frac{(\ell-m)!}{(\ell+m)!}}\, P_{\ell,\,m}(\cos\theta) \qquad (|m| \le \ell). \tag{1}$$

$P_{\ell,m}(\cos\theta)$ is a function known as an **associated Legendre function**, given in terms of a general argument x by

$$P_{\ell,m}(x) = \frac{1}{2^\ell \ell!}(1-x^2)^{m/2}\frac{d^{\ell+m}}{dx^{\ell+m}}(x^2-1)^\ell. \qquad (2)$$

In our case, $x \equiv \cos\theta$. Both Equations (1) and (2) are valid for m positive, negative, or zero; further details on the properties of these functions are given in Chapter 11 of Weber and Arfken.

For computational purposes, this form for the associated Legendre functions is not convenient, as it involves computing the $(\ell+m)$th derivative of $(x^2-1)^\ell$. More practical would be a form wherein $\Theta(\theta)$ is expressed directly as a series in terms of, say, $\sin\theta$ or $\cos\theta$. This can be achieved via a binomial-expansion method. The details of this manipulation are given in Appendix A2; the result is

$$\Theta(\theta) = \frac{1}{2^\ell \ell!}\sqrt{\frac{2\ell+1}{2}(\ell+m)!(\ell-m)!}\left(\sin^m\theta\right)\sum_{k=0}^{\left[\frac{\ell-m}{2}\right]}\left[(-1)^k\binom{\ell}{k}\binom{2\ell-2k}{\ell+m}\left(\cos^{\ell-m-2k}\theta\right)\right]. \qquad (3)$$

A few remarks on the nature of $\Theta(\theta)$ that will be useful for when we come to interpret plots of hydrogen atom wavefunctions can be made at this point. By studying Equation (3), you should be able to convince yourself that the sum appearing therein is a polynomial in $\cos\theta$ whose highest order (when $k=0$) is always $\ell-m$, and whose lowest order depends on the evenness or oddness of $\ell-m$. Neglecting numerical coefficients,

$$\ell-m \text{ even} \Rightarrow \Theta_{\ell,m}(\theta) \sim \sin^m\theta[\cos^{\ell-m}\theta + \cos^{\ell-m-2}\theta + \ldots + 1], \qquad (4a)$$

$$\ell-m \text{ odd} \Rightarrow \Theta_{\ell,m}(\theta) \sim \sin^m\theta[\cos^{\ell-m}\theta + \cos^{\ell-m-2}\theta + \ldots + \cos\theta]. \qquad (4b)$$

Consider first the factor of $\sin^m\theta$ that appears in these expressions. If $m \neq 0$, this term will force $\Theta_{\ell,m}(\theta) = 0$ along $\theta = 0$; that is, there will be an angular node along the z-axis. Conversely, if $m = 0$, there will never be an angular node along the z-axis.

Now consider the square brackets in Equations (4a) and (4b). In each case the polynomials in $\cos\theta$ will have $(\ell-m)$ zeros; that is, there will be $(\ell-m)$ angular nodes. In the case of $(\ell-m)$ even, $\Theta_{\ell,m}(\theta)$ will be nonzero along $\theta = \pi/2$. If, however, $(\ell-m)$ is odd, the square bracket will lead to an angular node along $\theta = \pi/2$. We can summarize these results as follows:

(i) If there is an angular node along the z-axis, then $m \neq 0$, and the total number of angular nodes will be $(\ell - m + 1)$, including the one along the z-axis. If there is not an angular node along z-axis, then we must have $m = 0$ and the total number of angular nodes will be $(\ell - m)$, or simply ℓ.

(ii) If there is an angular node along $\theta = \pi/2$, then $(\ell - m)$ must be odd; if there is not, then $(\ell - m)$ must be even. This rule is independent of and in addition to rule (i).

Finally, the complete solution to the angular part of Schrödinger's equation for a central potential, $Y_{\ell, m}(\theta, \phi) = \Theta_{\ell, m}(\theta)\Phi_m(\phi)$, is given by the product of Equations (6.5.1.9) and (3). Traditionally, a further multiplicative factor of $(-1)^m$ is included in this definition: $Y_{\ell, m}(\theta, \phi) = (-1)^m \Theta_{\ell, m}(\theta)\Phi_m(\phi)$. This factor, known as the Condon-Shortley phase, is a convention that serves to define spherical harmonics for negative values of m (see Chapter 11 of Weber and Arfken). Hence we have

$$Y_{\ell, m}(\theta, \phi) = \frac{(-1)^m}{2^\ell \ell!}\left\{\sqrt{\frac{2\ell+1}{4\pi}(\ell+m)!(\ell-m)!}\left(\sin^m \theta\right)\sum_{k=0}^{\left[\frac{\ell-m}{2}\right]}\left[(-1)^k\binom{\ell}{k}\binom{2\ell-2k}{\ell+m}\left(\cos^{\ell-m-2k}\theta\right)\right]\right\}e^{im\phi}. \quad (5)$$

These functions are known as **spherical harmonics**. Since both Θ and Φ were independently normalized, the $Y_{\ell, m}$ are as well. Spherical harmonics up to $l = 3$ are listed in Table 6.1.

EXAMPLE 6.4

Show that for $(\ell, m) = (3, 0)$, Equation (5) yields $Y_{3,0}$ as given in Table 6.1.

With $(\ell, m) = (3, 0)$, the upper index of summation will be 1, so we have

$$Y_{3,0} = \frac{1}{8}\sqrt{\frac{7}{4\pi}}\sum_{k=0}^{1}\left[(-1)^k\binom{3}{k}\binom{6-2k}{3}\right]\left(\cos^{3-2k}\theta\right)$$

$$= \frac{1}{8}\sqrt{\frac{7}{4\pi}}\left[\binom{3}{0}\binom{6}{3}\cos^3\theta - \binom{3}{1}\binom{4}{3}\cos\theta\right].$$

Table 6.1   Spherical Harmonics

$$Y_{0,0}(\theta, \phi) = \frac{1}{\sqrt{4\pi}}$$

$$Y_{1,0}(\theta, \phi) = \sqrt{\frac{3}{4\pi}} \cos\theta$$

$$Y_{1,\pm1}(\theta, \phi) = \mp\sqrt{\frac{3}{8\pi}} \sin\theta \, e^{\pm i\phi}$$

$$Y_{2,0}(\theta, \phi) = \sqrt{\frac{5}{4\pi}} \left(\frac{3}{2}\cos^2\theta - \frac{1}{2} \right)$$

$$Y_{2,\pm1}(\theta, \phi) = \mp\sqrt{\frac{15}{8\pi}} \sin\theta \cos\theta \, e^{\pm i\phi}$$

$$Y_{2,\pm2}(\theta, \phi) = \sqrt{\frac{15}{32\pi}} \sin^2\theta \, e^{\pm 2i\phi}$$

$$Y_{3,0}(\theta, \phi) = \sqrt{\frac{7}{16\pi}} (5\cos^3\theta - 3\cos\theta)$$

$$Y_{3,\pm1}(\theta, \phi) = \mp\sqrt{\frac{21}{64\pi}} \sin\theta \, (5\cos^2\theta - 1) \, e^{\pm i\phi}$$

$$Y_{3,\pm2}(\theta, \phi) = \sqrt{\frac{105}{32\pi}} \sin^2\theta \cos\theta \, e^{\pm 2i\phi}$$

$$Y_{3,\pm3}(\theta, \phi) = \mp\sqrt{\frac{35}{64\pi}} \sin^3\theta \, e^{\pm 3i\phi}$$

Recalling that

$$\binom{a}{b} = \frac{a!}{b!\,(a-b)!},$$

we have

$$Y_{3,0} = \frac{1}{8}\sqrt{\frac{7}{4\pi}} (20\cos^3\theta - 12\cos\theta).$$

Extract a factor of four from within the bracket and combine it with the factors outside to give

$$Y_{3,0} = \sqrt{\frac{7}{16\pi}} (5\cos^3\theta - 3\cos\theta),$$

in agreement with Table 6.1.

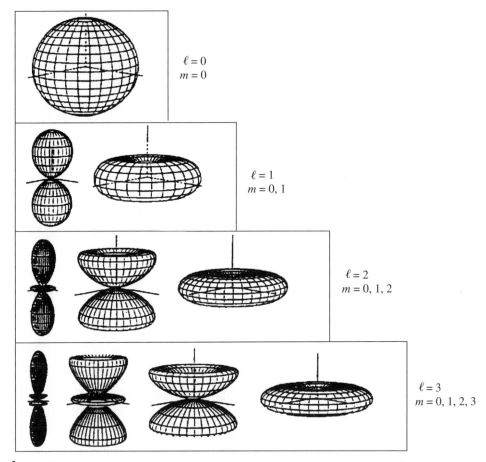

$\ell = 0$
$m = 0$

$\ell = 1$
$m = 0, 1$

$\ell = 2$
$m = 0, 1, 2$

$\ell = 3$
$m = 0, 1, 2, 3$

FIGURE 6.7   Polar diagrams of the absolute squares of spherical harmonics up to $\ell = 3$. Reproduced from Siegmund Brandt and Hans Dieter Dahmen, The Picture Book of Quantum Mechanics, John Wiley & Sons, Inc., New York, 1985, with the kind permission of the publisher.

Figure 6.7 shows pseudo-three-dimensional plots of $|Y_{\ell, m}|^2$ for various (ℓ, m). Study these figures carefully; recall that θ is measured from the vertically upward z-axis (north pole); since $|Y|^2$ is independent of ϕ, they are rotationally symmetric around the z-axis.

In Chapter 7 we will see that these functions manifest themselves in the probability distribution for finding the electron in an infinitesimal volume of space dV at (r, θ, ϕ) in a hydrogen atom:

$$P(r, \theta, \phi)\,dV = \psi^*\psi\,dV = |R(r)|^2\,|Y_{\ell, m}(\theta, \phi)|^2 r^2 \sin\theta\,dr\,d\theta\,d\phi. \tag{6}$$

The forms of the graphs in Figure 6.7 do not wholly dictate the probability distribution of the electron, as we have yet to determine the solution of the radial function $R(r)$ for the Coulomb potential. However, it is clear that the probability distributions will not be spherically symmetric; there will be regions of space wherein one is more or less likely to find the electron, depending on its (ℓ, m) state. Fundamentally, it is the shape of these $|Y|^2$ functions that dictate bonding orientations in molecules.

Finally, although it is not obvious from inspection of Equation (5), it can be shown that $Y_{\ell, -m} = (-1)^m Y_{\ell, m}^*$; a proof appears in Appendix A3.

■ Summary

The key concepts introduced in this chapter are separation of variables in Cartesian and spherical coordinates, degeneracy, angular momentum operators, and the solution of the angular part of Schrödinger's equation for central potentials in terms of spherical harmonics. Readers should be aware that definitions and notation for some of the special mathematical functions involved here can vary; the definitions of the associated Legendre functions and spherical harmonics used here are identical to those in Weber and Arfken.

Separation of variables is a standard technique used in the solution of ordinary and partial differential equations, and is treated in any good text on differential equations. Solutions of the SE in more than one dimension prove to be characterized by the presence of one quantum number for each dimension. Depending on the boundary conditions, different choices for the quantum numbers can lead to the same energy, a condition known as *degeneracy*.

The energy of a particle of mass m trapped in an infinite potential box of dimensions (a, b, c) is given in terms of the (n_x, n_y, n_z) quantum numbers by

$$E = \frac{h^2}{8m}\left(\frac{n_x^2}{a^2} + \frac{n_y^2}{b^2} + \frac{n_z^2}{c^2}\right), \quad (n_x, n_y, n_z) = 1, 2, 3, \dots .$$

The number of individual energy states lying below energy E is

$$N(E) = \frac{8^{3/2}\pi}{6}\frac{V m^{3/2}}{h^3}E^{3/2},$$

where $V = abc$ is the volume of the box.

Angular momentum is a concept of central importance in quantum mechanics, particularly in multibody systems where a careful accounting of the vector nature of

L is necessary. Operators for the x, y, and z components of angular momentum appear in Cartesian and spherical coordinates as

$$L_x \equiv -\iota\hbar\left(y\frac{\partial}{\partial z} - z\frac{\partial}{\partial y}\right) \equiv -\iota\hbar\left(-\sin\phi\frac{\partial}{\partial \theta} - \cot\theta\cos\phi\frac{\partial}{\partial \phi}\right),$$

$$L_y \equiv -\iota\hbar\left(z\frac{\partial}{\partial x} - x\frac{\partial}{\partial z}\right) \equiv -\iota\hbar\left(\cos\phi\frac{\partial}{\partial \theta} - \cot\theta\sin\phi\frac{\partial}{\partial \phi}\right),$$

and

$$L_z \equiv -\iota\hbar\left(x\frac{\partial}{\partial y} - y\frac{\partial}{\partial x}\right) \equiv -\iota\hbar\frac{\partial}{\partial \phi}.$$

(See Section 6.3 and Problem 6.7.)

The operator for the magnitude of the square of total angular momentum is

$$L^2 \equiv -\hbar^2\left[\frac{1}{\sin\theta}\frac{\partial}{\partial \theta}\left(\sin\theta\frac{\partial}{\partial \theta}\right) + \frac{1}{\sin^2\theta}\frac{\partial^2}{\partial \phi^2}\right].$$

With this result, the Hamiltonian (energy) operator for a system of mass μ can be written in spherical coordinates as

$$\mathbf{H} \equiv -\frac{\hbar^2}{2\mu r^2}\frac{\partial}{\partial r}\left(r^2\frac{\partial}{\partial r}\right) + \frac{L^2_{op}}{2\mu r^2} + V(r, \theta, \phi).$$

Schrödinger's equation in spherical coordinates for a particle of mass μ moving in a central potential $V(r)$ appears as

$$\frac{\hbar^2}{2\mu}\left\{\frac{1}{r^2}\frac{\partial}{\partial r}\left(r^2\frac{\partial}{\partial r}\right) + \frac{1}{r^2\sin\theta}\frac{\partial}{\partial \theta}\left(\sin\theta\frac{\partial}{\partial \theta}\right) + \frac{1}{r^2\sin^2\theta}\left(\frac{\partial^2}{\partial \phi^2}\right)\right\}\psi(r, \theta, \phi)$$

$$+ V(r)\psi(r, \theta, \phi) = E\psi(r, \theta, \phi).$$

This equation is separable into a radial part $R(r)$ and an angular part $Y(\theta, \phi)$ on assuming

$$\psi(r, \theta, \phi) = R(r)\, Y(\theta, \phi).$$

The angular wavefunctions Y are given by

$$Y_{\ell,m}(\theta,\phi) = \frac{(-1)^m}{2^\ell \ell!}\left[\sqrt{\frac{2\ell+1}{4\pi}(\ell+m)!(\ell-m)!}\left(\sin^m\theta\right)\sum_{k=0}^{\left\lfloor\frac{\ell-m}{2}\right\rfloor}\left[(-1)^k\binom{\ell}{k}\binom{2\ell-2k}{\ell+m}\left(\cos^{\ell-m-2k}\theta\right)\right]\right]e^{im\phi}.$$

The $Y_{\ell,m}$ are known as spherical harmonics. In these expressions, ℓ is the orbital angular momentum quantum number and m is the magnetic quantum number. Respectively, these two integers quantize the total and (conventionally) z-components of angular momentum of the system according as

$$L = \sqrt{\ell(\ell+1)}\hbar \quad (\ell = 0, 1, 2, \ldots),$$

and

$$L_z = m\hbar \quad (|m| \le \ell).$$

■ Problems

6-1(E) Consider an electron moving in an infinite potential box of dimensions $(1.0, 1.5, 1.9)$ Å. Tabulate all possible energy levels (in eV) for $(n_x, n_y, n_z) = 1$ to 3.

6-2(E) Consider an electron trapped in a box of volume 1 cubic centimeter. How many quantum states are available to the electron below $E = 10$ eV? How many states would lie between 10 eV and 10.01 eV?

6-3(E) For which of the following three-dimensional potentials would Schrödinger's equation be separable?

(a) $V(x, y, z) = x^2 y + \sin(z)$

(b) $V(x, y, z) = x^2 + y + \tan^{-1}(\sqrt{z})$

(c) $V(x, y, z) = e^x y^{7/2} z^2$

(d) $V(x, y, z) = y\sin(x) + z\cos(y) + y\tan(z)$

(e) $V(x, y, z) = y^{-4} + \sin^{-1}(e^{\sqrt{x}}) + \tan(z)$

(f) $V(x, y, z) = e^{xy\sqrt{z}}$

(g) $V(x, y, z) = e^{x+y-\sqrt{z}}$

6-4(E) In his development of blackbody theory, Planck assumed that photons in a blackbody cavity were of a continuum of wavelengths as opposed to the discrete wavelengths that the cavity could actually support on account of its finite dimensions. Planck's expression for the number of photon states between frequencies ν and $\nu + d\nu$ that a cavity of volume V could support was

$$N(\nu)\,d\nu = \frac{8\pi V}{c^3} \nu^2 d\nu.$$

Transform this expression into an equivalent wavelength form. Now consider a tiny volume, say 1 mm³. How many photon states are possible between $\lambda = 5000$ Å and $\lambda = 5001$ Å, typical visible-light wavelengths? Was Planck justified in his assumption of an essentially continuous distribution of frequencies/wavelengths?

6-5(I) Verify the expressions given in the text for the derivatives of the spherical-coordinate unit vectors, Equations (6.2.7).

6-6(I) Using the method demonstrated in Equation (6.3.9), evaluate the other three terms in Equation (6.3.8), and hence verify Equations (6.3.10) and (6.3.11) for L_{op}^2.

6-7(I) Following the method that was used to derive the expression for $(L_z)_{op}$ in Section 6.3, show that the operators for the x and y components of angular momentum in spherical coordinates are given by

$$L_x \equiv -\iota\hbar\left(-\sin\phi\,\frac{\partial}{\partial\theta} - \cot\theta\cos\phi\,\frac{\partial}{\partial\phi}\right)$$

and

$$L_y \equiv -\iota\hbar\left(\cos\phi\,\frac{\partial}{\partial\theta} - \cot\theta\sin\phi\,\frac{\partial}{\partial\phi}\right).$$

6-8(E) In Chapter 8 the *angular momentum raising and lowering operators* $L_{\pm} = L_x \pm \iota L_y$ will be introduced. From your results in Problem 6-7, show that in spherical coordinates these appear as

$$L_{\pm} \equiv \hbar e^{\pm\iota\phi}\left\{\pm\frac{\partial}{\partial\theta} + \iota\cot\theta\,\frac{\partial}{\partial\phi}\right\}.$$

6-9(A) Following the procedures of Sections 6.2 and 6.3, derive expressions for the L_{op}^2 operator in (a) Cartesian and (b) cylindrical coordinates.

6-10(I) In Example 6.2 it was shown that $[L_x, L_y] \equiv (\iota\hbar)L_z$. Prove likewise that

$$[L_y, L_z] \equiv (\iota\hbar)L_x,$$

and

$$[L_z, L_x] \equiv (\iota\hbar)L_y.$$

6-11(I) Prove that $[L_x, p_x] \equiv 0$, $[L_x, p_y] \equiv (\iota\hbar)p_z$, and $[L_x, p_z] \equiv -(\iota\hbar)p_y$. Permuting the coordinates leads also to the identities $[L_y, p_x] \equiv -(\iota\hbar)p_z$, $[L_y, p_y] \equiv 0$, $[L_y, p_z] \equiv (\iota\hbar)p_x$, $[L_z, p_x] \equiv (\iota\hbar)p_y$, $[L_z, p_y] \equiv -(\iota\hbar)p_x$, and $[L_z, p_z] \equiv 0$.

6-12(I) Prove that $[L_x, x] \equiv 0$, $[L_x, y] \equiv (\iota\hbar)z$, and $[L_x, z] \equiv -(\iota\hbar)y$. Permuting the coordinates leads also to the identities $[L_y, x] \equiv -(\iota\hbar)z$, $[L_y, y] \equiv 0$, $[L_y, z] \equiv (\iota\hbar)x$, $[L_z, x] \equiv (\iota\hbar)y$, $[L_z, y] \equiv -(\iota\hbar)x$, and $[L_z, z] \equiv 0$.

6-13(E) Show that Equation (6.4.6) follows from Equation (6.4.4) and the discussion in Section 6.3.

6-14(E) Prove that Equation (6.5.1.3) does not diverge for $m \rightarrow 0$.

6-15(I) In Section 6.5.2 it was remarked that the function $\Theta(\chi) = (1 - \chi^2)^{|m|/2}G(\chi)$ is indeterminate for $\chi \rightarrow \pm 1$. Use L'Hôpital's rule to prove this. Then try a different factorization for $\Theta(\chi)$, namely $\Theta(\chi) = (1 - \chi^2)^{-|m|/2}U(\chi)$. Show that the high-order terms in the resulting series solution for $U(\chi)$ behave in the same manner as do those for $G(\chi)$, and hence that $U(\chi)$ diverges for $\chi \rightarrow \pm 1$. From the uniqueness theorem for solutions of differential equations, what can you conclude about the way $G(\chi)$ was terminated in Section 6.5.2?

6-16(E) Verify the forms of the expressions for $\Theta_{\ell, m}(\theta)$ given in Equations (6.5.3.4a) and (6.5.3.4b).

6-17(I) Working directly from Equation (6.5.3.5), verify the expression given for $Y_{3, 1}$ in Table 6.1.

6-18(I) Using spherical coordinates, show that $[L^2, L_z]\psi = 0$ if ψ is of the form $\psi = \Theta(\theta)\Phi(\phi)$, that is, if ψ is a separable function of θ and ϕ. If you are ambitious, show as well that $[L^2, L_x]\psi = 0$ and $[L^2, L_y]\psi = 0$, but be warned that the algebra is messy. An easier method is explored in Section 8.1.

6-19(I) Show that if the potential function is a function only of the radial coordinate r [that is, $V = V(r)$ only] and that the wavefunction can be separated as $\psi(r, \theta, \phi) = R(r) g(\theta, \phi)$, then it follows that that $[H, L^2] \psi = 0$.

6-20(I) In more than one dimension, the "uncertainty packet" $\Delta r \Delta p$ is given by computing $\Delta r \Delta p = \sqrt{(\langle r^2 \rangle - \langle \mathbf{r} \rangle^2)(\langle p^2 \rangle - \langle \mathbf{p} \rangle^2)}$, where the square of a vector expectation value is given by a dot product as in $\langle \mathbf{r} \rangle^2 = \langle \mathbf{r} \rangle \cdot \langle \mathbf{r} \rangle$. In three dimensions it can be shown that the uncertainty principle appears as $\Delta r \Delta p \geq (\sqrt{3}/2)\hbar$ (see [5]). For a centrally symmetric potential in three dimensions we can put $\psi(r, \theta, \phi) = R(r) Y_{\ell m}(\theta, \phi)$, where the $Y_{\ell m}$ are the spherical harmonics of Section 6.5.3. Show that in such a case, $\langle \mathbf{r} \rangle = 0$ always. [*Hint:* Note that the $Y_{\ell m}$ are explicitly complex. Use spherical coordinates; write $\mathbf{r} = r\mathbf{r}$ where $\mathbf{r}$ is the radial unit vector in spherical coordinates, Equation (6.2.5)]. Since $\langle \mathbf{p} \rangle = 0$ for any time-dependent wavefunction (Section 4.2), the uncertainty packet for such wavefunctions reduces to $\Delta r \Delta p = \sqrt{\langle r^2 \rangle \langle p^2 \rangle}$.

6-21(I) In ordinary vector algebra, the cross-product of a vector with itself is always zero: $\mathbf{A} \times \mathbf{A} = 0$. When the vectors are operators, however, things can be different. Using spherical coordinates, show that the angular momentum operator behaves as $\mathbf{L} \times \mathbf{L} = (\iota\hbar)\mathbf{L}$.

7 | Central Potentials

■ 7.1 Introduction

In the preceding chapter, it was shown how solutions to Schrödinger's equation in spherical coordinates (r, θ, ϕ) for a mass μ moving in a central potential $V(r)$,

$$-\frac{\hbar^2}{2\mu}\left\{\frac{1}{r^2}\frac{\partial}{\partial r}\left(r^2\frac{\partial}{\partial r}\right) + \frac{1}{r^2\sin\theta}\frac{\partial}{\partial\theta}\left(\sin\theta\frac{\partial}{\partial\theta}\right) + \frac{1}{r^2\sin^2\theta}\left(\frac{\partial^2}{\partial\phi^2}\right)\right\}\psi(r,\theta,\phi)$$

$$+ V(r)\psi(r,\theta,\phi) = E\psi(r,\theta,\phi), \tag{6.4.1}$$

can be separated into radial and angular parts as $\psi(r, \theta, \phi) = R(r)Y(\theta, \phi)$. In terms of the operator for the squared angular momentum of the system, L_{op}^2 [Eq. (6.3.11)], this separation takes the form

$$-\frac{\hbar^2}{2\mu}\left\{\frac{1}{R}\frac{\partial}{\partial r}\left(r^2\frac{\partial R}{\partial r}\right)\right\} + [V(r) - E]r^2 = -\frac{1}{2\mu Y}(L_{op}^2 Y). \tag{6.4.6}$$

The solution of the angular function $Y(\theta, \phi)$ was developed in Section 6.5 as the spherical harmonic functions $Y_{\ell,m}(\theta, \phi)$:

$$Y_{\ell,m}(\theta,\phi) = \frac{(-1)^m}{2^\ell \ell!}\left\{\sqrt{\frac{2\ell+1}{4\pi}(\ell+m)!(\ell-m)!}\left(\sin^m\theta\right)\sum_{k=0}^{\left[\frac{\ell-m}{2}\right]}\left[(-1)^k\binom{\ell}{k}\binom{2\ell-2k}{\ell+m}\right]\left(\cos^{\ell-m-2k}\theta\right)\right\}e^{im\phi}$$

$$\tag{6.5.3.5}$$

where ℓ and m are respectively the orbital angular momentum and magnetic quantum numbers, with $\ell = 0, 1, 2, \ldots$ and $|m| \leq \ell$.

The eigenvalues of L_{op}^2 are given in Equation (6.5.2.18):

$$L_{op}^2 Y_{\ell, m}(\theta, \phi) = [\hbar^2 \ell(\ell + 1)] Y_{\ell, m}(\theta, \phi). \qquad (6.5.2.18)$$

In developing solutions for the radial part of Equation (6.4.6) for central potentials, it is conventional to put the equation in terms of ℓ by substituting the result (6.5.2.18) into the right side to yield

$$-\frac{\hbar^2}{2\mu}\left\{ \frac{1}{R}\frac{\partial}{\partial r}\left(r^2 \frac{\partial R}{\partial r} \right) \right\} + [V(r) - E]r^2 = -\frac{1}{2\mu Y}[\hbar^2 \ell(\ell + 1)]Y,$$

and then cancel the Y-functions and rearrange to the form

$$-\frac{\hbar^2}{2\mu}\left\{ \frac{1}{R}\frac{\partial}{\partial r}\left(r^2 \frac{\partial R}{\partial r} \right) - \ell(\ell + 1) \right\} + V(r)r^2 = Er^2. \qquad (1)$$

This expression is known as the *radial equation*. The magnetic quantum number m is "hidden" in the spherical harmonic $Y_{\ell, m}(\theta, \phi)$ appropriate to the angular momentum state ℓ for which Equation (1) is to be solved. Clearly, if we can solve for $R(r)$ for some potential $V(r)$, there will be a whole family of solutions available given by choosing different combinations of the ℓ and m quantum numbers.

Two other forms of the radial equation are commonly seen. The first casts the derivative into a more compact form by noting that

$$\frac{1}{R}\frac{\partial}{\partial r}\left(r^2 \frac{\partial R}{\partial r} \right) = \frac{r}{R}\frac{\partial^2}{\partial r^2}(rR), \qquad (2)$$

hence rendering Equation (1) as

$$-\frac{\hbar^2}{2\mu}\left\{ \frac{r}{R}\frac{\partial^2}{\partial r^2}(rR) - \ell(\ell + 1) \right\} + V(r)r^2 = Er^2. \qquad (3)$$

The other alternate form introduces the auxiliary function

$$U(r) = r R(r), \qquad (4)$$

in which case we have

$$\frac{d^2 U}{dr^2} + \frac{2\mu}{\hbar^2}\left\{E - V(r) - \frac{\ell(\ell+1)\hbar^2}{2\mu r^2}\right\}U(r) = 0. \tag{5}$$

In anticipation that the solution of Equations (1), (3), or (5) will lead to a quantum number n that dictates energy levels, the overall wavefunction ψ will be of the form

$$\psi_{n\ell m}(r, \theta, \phi) = R_n(r)Y_{\ell,m}(\theta, \phi) = \frac{U_n(r)}{r}Y_{\ell,m}(\theta, \phi). \tag{6}$$

The purpose of this chapter is to take up solutions to these various versions of the radial equation. We will begin by looking at two relatively simple cases, solutions for the infinite and finite spherical potential wells (Sections 7.2 and 7.3) for the specific case of $\ell = 0$. These situations represent spherically symmetric analogs of the three-dimensional rectangular box treated in Chapter 6. Solutions along these lines are of interest in nuclear physics, where nuclei can be modeled as spherical potential wells on the order of tens of MeV deep and $\sim 10^{-14}$ meters in radius. In Sections 7.4 and 7.5 we develop and examine a detailed solution for the hydrogenic Coulomb potential. It is difficult to overstate the importance of this solution in the history and continuing development of quantum physics; it truly is one of the crown jewels of quantum mechanics. Bohr's treatment of the hydrogen spectrum marked the real beginnings of quantum theory, and in his seminal paper on quantum mechanics, Schrödinger developed the solution of the wave equation for the Coulomb potential [1]. Being the only realistic atomic potential for which the SE is exactly soluble analytically, solutions for the Coulomb potential form the foundation on which our understanding of the physics of more complex atomic and molecular systems rests. As solutions of Schrödinger's equation are interpreted probabilistically, we can expect the resulting detailed workings it predicts for hydrogen to be very different from those of the Bohr model. But the Bohr and Schrödinger pictures must agree on at least one point: the permissible energy levels of the electron/proton system, as revealed by spectroscopic analysis.

■ 7.2   The Infinite Spherical Well

The infinite spherical well is an analog of the three-dimensional box potential discussed in Section 6.1. The particle (mass μ) is trapped in a spherical region of space of radius a within an impenetrable barrier defined by

$$V(r) = \begin{cases} \infty \, (r \geq a) \\ 0 \, (r < a). \end{cases} \tag{1}$$

This is illustrated in Figure 7.1.

The simplest case is a particle with zero angular momentum $\ell = 0$. (Solving the radial equation for $\ell \neq 0$ involves functions known as spherical Bessel and Neumann functions, exploration of which lies beyond the scope of this work.)

In this case, it proves most straightforward to work with version (5) of the radial equation. A subscript 0 is appended to U as a reminder that the solution is valid only for $\ell = 0$. Inside the well we have

$$\frac{d^2 U_0}{dr^2} + k^2 U_0 = 0, \tag{2}$$

where

$$k^2 = \frac{2\mu E}{\hbar^2}. \tag{3}$$

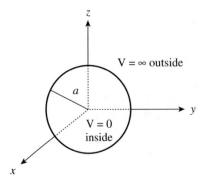

I FIGURE 7.1   Infinite Spherical Well.

Equations (1) and (2) are formally identical to those describing a one-dimension-al infinite potential well; this is why we chose version (5) of the radial equation. We can immediately write the solution as

$$U_0(r) = A\sin(kr) + B\cos(kr). \tag{4}$$

What boundary conditions apply in this case? It is important to bear in mind that the solution to the radial equation is not given by U directly but by $R = U/r$. To prevent divergence as $r \to 0$, we must have $U(r = 0) = 0$, which forces $B = 0$ in Equation (4). Furthermore, since the barrier is impenetrable, we must have $U(r = a) = 0$, or $ka = n\pi$. Hence

$$E_n(\ell = 0) = \frac{n^2\pi^2\hbar^2}{2\mu a^2}. \tag{5}$$

(The argument given here regarding the vanishing of $U(r)$ at $r = 0$ is too simplistic, although adequate for our purposes. Deeper details are covered in Shankar [2].) The energy levels for a particle with $\ell = 0$ in an infinite spherical well are identical to those of a one-dimensional infinite rectangular well with the width of the rectangular well replaced by the radius of the spherical well.

The total wavefunction in this case is

$$\psi_{n00}(r, \theta, \phi) = R_n(r)Y_{0,0}(\theta, \phi) = \frac{A}{\sqrt{4\pi r}}\sin\left(\frac{n\pi r}{a}\right).$$

Normalizing demands

$$\frac{A^2}{4\pi}\int_0^a\int_0^\pi\int_0^{2\pi}\left[\frac{1}{r^2}\sin^2\left(\frac{n\pi r}{a}\right)\right]r^2\sin\theta\,d\phi\,d\theta\,dr = 1,$$

which gives $A = \sqrt{2/a}$. Hence we have

$$\psi_{n00} = \frac{1}{\sqrt{2\pi ar}}\sin\left(\frac{n\pi r}{a}\right). \tag{6}$$

The expectation value of r for a particle in such a potential is given by

$$\langle r \rangle = \int_0^a \int_0^\pi \int_0^{2\pi} [\psi_{n00} r \psi_{n00}] r^2 \sin\theta \, d\phi \, d\theta \, dr$$

$$= \frac{1}{2\pi a} \left\{ \int_0^a r \sin^2(n\pi r/a) \, dr \right\} \left\{ \int_0^\pi \sin\theta \, d\theta \right\} \left\{ \int_0^{2\pi} d\phi \right\} = \frac{2}{a} \int_0^a r \sin^2(n\pi r/a) \, dr$$

$$= \frac{2}{a} \left[\frac{r^2}{4} - \frac{r \sin(n\pi r/a)}{4(n\pi/a)} - \frac{\cos(n\pi r/a)}{8(n\pi/a)^2} \right]_0^a = \frac{a}{2}. \tag{7}$$

$\langle r \rangle$ is independent of n: increasing the energy of the particle alters its probability distribution, but not its average position. If $\ell \neq 0$, $\langle r \rangle$ would be a function of both n and ℓ.

■ 7.3   The Finite Spherical Well

The spherical analog of the one-dimensional finite well treated in Chapter 3 is defined by

$$V(r) = \begin{cases} V_o \ (r \geq a) \\ 0 \ (r < a). \end{cases} \tag{1}$$

Such a potential might describe a particle trapped inside a nucleus along the lines of the alpha-decay problem treated in Chapter 3. We seek bound-state $(E < V_o)$ solutions of the radial equation for this potential; the solution for the energy levels of this potential closely parallels that for the one-dimensional finite well studied in Sections 3.3–3.5.

Once again, we consider the $\ell = 0$ case. Inside the well $(r < a)$, the radial equation is the same as that for the infinite spherical well, Equation (2) of the preceding section. Applying the boundary condition that $U(r = 0) = 0$ leads to the solution

$$R_0^{in}(r) = \frac{A \sin(k_1 r)}{r}, \quad k_1^2 = 2\mu E/\hbar^2 \ (r < a), \tag{2}$$

where μ is again the mass of the particle trapped in the potential. Outside the well $(r \geq a)$, the radial equation becomes

$$\frac{d^2 U_0^{out}(r)}{dr^2} = k_2^2 U_0^{out}(r), \tag{3}$$

where

$$k_2^2 = \frac{2m}{\hbar^2}(V_o - E).$$ (4)

The general form of the solution is

$$U_0^{out}(r) = C e^{k_2 r} + D e^{-k_2 r},$$

that is,

$$R_0^{out}(r) = \frac{C e^{k_2 r}}{r} + \frac{D e^{-k_2 r}}{r}.$$ (5)

Requiring $U(r) \to 0$ as $r \to \infty$ demands $C = 0$, reducing the solution to

$$R_0^{out}(r) = \frac{D e^{-k_2 r}}{r}.$$ (6)

Forcing the continuity of R and dR/dr at $r = a$ leads to two conditions:

$$A \sin(k_1 a) = D e^{-k_2 a},$$ (7)

and

$$A[a k_1 \cos(k_1 a) - \sin(k_1 a)] = -D e^{-k_2 a}[a k_2 + 1].$$ (8)

Dividing Equation (8) by Equation (7) eliminates A and D and yields a transcendental equation for the energy eigenvalues:

$$\xi \cot \xi = -\eta,$$ (9)

where we have defined

$$\xi = k_1 a$$ (10)

and

$$\eta = k_2 a.$$ (11)

From the definitions of k_1 and k_2, we can form a strength parameter for the spherical potential much like that for the one-dimensional finite potential of Chapter 3:

$$\xi^2 + \eta^2 = a^2(k_1^2 + k_2^2) = \frac{2\mu V_o a^2}{\hbar^2} = \text{constant} = R^2. \tag{12}$$

Equation (12) is that of a circle of radius R in the (ξ, η) plane: $\xi^2 + \eta^2 = R^2$; this is why the strength parameter is designated as R^2. The permissible bound-state energies are given by finding the values of ξ and η that satisfy Equations (9) and (12) simultaneously; that is, by finding the points of intersection of these equations in the (ξ, η) plane. From the definitions of k_1 and k_2, ξ and η must be positive, so our attention can be restricted to the first quadrant.

The situation is shown in Figure 7.2.

The quarter-circularlike arcs correspond to wells of different depths, specifically, $R = 1, 2, 4,$ and 6 in Equation (12). The points of intersection between the circles and the almost vertical cotangent curves ($\eta = -\xi\cot\xi$) correspond to the quantized energy levels. The $R = 1$ well possesses no bound states, while the other wells all bind one state each. Since the zeros of the cotangent function occur at $(2n - 1)\pi/2$, $n = 1, 2, 3, \ldots$, it follows that for a spherical well to possess n bound states it must have $R > (2n - 1)\pi/2$, or

$$V_o a^2 \geq \frac{(2n - 1)^2 h^2}{32\mu} \quad (\ell = 0). \tag{13}$$

It is interesting to compare this example with the one-dimensional finite potential well. In the present case there are no even and odd solutions to keep track of; that com-

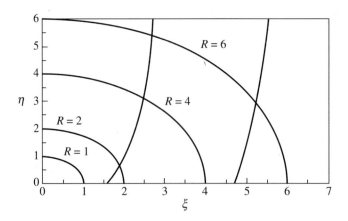

FIGURE 7.2   Illustration of the Solution for Energy Eigenvalues for a Finite Spherical Well.

plication arises in one dimension because the boundary conditions have to be applied at both sides of the one-dimensional well ($x = \pm L$), whereas r is not defined for $r < 0$. While a one-dimensional well will always have at least one bound state no matter how shallow it is, this is not the case for a spherical well.

EXAMPLE 7.1

How many energy states are available to an alpha-particle trapped in a finite spherical well of depth 50 MeV and radius $10^{-14}\ m$? Assume $\ell = 0$.
   From Equation (13),

$$(2n - 1)^2 < \frac{32 \mu a^2 V_o}{h^2}.$$

On substituting the appropriate numerical values we find

$$(2n - 1)^2 < \frac{32\,(6.646 \times 10^{-27} kg)\,(10^{-14} m)^2\,(8.010 \times 10^{-12} J)}{(6.626 \times 10^{-34} J - \sec)^2},$$

or,

$$(2n - 1)^2 < 388.$$

   From this we find $n < 10.4$: the alpha-particle has only ten bound states of $\ell = 0$ available.
   We can determine the energy of the lowest-energy bound state for this system as follows. From Equation (12) we have

$$\xi^2 + \eta^2 = \frac{2 \mu a^2 V_o}{\hbar^2} = 956.6.$$

Using this result to eliminate η in Equation (9) provides a constraint on ξ:

$$\xi \cot \xi + \sqrt{956.6 - \xi^2} = 0.$$

   The lowest-valued root of this equation is $\xi = 3.04305$, which gives, via Equation (10) and the definition of k_1 in Equation (2),

$$E = \frac{\xi^2 \hbar^2}{2 \mu a^2} = 0.48 \text{ MeV}.$$

■ 7.4 The Coulomb Potential

As emphasized in the introduction to this chapter, the hydrogenic, or Coulomb, potential is perhaps the single most important potential for which an exact solution of Schrödinger's equation can be obtained. Our model for the hydrogen atom consists of a single electron of charge $-e$ and a single proton of charge $+e$ separated by distance r. From electromagnetic theory we know that the potential energy of such an arrangement is

$$V(r) = -\frac{e^2}{4\pi\epsilon_o r}.$$ (1)

As indicated in Section 6.4, the importance of this potential demands that a full, rigorous solution be presented. In the analysis of the Bohr atom in Chapter 1, it was assumed that the proton's position could be considered as fixed in view of its much greater mass than that of the "orbiting" electron. This is not strictly true, of course, and leads to an analysis that cannot be generally applied to two-body systems. Hence, we open this section with a proof that Schrödinger's equation for any two-body system can be separated into a part that describes the motion of the center of mass (*CM*) of the system as a whole and a part that describes the "internal" energy levels of the system. The second part reduces the two-body problem to an equivalent one-body problem in a formulation that can be applied to *any* two body central-potential problem, and thus becomes the primary center of interest for the rest of the chapter.

Consult Figure 7.3, which shows two masses, m_A and m_B. [We revert here to using the symbol m to designate mass, as no confusion with the magnetic quantum number

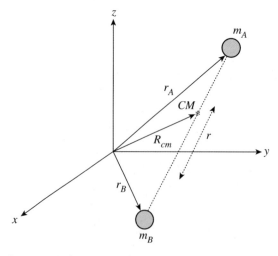

I FIGURE 7.3 Reduction of Two-body System to Equivalent One-body System.

is likely to arise. μ is reserved for the reduced mass of this two-body system, Equation (4), which is shown below.] With respect to the coordinate origin shown, they lie at vector positions $\mathbf{r}_A$ and $\mathbf{r}_B$. $\mathbf{R}_{CM}$ is the position of the center of mass of the two-mass system, which we know must lie along the line joining the two masses. From classical mechanics, this is given by

$$\mathbf{R}_{CM} = \frac{m_A \mathbf{r}_A + m_B \mathbf{r}_B}{m_A + m_B}. \tag{2}$$

It will prove helpful to have a symbol to represent the sum of the masses,

$$M = m_A + m_B, \tag{3}$$

and one to represent what is known as the **reduced mass** of the system:

$$\mu = \frac{m_A m_B}{m_A + m_B}. \tag{4}$$

A crucial concept here is that of the **relative coordinate** of the two masses, defined as

$$\mathbf{r}_{rel} = \mathbf{r}_A - \mathbf{r}_B. \tag{5}$$

By imagining a vector that goes from m_B to m_A, you should be able to convince yourself that the separation between the two masses is given by the magnitude of the vector $\mathbf{r}_A - \mathbf{r}_B$, or simply r_{rel}. If the potential energy of the system is a function only of the separation of the two particles, we can write it as $V(r_{rel})$.

Now, Schrödinger's equation for this system is

$$-\frac{\hbar^2}{2m_A}\nabla_A^2 \psi(\mathbf{r}_A, \mathbf{r}_B) - \frac{\hbar^2}{2m_B}\nabla_B^2 \psi(\mathbf{r}_A, \mathbf{r}_B) + V(r_{rel})\psi(\mathbf{r}_A, \mathbf{r}_B) = E\psi(\mathbf{r}_A, \mathbf{r}_B). \tag{6}$$

In writing this, note that ∇_A^2 will take derivatives only with respect to the coordinates of mass A; similarly for ∇_B^2 and mass B. $\psi(\mathbf{r}_A, \mathbf{r}_B)$ is a "joint probability" wavefunction that gives the probability of mass A being in a small volume of space at $\mathbf{r}_A$, while mass B is in some small volume of space at $\mathbf{r}_B$.

Given the success of the separation-of-variables approach of Chapter 6, one might be tempted to try a separation of the form $\psi(\mathbf{r}_A, \mathbf{r}_B) = \psi_A(\mathbf{r}_A)\psi_B(\mathbf{r}_B)$. However, you would discover quickly that this would not work because the potential energy is a function of the form $V(r_{rel}) = V(|\mathbf{r}_A - \mathbf{r}_B|)$, not separable into "$A$" and "$B$" coordinates. If the derivatives were with respect to r_{rel}, we might have some hope of separability. Further, since there are two masses, $\mathbf{r}_{rel} = \mathbf{r}_A - \mathbf{r}_B$ gives information only on their *relative* positions; we need some other piece of information to pin down their *absolute* positions with respect to the origin. This second coordinate is taken to be $\mathbf{R}_{CM}$, as defined in Equation (2). The point here is that we are going to transform Equation (6) from $(\mathbf{r}_A, \mathbf{r}_B)$ coordinates to $(\mathbf{r}_{rel}, \mathbf{R}_{CM})$ coordinates. In doing so we will find that Schrödinger's equation naturally splits into separate $\mathbf{r}_{rel}$ and $\mathbf{R}_{CM}$ subequations.

The Laplacian operators in Equation (6) need to be transformed to the new coordinates. We will illustrate this with the x-component of ∇_A^2; the other components and those of ∇_B^2 will then follow directly by inspection.

From multivariable calculus, this sort of transformation goes as

$$\frac{\partial}{\partial x_A} \equiv \left(\frac{\partial x_{CM}}{\partial x_A}\right)\frac{\partial}{\partial x_{CM}} + \left(\frac{\partial x_{rel}}{\partial x_A}\right)\frac{\partial}{\partial x_{rel}} \equiv \left(\frac{m_A}{M}\right)\frac{\partial}{\partial x_{CM}} + \frac{\partial}{\partial x_{rel}}. \tag{7}$$

$\partial/\partial x_B$ follows similarly but with a change of sign due to the second term in the right side of Equation (5):

$$\frac{\partial}{\partial x_B} \equiv \left(\frac{m_B}{M}\right)\frac{\partial}{\partial x_{CM}} - \frac{\partial}{\partial x_{rel}}. \tag{8}$$

On extending these to (y, z) components and then to second derivatives, the negative sign in Eq. (8) disappears due to a second application of ∇_B, resulting in

$$\nabla_A^2 \equiv \left(\frac{m_A}{M}\right)\nabla_{CM}^2 + \nabla_{rel}^2 \tag{9}$$

and

$$\nabla_B^2 \equiv \left(\frac{m_B}{M}\right)\nabla_{CM}^2 + \nabla_{rel}^2. \tag{10}$$

Now assume separability of the form $\psi(\mathbf{r}_A, \mathbf{r}_B) \equiv \psi_{CM}(\mathbf{R}_{CM})\psi_{rel}(\mathbf{r}_{rel})$ and substitute Equations (9) and (10) into Equation (6). Remembering that derivatives with respect to CM coordinates do not affect rel coordinates and vice-versa, we find

$$-\frac{\hbar^2 m_A}{2 M^2}\psi_{rel}\nabla_{CM}^2\psi_{CM} - \frac{\hbar^2 m_B}{2 M^2}\psi_{rel}\nabla_{CM}^2\psi_{CM}$$
$$-\frac{\hbar^2}{2m_A}\psi_{CM}\nabla_{rel}^2\psi_{rel} - \frac{\hbar^2}{2m_B}\psi_{CM}\nabla_{rel}^2\psi_{rel} + V(r_{rel})\psi_{CM}\psi_{rel} = E\psi_{CM}\psi_{rel}. \tag{11}$$

On dividing through by $\psi_{CM}\psi_{rel}$, Equation (11) becomes

$$\left[-\frac{\hbar^2}{2M}\frac{1}{\psi_{CM}}\nabla^2_{CM}\psi_{CM}\right] + \left[-\frac{\hbar^2}{2\mu}\frac{1}{\psi_{rel}}\nabla^2_{rel}\psi_{rel} + V(r_{rel})\right] = E. \tag{12}$$

In Equation (12), the term in the first square bracket deals with only *CM* coordinates, whereas that in the second square bracket involves only relative coordinates: the equation has been separated. Note that the reduced mass appears in the relative-coordinates part of Equation (12). Writing $E = E_{CM} + E_{rel}$, we then have two independent equations:

$$-\frac{\hbar^2}{2M}\nabla^2_{CM}\psi_{CM} = E_{CM}\psi_{CM} \tag{13}$$

and

$$-\frac{\hbar^2}{2\mu}\nabla^2_{rel}\psi_{rel} + V(r_{rel})\psi_{rel} = E_{rel}\psi_{rel}. \tag{14}$$

Study Equations (13) and (14) carefully. Equation (13) is Schrödinger's equation for a "free" particle; that is, one where $V = 0$. This equation describes the "motion" of the *CM* of our two-particle system and tells us that the kinetic energy of the *CM* is a continuous variable. In fact, if the coordinate origin in Figure 7.3 had been put at the *CM*, only Equation (14) would have emerged from the derivation.

Equation (14) is of the form of Schrödinger's equation for a single particle, but with the mass of the particle being the reduced mass of the two-particle system. By separating into *CM* and relative coordinates, we have reduced the two-mass system to an equivalent single-particle system.

The advantage of this approach is powerful: it applies to *any* two-body central-force potential. Because we have recovered Schrödinger's equation, the angular/radial separation carried out in Chapter 6 and all that follows from it—in particular the various forms of the radial equation given in Section 7.1—retain their validity: we need only replace the single-particle mass with reduced mass of Equation (4). In practice, it is customary to drop the *rel* subscripts from Equation (14).

Section 8.4 deals with some further separation-of-variables issues in multiparticle systems, particularly in regard to the role of distinguishable and indistinguishable particles. At present, our task is to solve the radial equation of the hydrogenic electron/proton system. The reduced mass of this system is

$$\mu = \frac{m_e m_p}{m_e + m_p} = \frac{m_e}{1 + m_e/m_p}, \tag{15}$$

which will be only very slightly less than the electron mass. For this reason, this expression is often called the *reduced electron mass*, designated μ_e, a notation we adopt. As an example of the power of this two-body-reduction approach, consider a hydrogen atom where the proton is replaced by a positive electron; that is, a positron. Such a species is known as "positronium." The same radial wavefunctions and energies that we derive below for the hydrogenic case will also be valid for positronium upon substituting the appropriate reduced mass, which would be $m_e/2$. We are, in effect, about to solve many problems at once.

The form of the radial equation we will use here is that of Equation (5) in Section 7.1:

$$-\frac{\hbar^2}{2\mu_e}\left\{\frac{d^2}{dr^2} - \frac{\ell(\ell+1)}{r^2}\right\}U(r) + V(r)U(r) = EU(r). \tag{16}$$

We seek solutions for the particular case of the Coulomb potential, Equation (1) in the present section:

$$\left\{-\frac{\hbar^2}{2\mu_e}\frac{d^2}{dr^2} + \frac{\hbar^2\ell(\ell+1)}{2\mu_e r^2} - \frac{e^2}{4\pi\epsilon_o r}\right\}U(r) = EU(r). \tag{17}$$

The various physical constants appearing in Equation (17) threaten to make subsequent algebra awkward. In Chapter 5 we saw that the algebra attending solutions of Schrödinger's equation can be simplified by casting it in a dimensionless form by finding combinations of the constants involved in a problem that have dimensions of length and energy. In the present case, such combinations are already in hand: the Bohr radius and the Rydberg energy for hydrogen from Chapter 1 (Equations 1.3.7 and 1.3.15), now modified to have the reduced electron mass in place of the normal electron mass. Labeling these as a_o and E_r, respectively, we now define dimensionless coordinates ρ and ϵ according as

$$r = \left(\frac{4\pi\epsilon_o\hbar^2}{\mu_e e^2}\right)\rho = a_o\rho, \tag{18}$$

and

$$E = \left(\frac{\mu_e e^4}{32\pi^2\epsilon_o^2\hbar^2}\right)\epsilon = E_r\epsilon. \tag{19}$$

Such dimensionless coordinates are also known as reduced variables, hence the notation E_r for the ground-state energy. With these definitions we have

$$\frac{d}{dr} = \frac{1}{a_o}\frac{d}{d\rho} \quad \text{and} \quad \frac{d^2}{dr^2} = \frac{1}{a_o^2}\frac{d^2}{d\rho^2}. \tag{20}$$

On substituting for r and E in terms of ρ and ϵ in Equation (17), we find that no physical constants appear in the transformed equation:

$$-\frac{d^2U}{d\rho^2} + \frac{\ell(\ell+1)}{\rho^2}U - \frac{2}{\rho}U = \epsilon U. \tag{21}$$

This is a second-order linear differential equation with nonconstant coefficients; evidently we will have to seek a series solution for U. However, as in the case of the harmonic oscillator, we can simplify the ultimate form of the final result by establishing asymptotic solutions for U. Here we have two cases: $U(\rho)$ as $\rho \to \infty$ and as $\rho \to 0$. We examine these two extremes separately.

Case of $\rho \to 0$

As $\rho \to 0$, the second term in Equation (21) dominates by virtue of the factor of ρ^{-2}, leaving

$$\frac{d^2U}{d\rho^2} \sim \frac{\ell(\ell+1)}{\rho^2}U \quad (\rho \to 0). \tag{22}$$

Now, as $\rho \to 0$, we must have $U \to 0$ to keep the wavefunction finite. We might therefore expect some power-law solution of the form $U(\rho) = A\rho^k$. This would demand

$$k(k-1)A\rho^{k-2} = \ell(\ell+1)A\rho^{k-2},$$

or $k(k-1) = \ell(\ell+1)$, which gives $k = -\ell$ or $\ell+1$. Since ℓ is restricted to positive integers or zero, the $k = -\ell$ solution could lead to a negative value for k. This is not physically acceptable, as it would cause U to diverge at the origin and hence be non-normalizable. Consequently, we take

$$U(\rho) \propto \rho^{\ell+1}, \quad (\rho \to 0). \tag{23}$$

[Aside: The behavior of $U(\rho)$ as $\rho \to 0$ is more subtle than this argument suggests. The function that ultimately is to be normalized is $R = U/r$, that is,

$\int R^2 r^2 dr = \int U^2 dr$. It is possible for a function to have an infinite value at some point but still have a finite integral over a domain that includes that point, for example, $U(\rho) = 1/(\rho - a)$ with $a > 0$. But a simple inverse power of ρ such as $\rho^{-\ell}$ is not such a function and so must be rejected. See [2] for more details. Further, the preceding argument appears to fail for $\ell = 0$ since the ρ^{-2} term in Equation (21) would vanish, leaving $d^2 U/d\rho^2 \sim -(2/\rho)U$ as the dominant behavior. No consistent solution of the form $U(\rho) = A\rho^k$ can be found for this case; it is only because both factors of ρ in the equation between Equations (22) and (23) are raised to the same power (and hence cancel) that this derivation works. If $\ell = 0$, however, a series solution of the form $U \sim \Sigma \rho^n$ is workable. The result is a series that can be folded into the general series solution of Equations (26) and (31), so no separate derivation need be made for this case.]

Case of $\rho \to \infty$

In this case the second and third terms in Equation (21) vanish to leave

$$\frac{d^2 U}{d\rho^2} \sim \epsilon U \quad (\rho \to \infty). \tag{24}$$

This simple differential equation has two possible solutions: $U(\rho) \propto e^{\pm \sqrt{-\epsilon}\rho}$. Since we are seeking bound-state energies, $\epsilon < 0$; that is, $\sqrt{-\epsilon}$ is positive real. The solution corresponding to the positive sign in the exponential is unacceptable as it would cause U to diverge as $\rho \to \infty$, so we take

$$U(\rho) \propto e^{-\sqrt{-\epsilon}\rho} \quad (\rho \to \infty). \tag{25}$$

General Case

Combining Equations (23) and (25), we can infer that, in general,

$$U(\rho) = F(\rho)\rho^{\ell+1} e^{-\sqrt{-\epsilon}\rho}, \tag{26}$$

where $F(\rho)$ is some polynomial in ρ.

Substituting Equation (26) into Equation (21) yields a differential equation for $F(\rho)$:

$$\frac{d^2 F}{d\rho^2} + \left\{\frac{2D}{\rho} + 2\gamma\right\}\frac{dF}{d\rho} + \left\{\frac{2\gamma D}{\rho} + \frac{2}{\rho}\right\}F(\rho) = 0, \tag{27}$$

where we have defined

$$\gamma = -\sqrt{-\epsilon}, \tag{28}$$

and

$$D = \ell + 1. \tag{29}$$

Multiplying through Equation (27) by ρ renders it as

$$\rho\frac{d^2F}{d\rho^2} + 2(D + \gamma\rho)\frac{dF}{d\rho} + 2(\gamma D + 1)F = 0. \tag{30}$$

We now attempt a series solution for $F(\rho)$ of the form

$$F(\rho) = \sum_{k=0}^{\infty} b_k\rho^k. \tag{31}$$

Substituting this trial sum into Equation (30) yields, after the usual manipulations to bring all of the terms in ρ to the same power,

$$\begin{aligned} &[2Db_1 + 2b_0(\gamma D + 1)] \\ &+ \sum_{k=1}^{\infty}[b_{k+1}(k+1)(k+2D) + 2b_k(\gamma k + \gamma D + 1)]\rho^k = 0. \end{aligned} \tag{32}$$

Since ρ is not in general equal to zero, the quantities in square brackets must both vanish. This gives

$$b_1 = -\frac{(\gamma D + 1)}{D}b_0, \tag{33}$$

and

$$b_{k+1} = -\frac{2[\gamma(k + \ell + 1) + 1]}{(k+1)[k + 2(\ell+1)]}b_k. \tag{34}$$

In writing Equation (34) we have used Equation (29) to eliminate D. Note that Equation (33) is just Equation (34) for $k = 0$. Equation (34) is our recursion relation.

As always, the essential question is, "Does the series converge for all values of ρ?" We explore this by examining the behavior of Equation (34) for large values of k:

$$b_{k+1} \approx -\left(\frac{2\gamma}{k}\right) b_k. \tag{35}$$

The ratio of two successive terms in the series for $F(\rho)$ then behaves as

$$\left[\frac{\text{Term}(n+1)}{\text{Term}(n)}\right]_{\substack{\text{series} \\ \text{solution}}} = \frac{b_{k+1}}{b_k}\rho \sim -\left(\frac{2\gamma}{k}\right)\rho. \tag{36}$$

Now, from Equation (5.3.16), the ratio of successive terms of the general exponential series for $\exp(\eta\rho^p)$ is, for large values of the expansion index n,

$$\left[\frac{\text{Term}(n+1)}{\text{Term}(n)}\right]_{\text{exponential}} \sim \frac{\eta\rho^p}{n}. \tag{37}$$

Comparing Equations (36) and (37) shows that we have $p = 1$ and $\eta = -2\gamma$. This means that, asypmtotically,

$$F(\rho) \sim e^{-2\gamma\rho}. \tag{38}$$

Since $\gamma = -\sqrt{-\epsilon}$ we must have $\gamma < 0$, which means that $F(\rho)$ diverges. However, the solution to the radial equation, $U(\rho)$, is the product of $F(\rho)$ and two other functions (Equation 26), so the question of the overall convergence or divergence of $U(\rho)$ remains. Looking at the asymptotic behavior of all three terms together gives

$$U(\rho) = F(\rho)\rho^{\ell+1}e^{-\sqrt{-\epsilon}\rho} \sim e^{-2\gamma\rho}\rho^{\ell+1}e^{\gamma\rho} \sim e^{-\gamma\rho}\rho^{\ell+1} \sim \rho^{\ell+1}e^{+\sqrt{-\epsilon}\rho},$$

which is clearly divergent. The only way to prevent this catastrophe is to assume that the series for $F(\rho)$ terminates at some finite n. Assuming $b_k = 0$ for values of k greater than some limiting value N, the recursion relation demands

$$\gamma N + \gamma(\ell + 1) + 1 = 0,$$

or,

$$\gamma(N + \ell + 1) = -1. \tag{39}$$

Inasmuch as $\ell = 0, 1, 2, \ldots, (N + \ell + 1) = 1, 2, 3, \ldots$. If we define

$$n = N + \ell + 1, \tag{40}$$

then the termination condition imposes a restriction on γ:

$$\gamma = -\sqrt{-\epsilon} = -\frac{1}{n},$$

or,

$$\epsilon = -\frac{1}{n^2}. \tag{41}$$

Since the minimum value that N can take is 0, we can write

$$(\ell + 1) \leq n, \qquad (n \geq 1). \tag{42}$$

Recalling the definition of ϵ in terms of the energy E, Equation (19), we find

$$E_n = E_r \epsilon = -\frac{E_r}{n^2} = -\frac{\mu_e e^4}{32 \pi^2 \epsilon_o^2 \hbar^2 n^2} \quad (n \geq 1). \tag{43}$$

Equation (43) gives the hydrogen-atom bound-state energies predicted by Schrödinger's equation: they are identical to those predicted by the Bohr model when the reduced mass of the electron is used.

The solution for the radial part of the hydrogen-atom wavefunction can now be expressed as

$$R_{n\ell}(r) = \frac{1}{r} U(r) = \frac{1}{r} F(\rho) \rho^{\ell+1} e^{-\sqrt{-\epsilon}\rho}$$

$$= \frac{1}{r} F(r/a_o) (r/a_o)^{\ell+1} \exp(-r/na_o)$$

$$= \frac{1}{r} (r/a_o)^{\ell+1} \exp(-r/na_o) \sum_{k=0}^{n-\ell-1} b_k (r/a_o)^k. \tag{44}$$

There is one arbitrary constant, b_0. Selecting this constant such that $R_{n\ell}$ is normalized for a given (n, ℓ),

$$\int_0^\infty R_{n\ell}^2(r) r^2 \, dr = 1,$$

leads to the following results (Pauling & Wilson, Appendix VII):

$$R_{n\ell}(r) = A_{n\ell}e^{-r/na_o}(2r/na_o)^\ell L_{n-\ell-1}^{2\ell+1}(2r/na_o), \tag{45}$$

where $A_{n\ell}$ is given by

$$A_{n\ell} = \sqrt{\frac{4(n-\ell-1)!}{a_o^3 n^4 (n+\ell)!}}, \tag{46}$$

and where $L_{n-\ell-1}^{2\ell+1}(x)$ denotes an **associated Laguerre polynomial** in argument x:

$$L_{n-\ell-1}^{2\ell+1}(x)=\sum_{k=0}^{n-\ell-1}(-1)^k\binom{n+\ell}{n-\ell-1-k}\frac{x^k}{k!}$$

$$=\sum_{k=0}^{n-\ell-1}\frac{(-1)^k(n+\ell)!}{(n-\ell-1-k)!(2\ell+1+k)!\,k!}x^k. \tag{47}$$

In our case, $x = (2r/na_o)$. Readers are warned that definitions of the Laguerre polynomials differ from text to text; that quoted here is consistent with the usages in Weber and Arfken (Section 13.2) and in Pauling and Wilson. The first few radial wavefunctions are given in Table 7.1. In these expressions, the radial coordinate r always appears divided by the Bohr radius, a natural unit of length for hydrogenic systems.

Table 7.1   **Hydrogen Radial Wavefunctions $R_{n\ell}(r)$.**

$$R_{10}(r) = \frac{2}{a_o^{3/2}}e^{-r/a_o} \qquad R_{20}(r) = \frac{1}{(2a_o)^{3/2}}(2-r/a_o)e^{-r/2a_o}$$

$$R_{21}(r) = \frac{1}{\sqrt{3}(2a_o)^{3/2}}(r/a_o)e^{-r/2a_o} \qquad R_{30}(r) = \frac{2}{(3a_o)^{3/2}}\left[1-\frac{2r}{3a_o}+\frac{2r^2}{27a_o^2}\right]e^{-r/3a_o}$$

$$R_{31}(r) = \frac{4\sqrt{2}}{9(3a_o)^{3/2}}(r/a_o)\left[1-\frac{r}{6a_o}\right]e^{-r/3a_o} \quad R_{32}(r) = \frac{2\sqrt{2}}{27\sqrt{5}(3a_o)^{3/2}}(r/a_o)^2 e^{-r/3a_o}$$

To summarize to this point, three quantum numbers, (n, ℓ, m), are needed for a complete description of the hydrogenic wavefunctions. Quantum number n (the principal quantum number) dictates the energy level of the system. A given energy level can be realized by n states of total orbital angular momentum given by $L = \sqrt{\ell(\ell + 1)}\hbar$, $0 \leq \ell \leq (n - 1)$ as deduced in Chapter 6, and each of these realizations can be obtained for a number of L_z states enumerated by $-\ell \leq m \leq \ell$, that is, there are $(2\ell + 1)$ possible values of m for each value of ℓ. To get the total number of substates for a given energy level n we sum the values of $(2\ell + 1)$ over all possible values of ℓ:

$$\text{degeneracy of level } E_n = \sum_{\ell=0}^{n-1}(2\ell + 1) = 2\sum_{\ell=0}^{n-1}\ell + \sum_{\ell=0}^{n-1}(1)$$

$$= (n)(n - 1) + n = n^2. \tag{48}$$

Upon accounting for electron spin (Chapter 8), this degeneracy actually proves to be $2n^2$.

EXAMPLE 7.2

In writing the solution of Equation (30)

$$\rho\frac{d^2F}{d\rho^2} + 2(D + \gamma\rho)\frac{dF}{d\rho} + 2(\gamma D + 1)F = 0$$

as a series of the form

$$F(\rho) = \sum_{k=0}^{\infty}b_k\rho^k,$$

we neglected to account for the possibility of any indicial term in the power of ρ, that is, for a solution of the form

$$F(\rho) = \sum_{k=0}^{\infty}b_k\rho^{k+c}.$$

Rework the solution of (30) with such an indicial term.

Substituting this new expression for F into the differential equation gives

$$\sum_{k=0}^{\infty}(k + c)(k + c - 1 + 2D)b_k\rho^{k+c-1} + 2\sum_{k=0}^{\infty}[\gamma(k + c + D) + 1]b_k\rho^{k+c} = 0.$$

Expanding out the first term by one step gives

$$c(c - 1 + 2D)b_0\rho^{c-1} + \sum_{k=1}(k + c)(k + c - 1 + 2D)b_k\rho^{k+c-1}$$

$$+ 2\sum_{k=0}[\gamma(k + c + D) + 1]b_k\rho^{k+c} = 0.$$

In the first summation, define a new index $j = k - 1$ in the usual way. This gives

$$c(c - 1 + 2D)b_0\rho^{c-1} + \sum_{j=0}(j + c + 1)(j + c + 2D)b_{j+1}\rho^{j+c}$$

$$+ 2\sum_{k=0}[\gamma(k + c + D) + 1]b_k\rho^{k+c} = 0.$$

The two summations can now be combined as

$$c(c - 1 + 2D)b_0\rho^{c-1} + \sum_{k=0}\{(k + c + 1)(k + c + 2D)b_{k+1} + 2[\gamma(k + c + D) + 1]b_k\}\rho^{k+c} = 0.$$

With $D = \ell + 1$, we have the indicial condition

$$c(c + 2\ell + 1)b_0 = 0$$

and the recursion relation

$$b_{k+1} = -\frac{2[\gamma(k + c + \ell + 1) + 1]}{(k + c + 1)(k + c + 2\ell + 2)}b_k.$$

Note that this expression is identical to Equation (34) when $c = 0$. Presuming that $b_0 \neq 0$ (or else we would have a null solution), the recursion relation indicates that $c = 0$ or $c = -(2\ell + 1)$. $c = 0$ is the "standard" solution already derived; let us examine the consequences of taking $c = -(2\ell + 1)$.

In this case, the recursion relation will appear as

$$b_{k+1} = -\frac{2[\gamma(k - \ell) + 1]}{(k - 2\ell)(k + 1)}b_k.$$

While this recursion relation has the same asymptotic form as that for $c = 0$, $b_{k+1} \sim -(2\gamma/k)b_k$, it has a serious problem: a factor of $k - 2\ell$ appears in the denominator. If $k = 2\ell$, then $b_{k+1} = \infty$, and the resulting series would be impossible to normalize. Consequently, we are forced to discard $c \neq 0$ as unphysical.

■ 7.5   Hydrogen Atom Probability Distributions

As can be seen from Tables 6.1 and 7.1, the complete hydrogen-atom wavefunctions $\psi_{n\ell m}(r, \theta, \phi) = R_{n\ell}(r) Y_{\ell m}(\theta, \phi)$ are quite involved. The first few of these are recorded in Table 7.2. In this table, we have suppressed the fact that some of the spherical harmonics are negative (Table 6.1).

A more extensive tabulation of these wavefunctions is given in Chapter V of Pauling and Wilson. These results can be extended to the case of a general single-electron hydrogenic atom; that is, a single electron orbiting a nucleus of charge $+Ze$, by replacing a_o by a_o/Z wherever it appears.

The probability of finding the electron in a volume of space $dV = r^2 \sin\theta \, dr \, d\theta d\phi$ is given by

$$\text{Probability}(\text{electron in } dV) = \psi^*\psi \, dV = \psi^*\psi \, r^2 \sin\theta \, dr \, d\theta \, d\phi. \tag{1}$$

Table 7.2   **Hydrogen Atom Wavefunctions $\psi_{n\ell m}(r, \theta, \phi)$.**

$$\psi_{100} = \frac{1}{\sqrt{\pi} a_o^{3/2}} e^{-r/a_o}$$

$$\psi_{200} = \frac{1}{4\sqrt{2\pi} a_o^{3/2}} (2 - r/a_o) e^{-r/2a_o}$$

$$\psi_{210} = \frac{1}{4\sqrt{2\pi} a_o^{3/2}} (r/a_o) e^{-r/2a_o} \cos\theta$$

$$\psi_{21\pm 1} = \frac{1}{8\sqrt{\pi} a_o^{3/2}} (r/a_o) e^{-r/2a_o} \sin\theta \, e^{\pm\iota\phi}$$

$$\psi_{300} = \frac{1}{81\sqrt{3\pi} a_o^{3/2}} \left[27 - 18\frac{r}{a_o} + 2\frac{r^2}{a_o^2} \right] e^{-r/3a_o}$$

$$\psi_{310} = \frac{\sqrt{2}}{81\sqrt{\pi} a_o^{3/2}} (r/a_o)(6 - r/a_o) e^{-r/3a_o} \cos\theta$$

$$\psi_{31\pm 1} = \frac{1}{81\sqrt{\pi} a_o^{3/2}} (r/a_o)(6 - r/a_o) e^{-r/3a_o} \sin\theta \, e^{\pm\iota\phi}$$

$$\psi_{320} = \frac{1}{81\sqrt{6\pi} a_o^{3/2}} (r/a_o)^2 e^{-r/3a_o} (3\cos^2\theta - 1)$$

$$\psi_{32\pm 1} = \frac{1}{81\sqrt{\pi} a_o^{3/2}} (r/a_o)^2 e^{-r/3a_o} \sin\theta \cos\theta \, e^{\pm\iota\phi}$$

$$\psi_{322} = \frac{1}{162\sqrt{\pi} a_o^{3/2}} (r/a_o)^2 e^{-r/3a_o} \sin^2\theta \, e^{\pm 2\iota\phi}$$

A central physical concept here is that of a **probability density**—literally, the probability per unit volume of space of finding the electron at a given position. We use the symbol P to designate probability density:

$$P = \frac{probability\ of\ finding\ electron\ in\ dV}{dV} = \psi^*\psi. \tag{2}$$

To visualize these probability density distributions in three dimensions requires an imaginative ability bordering on clairvoyance. To illustrate some of the important points, we consider the (1, 0, 0) and (2, 0, 0) states in particular.

7.5.1   The (1, 0, 0) State of Hydrogen

The wavefunction for the (1, 0, 0) (= ground state) of hydrogen is given by

$$\psi_{100} = \frac{1}{\sqrt{\pi}\,a_o^{3/2}}e^{-r/a_o}. \tag{1}$$

The probability density for this state is given by

$$P_{100} = \psi_{100}^*\psi_{100} = \frac{1}{\pi a_o^3}e^{-2r/a_o}. \tag{2}$$

Note that P_{100} is independent of θ; that is, the ground-state electron cloud is spherically symmetric about the nucleus. The position of highest *probability density* for the electron is at the nucleus itself. However, the most likely *radius* is not $r = 0$, as the following argument shows. Imagine surrounding the nucleus with concentric spherical shells each of thickness Δr; the volume of each shell will be $4\pi r^2 \Delta r$. The probability of finding the electron within the shell at radius r will be

P (electron in shell at radius r) = P_{100} (volume of shell)

$$= \frac{4}{a_o^3}\left(r^2 e^{-2r/a_o}\right)\Delta r. \tag{3}$$

In what shell are we most likely to find the electron? This can be determined by maximizing P with respect to r to find the most probable radius r_{mp}:

$$\left(\frac{dP}{dr}\right)_{r=r_{mp}} = 0.$$

Therefore,

$$\frac{d}{dr}\left(r^2 e^{-2r/a_o}\right) = 2re^{-2r/a_o} - (2/a_o)r^2 e^{-2r/a_o} = 0,$$

or, on canceling a factor of $[r\,e^{-2r/a_o}]$,

$$(r_{mp})_{100} = a_o.$$

The most probable radius for the electron in the ground state of hydrogen is exactly one Bohr radius! This most probable radius, a_o, is different from the position of greatest probability density ($r = 0$) because there are more "points" near $r = a_o$ than there are near $r = 0$, albeit with the former each individually less probable than the latter. From this result one might hypothesize (in analogy with the Bohr model) that $(r_{mp})_{n\ell m} = n^2 a_o$, but we will see in the following subsection that this is in fact not the case.

According to Equation (3), the probability of finding an electron in the ground state at radius r is proportional to $r^2 e^{-2r/a_o}$. This function is shown graphically in Figure 7.4, and is known as a radial probability distribution function. [Specifically, $P(r) = 4\pi r^2 R_{n\ell}^2(r)$; the scale on the x-axis is in terms of Bohr radii. The units of $P(r)$ are m^{-1}.]

EXAMPLE 7.3

The exponential tail in Figure 7.4 indicates that the average radial position (expectation value) of the electron will be beyond a_o. Compute the average radial distance of the electron from the proton in the (1, 0, 0) state of hydrogen.

From the concepts developed in Chapter 4, this is given by

$$\langle r_{100}\rangle = \langle\psi_{100}^*|r|\psi_{100}\rangle = \int_0^\infty \int_0^\pi \int_0^{2\pi} \psi_{100}^* r \psi_{100} r^2 \sin\theta \, dr \, d\theta \, d\phi$$

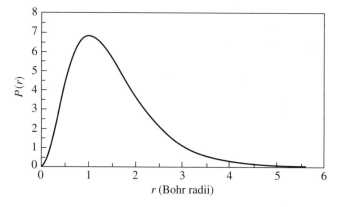

| FIGURE 7.4   Radial Probability Distribution for the Ground State of Hydrogen.

$$= \frac{1}{\pi a_o^3}\left(\int_0^\infty r^3 e^{-2r/a_o}dr\right)\left(\int_0^\pi \sin\theta\, d\theta\right)\left(\int_0^{2\pi} d\phi\right)$$

$$= \frac{1}{\pi a_o^3}\left(\frac{3a_o^4}{8}\right)(2)(2\pi) = 3a_o/2.$$

The interpretation of this result is that the average value of observations of the radial positions of electrons in many ground-state hydrogen atoms would be $1.5a_o$ from the nucleus. You should be able to show that this result is consistent with the result of Example 4.2.

EXAMPLE 7.4

What is the probability of finding the electron within distance r of the proton in the $(1, 0, 0)$ state of hydrogen?

The probability of finding the electron within any volume of space dV is always given by $\psi^*\psi dV$. To answer this question, we need to integrate this over all volume out to radius r; that is, over all values of θ and ϕ for $r = 0$ to r:

$$P_{100}(\leq r) = \int_0^r \int_0^\pi \int_0^{2\pi} \psi_{100}^*\psi_{100}^* r^2 \sin\theta\, dr\, d\theta\, d\phi = \frac{4}{a_o^3}\left(\int_0^r r^2 e^{-2r/a_o}dr\right)$$

$$= 1 - e^{-2r/a_o}[2(r/a_o)^2 + 2(r/a_o) + 1].$$

From this result we find the probability of finding the electron within one Bohr radius (that is, $r = a_o$) of the nucleus to be 0.323, and within two Bohr radii to be 0.762. The probability of finding the electron beyond 10 Bohr radii is only about 0.003. As $r \to \infty$, $P(\leq r) \to 1$. The run of this cumulative probability for the $(1, 0, 0)$ state of hydrogen is shown in Figure 7.5.

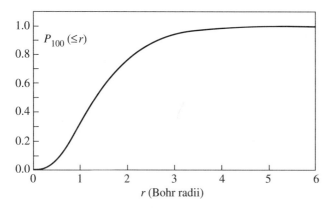

| FIGURE 7.5 Cumulative Probability Density for the (1, 0, 0) State of Hydrogen.

7.5.2 The (2, 0, 0) and Other States of Hydrogen

As a second example, consider the (2, 0, 0) or "first excited state" of hydrogen:

$$\psi_{200} = \frac{1}{\sqrt{32\pi a_o^{3/2}}}(2 - r/a_o)e^{-r/2a_o}. \tag{1}$$

Let us test our previous hypothesis that the most probable radius for this state should be $4a_o$. To do this we find the value of r that satisfies

$$\frac{d}{dr}\left[r^2(2 - r/a_o)^2 e^{-r/a_o}\right] = 0. \tag{2}$$

On computing the derivative and canceling common factors of $\exp(-r/a_o)$ and $(2 - r/a_o)$, we are left with a quadratic equation in (r/a_o):

$$(r/a_o)^2 - 6(r/a_o) + 4 = 0,$$

which has two real solutions,

$$(r_{mp})_{200} = 0.764\,a_o \quad \text{or} \quad 5.236\,a_o, \tag{3}$$

neither of which corresponds to our hypothesis. On back-substituting, it is easy to show that the second solution maximizes $(r\,R_{200})^2$. As shown in Figure 7.6, the radial probability distribution for this state consists of an inner shell peaking at 0.76 Bohr radii nested within a shell of higher–probability density peaking at 5.236 Bohr

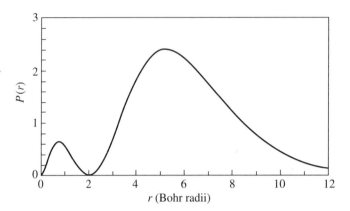

I FIGURE 7.6 Radial Probability Distribution for the (2, 0, 0) State of Hydrogen.

radii. As a general rule, the most probable radius for energy level n is $n^2 a_o$ only when $\ell = n - 1$ (see Appendix A.4).

Other Hydrogenic States

Figures 7.7(a) and 7.7(b) show radial probability distributions for a number of (n, ℓ) states (the value of m does not affect these functions). For given (n, ℓ), there are a number of radii where the value of $P(r)$ is zero (nodes); that is, where we would never expect to find the electron. In general the number of such nodes is given by $n - \ell - 1$; a proof of this is given in Appendix A.4. Also, examination of Equation (7.3.44) shows that $R_{n\ell}(0) = 0$ for $\ell \neq 0$, always; similarly, $R_{n\ell}(0) \neq 0$ when $\ell = 0$.

If you look carefully at Figure 7.7 it appears that the electron will on average reside closest to the nucleus when $\ell = n - 1$ for a given value of n. This is in fact generally true, as you will show in Problem 7-18. We can construct a classical analogy to this result by considering planets orbiting the Sun. If the orbits of two planets are of equal total energy, then the Keplerian ellipses that describe their orbits will have identical semimajor axes. The precise shapes of the orbits, however, will depend on the planets' orbital angular momenta: *lesser* angular momentum means a *more eccentric* orbit because in a skinny, elongated orbit the **r** and **p** vectors in the angular momentum **L** = **r** × **p** are nearly parallel for most of the orbit. It turns out that the time-averaged distance of a planet from the Sun, $\langle r_{planet} \rangle$, is greater for one in a high-eccentricity orbit than for one in a low-eccentricity orbit of the same energy; this is because the planet spends much of its time moving at low speeds far from the Sun. Conversely, a lower value of $\langle r_{planet} \rangle$ will be associated with greater **L**, and this is what Figure 7.7 shows: $\langle r \rangle$ is least when ℓ is greatest for a fixed value of n (fixed total energy). Problem 7-19 explores this analogy further. This comparison should not be taken too

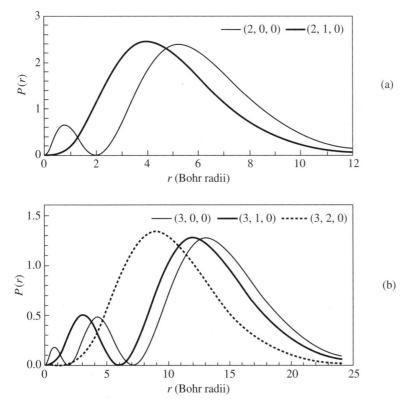

I FIGURE 7.7   Hydrogen Radial Probability Distributions for (a) $n = 2$ and (b) $n = 3$.

literally, however, as the three-dimensional electron probability distributions (Figure 7.10) look nothing like classical orbits.

The radial probability distributions do not, however, tell the entire story. Because the $\psi_{n,\ell,m}$ have an angular dependence as well (through the spherical harmonics), the electron clouds are in general not spherically symmetric about the nucleus. Attempts to represent $\psi_{n,\ell,m}(r, \theta, \phi)$ graphically are always plagued by the difficulty that one is attempting to represent on a two-dimensional surface a function that associates an amplitude with each point in three-dimensional space. One approach is to pseudo-three-dimensionally plot the value of $|\psi|$ in a plane cutting through the nucleus; by convention, this is usually taken to be the $\phi = 0$ plane; that is, the xz-plane. (Actually, the choice of plane is irrelevant as $|\psi|$ is rotationally symmetric about the z-axis, but choosing $\phi = 0$ is computationally simplest.) Such plots are shown in Figure 7.8. To get an impression of the full three-dimensional probability distribution, it is necessary to imagine rotating these figures about the z-axis. In these figures, $|\psi|$ is plotted as opposed to the more physically mean-

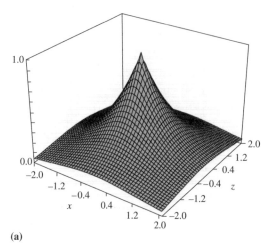

(a)

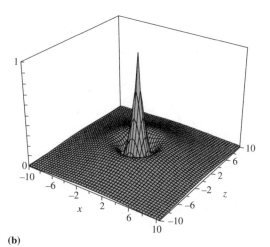

(b)

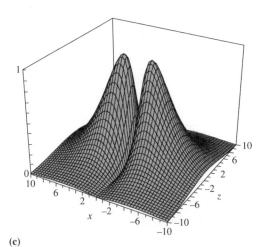

(c)

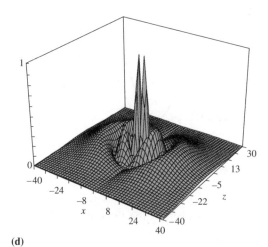

(d)

FIGURE 7.8 (a) $|\psi|$ Surface for $(n, \ell, m) = (1, 0, 0)$.
(b) $|\psi|$ Surface for $(n, \ell, m) = (2, 0, 0)$.
(c) $|\psi|$ Surface for $(n, \ell, m) = (2, 1, 1)$.
(d) $|\psi|$ Surface for $(n, \ell, m) = (4, 1, 1)$.
(e) $|\psi|$ Surface for $(n, \ell, m) = (5, 3, 1)$.

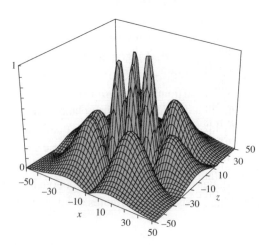

(e)

ingful $|\psi|^2$ in order to render smaller-amplitude features more apparent. The scales along the axes are in Bohr radii; note that the various figures are to different scales in the xz-plane. For convenience of plotting, the vertical scales have been normalized to unity at the maximum value of $|\psi|$ for each case; what is important are the *shapes* of the curves.

A number of features can be seen in these figures. The single peak in Figure 7.8(a), $(n, \ell, m) = (1, 0, 0)$, represents the purely radial exponential function characteristic of the hydrogen ground state; when rotated about the z-axis, $|\psi|$ is spherically symmetric and has its maximum value at the origin. The $(n, \ell, m) = (2, 0, 0)$ state likewise has a central peak and is spherically symmetric, but there is a radial node (a radius at which $\psi = 0$) located at $r = 2a_o$ (see Table 7.2), followed by a second maximum at $r = 4a_o$. On moving to $(n, \ell, m) = (2, 1, 1)$, no radial nodes are present, but there is an angular node at $\theta = 0$ (recall that θ is measured from the positive z-axis). For $(n, \ell, m) = (4, 1, 1)$ and $(5, 3, 1)$, both radial and angular nodes are present, with both having a central radial node; that is, $\psi = 0$ at $r = 0$.

By following reasoning similar to that in the discussion of the radial probability distributions $P(r)$, it is possible to show that two cases obtain for the radial wavefunctions $R_{n\ell}(r)$. If $\ell = 0$, then there will be no central radial node and there will be a total of $(n - 1)$ radial nodes. On the other hand, if $\ell \neq 0$, then there will be a central radial node, and the total number of radial nodes (including the central one, but not that at $r = \infty$) will be $(n - \ell)$.

Given plots such as those in Figure 7.8, these rules, when combined with those developed at the end of Section 6.5.3 for interpreting the associated Legendre functions $\Theta_{\ell,m}(\theta)$, can be used to make inferences as to what values of (n, ℓ, m) are involved. Figure 7.9 summarizes these rules in flowchart form. In some cases one can uniquely specify (n, ℓ, m) from the $|\psi|$ plot alone. As an example of such a case, consider $(n, \ell, m) = (2, 0, 0)$. Here there is one (noncentral) radial node and no angular nodes. The lack of a central radial node implies $\ell = 0$, which by default means $m = 0$. The presence of one radial node then demands $n = 2$. In contrast, $(n, \ell, m) = (5, 3, 1)$ is a case where the (n, ℓ, m) values cannot be uniquely reconstructed from an examination of $|\psi|$ (x, z) alone. In this case we have two radial nodes (including a central one) and three angular nodes, including one along the z-axis. The presence of a central radial node indicates that $\ell \neq 0$ and $n - \ell = 2$. The presence of an angular node along the z-axis indicates $m \neq 0$ and $\ell - m = 2$. Beyond these constraints, we cannot further specify (n, ℓ, m). As a rule of thumb, however, the radial extent of a wavefunction is largely confined to $r < 2n^2 a_o$, so examination of the scales in the plots, if they are provided, can be helpful in such otherwise nonunique cases.

The shapes of the atomic orbitals one obtains on rotating such plots around the z-axis dictate the orientations in which atoms will bind to form molecules. The successful prediction of these bonding angles, which is beyond the scope of this book,

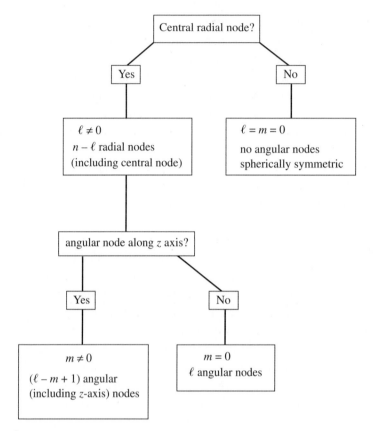

I FIGURE 7.9   Flowchart for Analysis of $|\psi|$ (x, z) Plots.

represented a major success for the wave theory of quantum mechanics over the older semiclassical theory.

Figure 7.10 shows grayscale representations of all hydrogen states up to $n = 5$. These plots appear as if one were looking at those in Figure 7.8 from above: the x-axes increase to the right and the z-axes increase upward; that is, we are viewing the $\phi = 0$ plane. The full width of each figure depends on the principle quantum number depicted and is equal to 4, 20, 40, 80, and 100 Bohr radii for $n = 1$, 2, 3, 4, and 5, respectively. States with negative values of m are not shown, as the only effect of a negative value of m is to negate the associated Legendre function $\Theta_{\ell, m}(\theta)$ when m is odd; this will have no effect in a plot of $|\psi|$ (Negating m also conjugates the wavefunction through Φ, but this again will have no effect on a plot of $|\psi|$). Readers should check that the radial and angular node conditions given in Figure 7.9 are satisfied in each case. Also, it is worthwhile comparing these images to Figure 6.7 to see the effect of the spherical harmonics on the probability distributions.

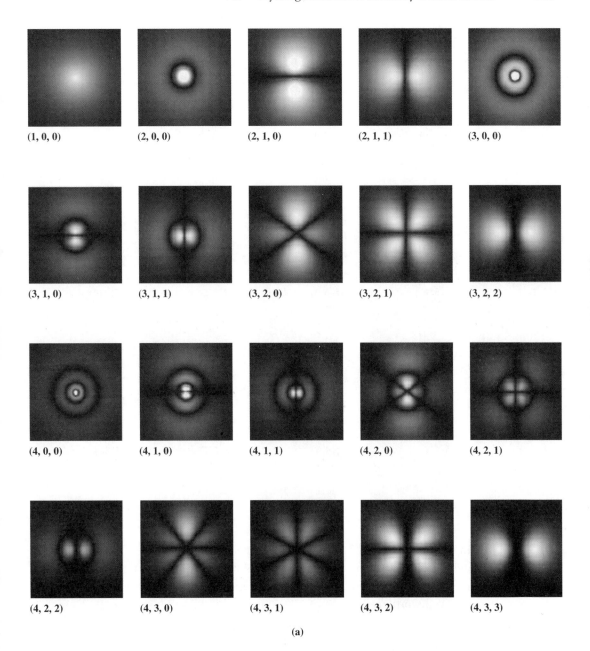

(1, 0, 0)   (2, 0, 0)   (2, 1, 0)   (2, 1, 1)   (3, 0, 0)

(3, 1, 0)   (3, 1, 1)   (3, 2, 0)   (3, 2, 1)   (3, 2, 2)

(4, 0, 0)   (4, 1, 0)   (4, 1, 1)   (4, 2, 0)   (4, 2, 1)

(4, 2, 2)   (4, 3, 0)   (4, 3, 1)   (4, 3, 2)   (4, 3, 3)

(a)

FIGURE 7.10 (a) Grayscale Representations of $|\psi|$ (x, z) for Hydrogen states to $n = 4$. (b) Grayscale Representations of $|\psi|$ (x, z) for Hydrogen $n = 5$ states.

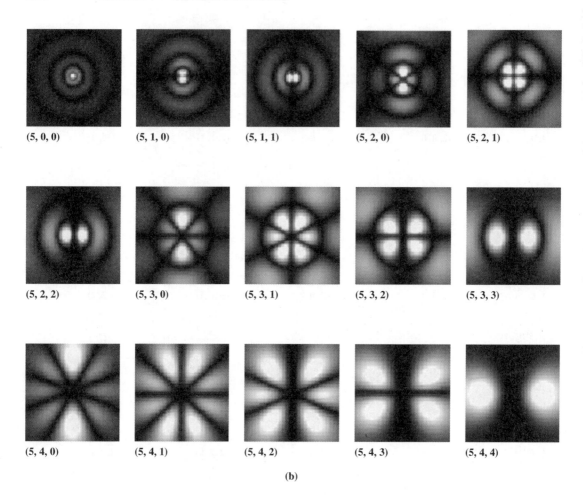

(b)

FIGURE 7.10 (continued)

In a classic paper, H.E. White [3] described the construction of an ingenious set of models of the *xz*-plane hydrogenic probability distributions, which, when set in motion and photographed, produced figures analogous to those in Figure 7.10. His paper is well worth reading.

■ 7.6 The Effective Potential

In this section we briefly consider another way of thinking about the Coulomb potential that emphasizes some important qualitative points. This is done by casting the radial equation into what is known as *effective potential* form.

Consider the dimensionless radial equation for the Coulomb potential, Equation (7.4.21):

$$-\frac{d^2U}{d\rho^2} + \frac{\ell(\ell+1)}{\rho^2}U - \frac{2}{\rho}U = \epsilon U. \tag{7.4.21}$$

If we define the effective potential as

$$V_{eff} = -\frac{2}{\rho} + \frac{\ell(\ell+1)}{\rho^2}, \tag{1}$$

then the radial equation has the form

$$-\frac{d^2U}{d\rho^2} + V_{eff}U = \epsilon U. \tag{2}$$

This form looks exactly like the regular one-dimensional Schrödinger equation.

Figure 7.11 shows plots of V_{eff} vs. ρ for $\ell = 0$, 1, 2, and 3. The qualitative difference between the curve for $\ell = 0$ and those for $\ell \neq 0$ is striking: for the latter, the combination of the two terms in Equation (1) leads to potential wells with infinite walls as $\rho \to 0$; this is why there are central radial nodes ($R = 0$) in every panel of Figure 7.10 when $\ell \neq 0$.

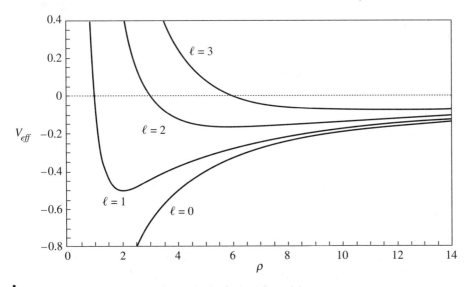

I FIGURE 7.11 Effective Potential Curves for the Coulomb Potential.

The $\ell(\ell + 1)/\rho^2$ term in the effective potential is known as a "centrifugal" term and contributes a repulsive potential that has the effect of driving the electron away from the nucleus. The repulsion becomes stronger as ℓ increases: each curve reaches a minimum at $\rho = \ell(\ell + 1)$ where $V_{eff} = -1/[\ell(\ell + 1)]$. Thus as ℓ increases we can expect to find the electron residing further and further from the nucleus; this is consistent with the statement in the preceding section that the most probable radius is $n^2 a_o$ when $\ell = n - 1$. All of the curves approach $V_{eff} = 0$ from below as $\rho \to \infty$; the way in which they merge together conveys a sense of why the Bohr energy levels get closer and closer together as $n \to \infty$.

■ 7.7   Some Philosophical Remarks

In solving Schrödinger's equation for hydrogen we have been rewarded with results of remarkable elegance and beauty. From a purely mathematical point of view we are fortunate that Schrödinger's equation for a two-body problem can be separated into center-of-mass and relative-coordinate subequations, and that the latter can be further separated into three independent one-dimensional equations. The solutions of these equations required the imposition of various boundary conditions, requirements that in each case led to the introduction of a quantum number restricted to certain integral values. The purely radial Coulomb potential function makes its influence known only in the radial equation and the subsequent quantization of energy levels. The quantization of L and L_z will be a feature of any central potential, independent of the precise form of the potential.

What has been lost in this solution is the intuitively powerful concept of Bohr orbits. Instead of a planetary electron circling its nuclear Sun in some well-defined orbit, our view of the atom has evolved into amorphous clouds of probability density that peak here and there while extending to infinity.

Finally, beyond the evidence of spectra, how can we know whether or not this picture of probability distributions is fundamentally correct? Direct experimental evidence for probability "orbitals" can be obtained via a technique known as electron momentum spectroscopy. With this technique it is possible to measure the distribution of electron orbitals in individual atoms as well as in molecules and solids [see Vos, M. and McCarthy, I., "Measuring orbitals and bonding in atoms, molecules, and solids," *American Journal of Physics* 1997;65:544]. When this technique is applied to hydrogen atoms, the measured orbitals prove to be in excellent agreement with what is deduced from solutions of Schrödinger's equation [Lohmann, B. and Weingold, E., "Direct Measurement of the Electron Momentum Probability Distribution in Atomic Hydrogen," *Physics Letters* 1981;86A:139]. Any debate as to the meaning or interpretation of quantum mechanics pales before its success in yielding precise, verifiable, *correct* predictions of measurable quantities in the atomic domain.

■ Summary

The radial equation for a system of mass μ moving in a central potential $V(r)$ has the equivalent forms

$$-\frac{\hbar^2}{2\mu}\left\{\frac{1}{R}\frac{\partial}{\partial r}\left(r^2\frac{\partial R}{\partial r}\right) - \ell(\ell + 1)\right\} + V(r)r^2 = Er^2,$$

$$-\frac{\hbar^2}{2\mu}\left\{\frac{r}{R}\frac{\partial^2}{\partial r^2}(rR) - \ell(\ell + 1)\right\} + V(r)r^2 = Er^2,$$

and

$$\frac{d^2U}{dr^2} + \frac{2\mu}{\hbar^2}\left\{E - V(r) - \frac{\ell(\ell + 1)\hbar^2}{2\mu r^2}\right\}U(r) = 0$$

where $U(r) = rR(r)$. The overall wavefunction ψ is of the form

$$\psi_{n\ell m}(r, \theta, \phi) = R_n(r)Y_{\ell, m}(\theta, \phi) = \frac{U_n(r)}{r}Y_{\ell, m}(\theta, \phi).$$

For a zero angular momentum ($\ell = 0$) particle of mass μ in an infinite spherical well, the energy levels are analogous to those of an infinite rectangular well of width L, with L replaced by the radius a of the spherical well:

$$E(\ell = 0) = \frac{n^2\pi^2\hbar^2}{2\mu a^2}.$$

For a particle of mass μ with $\ell = 0$ moving in a spherical potential of finite depth V_o and radius a, the condition that the well possess n bound states is given by

$$V_o a^2 \geq \frac{(2n - 1)^2 h^2}{32\mu} \quad (\ell = 0).$$

The solution of Schrödinger's equation for the Coulomb potential,

$$V(r) = -\frac{e^2}{4\pi\epsilon_o r},$$

forms the cornerstone of our understanding of atomic structure. The solution of the radial part of the SE for this potential is

$$R_{n\ell}(r) = A_{n\ell} e^{-r/na_o}(2r/na_o)^\ell L^{2\ell+1}_{n-\ell-1}(2r/na_o),$$

where a_o is the Bohr radius and where $A_{n\ell}$ is a normalization constant given by

$$A_{n\ell} = \sqrt{\frac{4(n-\ell-1)!}{a_o^3 n^4 (n+\ell)!}}.$$

$L^{2\ell+1}_{n-\ell-1}$ denotes an associated Laguerre polynomial, which for general argument x is given by

$$L^{2\ell+1}_{n-\ell-1}(x) = \sum_{k=0}^{n-\ell-1} (-1)^k \binom{n+\ell}{n-\ell-1-k} \frac{x^k}{k!}$$

$$= \sum_{k=0}^{n-\ell-1} \frac{(-1)^k (n+\ell)!}{(n-\ell-1-k)! (2\ell+1+k)! \, k!} x^k.$$

In the hydrogenic case, $x = 2r/na_o$. The energy levels of the hydrogen atom are given by

$$E_n = -\frac{\mu_e e^4}{32\pi^2 \epsilon_0^2 \hbar^2 n^2} \quad (n \geq 1),$$

where μ_e is the reduced mass of the electron/proton system. Note that ℓ can take on integer values from 0 to $(n-1)$. The degeneracy of energy level n is n^2.

Although the Schrödinger and Bohr models of the hydrogen atom predict the same energies, any strict comparison ends there. In the Schrödinger picture, the orbital radius of the electron is *not* quantized. Instead, one has some probability (possibly zero) of finding the electron in any given position; for most states, this probability is a function of both r and θ. For a given principal quantum number n there are preferred regions where one is more likely (but not guaranteed) to find the electron.

■ Problems

7-1(E) Show that for an alpha-particle moving in an infinite spherical well with $\ell = 0$ and $a = 10^{-15}$ m, $E_\alpha = (51.6\, n^2)$ MeV.

7-2(E) Derive an expression for $\langle r^2 \rangle$ for a particle in the $\ell = 0$ state of the infinite spherical well.

7-3(I) Normalize the wavefunction for the $\ell = 0$ finite spherical well. In terms of ξ and η, derive an expression for the probability of finding the particle outside the well. Evaluate your result numerically for the case discussed in Example 7.1.

7-4(I) Apply the results of Problem 6-20 to the infinite spherical well wavefunctions ($\ell = 0$) of Section 7.2. It is helpful to recall that for a mass m, $\langle p^2 \rangle = 2m \langle KE \rangle$ where $\langle KE \rangle$ is the kinetic energy. Is the uncertainty principle satisfied?

7-5(I) A particle trapped in a potential well of depth V_0 at energy level E is said to possess a *binding energy* $E_B = V_0 - E$; this is the amount of energy one would have to supply to the particle to free it from the well. A *deuteron* is a nucleus formed by the bonding of a neutron and a proton under the action of nuclear forces. Assume that the corresponding potential can be modeled as a finite spherical well of radius $a = 2 \times 10^{-15}$ m and that the deuteron acts as a single particle of mass equivalent to the reduced mass of the neutron/proton pair. Assume further that the deuteron is in an $\ell = 0$ ground state. Experimentally, the deuteron has a binding energy of 2.23 MeV. What is the depth of the potential well?

7-6(I) Consider a radial analog of the harmonic potential, $V(r) = (k/2)r^2$ $(0 \le r \le \infty)$. Show that if we define α, ϵ, and λ as in Section 5.1 and put $\rho = \alpha r$, then the radial equation for $U(r)$ [Equation (7.1.5)] reduces to

$$\frac{d^2 U}{d\rho^2} + \left\{ \lambda - \rho^2 - \frac{\ell(\ell + 1)}{\rho^2} \right\} U = 0.$$

Now, from the development in Section 7.4 it should be clear that for any central potential that does not diverge more strongly than $1/\rho^2$ as $\rho \to 0$, then $U(\rho) \sim \rho^{\ell+1}$ as $\rho \to 0$. This potential satisfies this requirement. Further, as $\rho \to \infty$, this differential equation has exactly the same form as that for the one-dimensional harmonic oscillator (Equation 5.2.1 with ρ in place of ξ), so we must have $U \sim e^{-\rho^2/2}$ as $\rho \to \infty$. As in Section 7.4, then, we can posit that the overall solution must be of the form $U(\rho) = F(\rho)\rho^{\ell+1}e^{-\rho^2/2}$. Show that $F(\rho)$ must satisfy

$$\frac{d^2 F}{d\rho^2} + 2\left\{ \frac{(\ell + 1)}{\rho} - \rho \right\} \frac{dF}{d\rho} + \{\lambda - (2\ell + 3)\}F = 0.$$

This result is known as the Kummer-Laplace equation; its solution usually proceeds in terms of hypergeometric functions.

7-7(E) An electron is trapped in a finite spherical potential of radius 10^{-14} meters. If it is in an $\ell = 0$ state, what must be the minimum depth of the potential (in MeV) to bind the electron? Compare to the results of Problem 4-16.

7-8(A) Consider a linear central potential of the form $V(r) = kr$ $(0 \leq r \leq \infty)$. Show that if we define $\rho = \alpha r$ and $\lambda = \epsilon E$ with $\alpha = (km/\hbar^2)^{1/3}$ and $\epsilon = (m/k^2\hbar^2)^{1/3}$, then the radial equation can be expressed in the dimensionless form

$$\frac{d^2U}{d\rho^2} - \frac{\ell(\ell+1)}{\rho^2}U + 2(\lambda - \rho)U = 0.$$

(See Problem 5-9; m = mass, not magnetic quantum number.) Now show that as $\rho \to \infty$, U must have the asymptotic form $U(\rho) \sim e^{-\gamma\rho^{3/2}}$ where $\gamma = 2\sqrt{2}/3$. From the logic of Problem 7-6 we can then propose a general solution for this potential of the form $U(\rho) = F(\rho)\rho^{\ell+1}e^{-\gamma\rho^{3/2}}$. Hence show that $F(\rho)$ must satisfy

$$\rho\frac{d^2F}{d\rho^2} + 2(\ell + 1 - \sqrt{2}\rho^{3/2})\frac{dF}{d\rho} + [2\lambda\rho - \sqrt{2}(2\ell + 5/2)\rho^{1/2}]F = 0.$$

7-9(E) In Equation (7.4.18) we redefined the Bohr radius to involve the reduced mass of the electron/proton system as opposed to just the electron mass, as was used in Chapter 1. Consider a proton and an antiproton "orbiting" each other under the force of their Coulomb attraction. What is the Bohr radius of this system?

7-10(I) Working directly from Equations (7.4.34) and (7.4.44), determine the value of the expansion coefficient b_0 such that $R_{31}(r)$ will be properly normalized. Verify your result by consulting Table 7.1.

7-11(I) Determine $\langle r \rangle$ and $\langle 1/r \rangle$ for a hydrogen atom in the (2, 1, 0) state. Verify that the most probable value of r for an electron in this state is $4a_o$. What is the probability of finding the electron between 3.9 and 4.1 Bohr radii from the nucleus?

7-12(I) Working directly from the expressions given in Chapter 6 for the spherical harmonics, verify by explicit calculation the expression given for $\psi_{3, 1, -1}$ in Table 7.2. Use your result from Problem 7-10.

7-13(E) For a hydrogen atom in the (1, 0, 0) state, what value of r corresponds to a cumulative probability of 50% of finding the electron within r?

7-14(E) Prove that the (1, 0, 0) and (2, 1, 0) states of hydrogen are orthogonal.

7-15(E) Verify the assertion made in Section 7.5.2 that the most probable radius for the electron in the (2, 0, 0) state of hydrogen is 5.236 a_o.

7-16(I) Apply the results of Problem 6-20 to the (1, 0, 0) state of hydrogen to compute $\Delta r \Delta p$ for this state; see also the hint in Problem 7-4. Is your result consistent with the uncertainty principle?

7-17(I) Write a computer program to generate the radial probability distribution function for any (n, ℓ) such as are shown in Figures 7.4, 7.6, and 7.7. Verify your results against those shown in those figures.

7-18(A) To compare the results of wave-mechanical calculations with those in the Bohr theory, it is useful to develop an expression for $\langle r \rangle$ for any hydrogenic state. Given that the Laguerre polynomials defined in Equation (7.4.47) obey the following relations,

$$\int_0^\infty e^{-x} x^K L_N^K(x) L_M^K(x) \, dx = \frac{(N + K)!}{N!} \delta_N^M,$$

and

$$x L_N^K(x) = (2N + K + 1) L_N^K(x) - (N + K) L_{N-1}^K(x) - (N + 1) L_{N+1}^K(x),$$

where $\delta_N^M = 1$ if $M = N$, (zero otherwise), show that $\langle r \rangle = (a_o/2)[3n^2 - \ell(\ell + 1)]$. Show also that $\langle 1/r \rangle = n^2 a_o$. *Hint:* Do not confuse N and M with the quantum numbers n and m; the uppercase indices used in the relations given here are general.

7-19(I) Because Coulombic and gravitational forces are both inverse-square, a number of interesting analogies can be made between them. In Newtonian gravitational mechanics, the mean distance of a planet from the Sun is given by $\langle r_{planet} \rangle = a (1 + e^2/2)$, where a is the semimajor axis and e is the eccentricity of the orbit. Further, if the gravitational potential is written as $V(r) = -K/r$, then a and e are given by

$$a = -K/2E$$

and

$$e^2 = 1 - \frac{2|E|L^2}{mK^2},$$

where m is the mass of the planet, E is the total energy (< 0) of the orbit, and L is the planet's orbital angular momentum. Using the expression for K for the Coulomb potential (watch your signs!), and those for the energies and angular momenta of the various states of the hydrogen atom in terms of the quantum numbers n and ℓ, show that $\langle r_{planet} \rangle$ reduces to that derived in the previous problem for the mean distance of the electron from the proton.

7-20(E) For an electron orbiting a nucleus of Z protons, the hydrogen atom wavefunctions are as given in Table 7.2 with $a_o \rightarrow a_o/Z$. Also, if the nucleus comprises a total of A nucleons, its radius is given approximately by $r \sim kA^{1/3}$, where $k = 1.2 \times 10^{-15}$ m. Show that to a good approximation the probability that an electron in the $(1, 0, 0)$ state will be found *within* the nucleus is given by $P \sim (4A/3)(kZ/a_o)^3$. What is P for a hydrogen atom? For a lone electron orbiting a uranium-238 nucleus? Nuclei can in this way occasionally "swallow" electrons, a process known as *electron capture*. The electron combines with a nuclear proton to yield a neutron, thus lowering the atom by one place in the periodic table.

7-21(I) Using the angular momentum operators developed in Chapter 6, verify that $\langle L_x \rangle = 0$ for the $(2, 1, 1)$ state of hydrogen. Refer to the results of Problem 6-7.

7-22(I) Verify the assertions made following Figure 7.6 regarding the number of nodes in the radial wavefunctions $R_{n,\ell}(r)$.

7-23(I) Using the rules developed in the text for interpreting plots of $|\psi|$, how many and what type of nodes would you expect to find in the case of $(n, \ell, m) = (6, 2, 1)$? Check your conclusions against the accompanying figure.

7-24(A) Consider a particle of mass μ trapped in an infinite cylindrical well of radius a and height L defined by

$$V(\rho,\phi,z) = \begin{cases} 0, 0 \le \rho \le a, 0 \le z \le L, 0 \le \phi \le 2\pi \\ \infty, \rho \ge a, z \le 0, z \ge L, 0 \le \phi \le 2\pi. \end{cases}$$

(a) Set up Schrödinger's equation for this potential. Use cylindrical coordinates.

(b) Setting $\psi(\rho, \phi, z) = R(\rho)\Phi(\phi)Z(z)$, show that the z-dependence can be separated as in the one-dimensional infinite well; that is, if the separation constant is written as $-k_z^2$, then the z-dependence solution is

$$Z = \sqrt{\frac{2}{L}}\sin(k_z z), k_z = n_z\pi/L, n_z = 1, 2, 3, \dots .$$

(c) Show that the ϕ-dependence then separates as in the hydrogen atom; that is, if the separation constant is written as $-m^2$, then the ϕ-dependence solution is

$$\Phi = \frac{1}{\sqrt{2\pi}}e^{\iota m\phi}, m = 0, \pm1, \pm2, \pm3, \dots .$$

(d) With your results from parts (b) and (c), show that Schrödinger's equation can be put in the form

$$\rho^2\frac{d^2R}{d\rho^2} + \rho\frac{dR}{d\rho} + [k^2\rho^2 - m^2]R = 0,$$

where

$$k^2 = 2\mu E/\hbar^2 - k_z^2.$$

This differential equation is known as *Bessel's equation*; its solution is treated in any good text on mathematical physics. The solutions to this equation depend on the value of the azimuthal separation constant m and are known as Bessel functions of argument $k\rho$ and order m, usually designated $J_m(k\rho)$. In the present case of an infinite cylindrical well of radius a, the energy eigenvalues are given by demanding that $J_m(ka) = 0$. A Bessel function of order m has an infinite number of zeros; they can be designated as Q_{pm}, which is read as "zero number p ($p = 1, 2, 3, \dots$) of order m." Hence, the eigenvalue condition becomes $ka = Q_{pm}$. For $m = 0$, the lowest zero is $Q_{10} = 2.4048\dots$.

For an electron trapped in such a well with $L = 50$ Å and $a = 10$ Å, what is the lowest energy state?

7-25(I) In Problem 6-19 it was shown that for a potential function of the form $V = V(r)$ and for wavefunctions of the separable form $\psi(r, \theta, \phi) = R(r)\, g(\theta, \phi)$, the Hamiltonian and L^2 operators commute; that is, $[H, L^2] = 0$. It is also true that the operators for $\mathbf{L}$ and L^2 commute: $[L^2, \mathbf{L}] = 0$. For central potentials, L^2 can be written as $L^2 = g(r) - 2mr^2 H$ (Equation 6.3.13). Use this expression in the identity $[L^2, \mathbf{L}] = 0$ to prove that $[H, \mathbf{L}] = 0$; assume that ψ is separable into the form $\psi = R\Theta\Phi$.

7-26(I) In the infancy of quantum mechanics there was considerable debate as to the probabilistic interpretation of ψ. Suppose that a friend proposes that the electron in a hydrogen atom in fact loses its identity as a particle, becoming instead a smeared-out cloud of electric charge whose density is distributed as $\psi^*\psi$. How would you respond to this argument?

8 Further Developments with Angular Momentum and Multiparticle Systems

This chapter is a catchall in which we take up some more advanced aspects of angular momentum and multiparticle systems. This material should be considered optional; returning to it later or skipping it entirely will have no effect on your understanding of Chapters 9–11. As each section of this chapter is independent of all others, problems are placed at the end of their respective sections as opposed to the usual procedure of placing them all at the end of the chapter. No summary is provided for this chapter.

In Section 6.3 it was remarked that it is possible to define angular momentum raising and lowering operators. These operators are the subject of Section 8.1. Section 8.2 is devoted to a discussion of the famous Stern–Gerlach experiment. This experiment, designed to test for quantization of angular momentum, revealed not only that such quantization exists but that, in addition, electrons possess a previously unknown property, which has come to be called *spin angular momentum*. Section 8.3 examines a simple application of quantized angular momentum, that of understanding the rotational states of diatomic molecules. Section 8.4 examines some consequences of the separability of Schrödinger's equation similar to the center-of-mass and relative-coordinates separation of Chapter 7.

■ 8.1 Angular Momentum Raising and Lowering Operators

To begin, it is helpful to summarize various properties of the angular momentum operators that were introduced in Chapter 6. We drop the "op" notation for convenience.

The operators for the (x, y, z) components of $\mathbf{L}$ can be written in Cartesian coordinates as

$$L_x = -\iota\hbar\left(y\frac{\partial}{\partial z} - z\frac{\partial}{\partial y}\right), \tag{1}$$

$$L_y = -\iota\hbar\left(z\frac{\partial}{\partial x} - x\frac{\partial}{\partial z}\right), \tag{2}$$

and

$$L_z = -\iota\hbar\left(x\frac{\partial}{\partial y} - y\frac{\partial}{\partial x}\right). \tag{3}$$

These operators satisfy the commutation relations (Problem 6-10)

$$[L_x, L_y] \equiv (\iota\hbar)L_z, \tag{4}$$

$$[L_y, L_z] \equiv (\iota\hbar)L_x, \tag{5}$$

and

$$[L_z, L_x] \equiv (\iota\hbar)L_y. \tag{6}$$

The operators for L^2 and L_z satisfy (Problem 6-18)

$$[L^2, L_z] \equiv 0. \tag{7}$$

Also, L^2 and L_z generate eigenvalues according as (Equations 6.5.2.18 and 20)

$$L^2 Y_{\ell, m} = \hbar^2 \ell(\ell + 1) Y_{\ell, m}, \tag{8}$$

and

$$L_z Y_{\ell, m} = m\hbar Y_{\ell, m}. \tag{9}$$

We reiterate that "m" here is the magnetic quantum number, not a mass (indeed, mass makes no appearance in this section).

Before defining new raising and lowering operators, it is helpful to look at the commutator $[L^2, L_x]$. Again we let the operators act on some dummy wavefunction to help keep the order of things straight:

$$[L^2, L_x]\psi = L^2(L_x\psi) - L_x(L^2\psi)$$

$$= (L_x^2 + L_y^2 + L_z^2)(L_x\psi) - L_x(L_x^2 + L_y^2 + L_z^2)\psi.$$

Both terms in this expression will give rise to terms of the form $L_x^3 \psi$, which will cancel each other. The remaining terms give

$$[L^2, L_x]\psi = (L_y^2 + L_z^2)(L_x \psi) - L_x(L_y^2 + L_z^2)\psi$$

$$= (L_y^2 L_x - L_x L_y^2)\psi + (L_z^2 L_x - L_x L_z^2)\psi$$

$$= [L_y^2, L_x]\psi + [L_z^2, L_x]\psi, \tag{10}$$

where square brackets again denote commutators.

We can rewrite the commutators in Equation (10) with the help of Equation (4.4.5):

$$[L_y^2, L_x] \equiv L_y[L_y, L_x] + [L_y, L_x]L_y, \tag{11}$$

and

$$[L_z^2, L_x] \equiv L_z[L_z, L_x] + [L_z, L_x]L_z. \tag{12}$$

Substituting Equations (4)–(6) into Equations (11) and (12) gives

$$[L_y^2, L_x] \equiv -(\iota\hbar)L_y L_z - (\iota\hbar)L_z L_y \tag{13}$$

and

$$[L_z^2, L_x] \equiv +(\iota\hbar)L_z L_y + (\iota\hbar)L_y L_z. \tag{14}$$

Equations (13) and (14), when back-substituted into Equation (10), give

$$[L^2, L_x] \equiv 0. \tag{15}$$

By an exactly analogous process, it can be shown that

$$[L^2, L_y] \equiv 0. \tag{16}$$

(See also Problem 6-18.)

As an aside, Equations (7), (15), and (16) together indicate that the operators for squared angular momentum and the total vector angular momentum itself commute:

$$[L^2, \mathbf{L}] \equiv 0. \tag{17}$$

We are now in a position to introduce the *angular momentum raising and lowering operators*

$$L_+ \equiv L_x + \iota L_y$$

and

$$L_- \equiv L_x - \iota L_y,$$

which can be abbreviated as

$$L_\pm \equiv L_x \pm \iota L_y. \tag{18}$$

To discover what these operators raise and lower, consider the commutator formed by L_z and $L_\pm$:

$$[L_z, L_\pm] \equiv L_z L_\pm - L_\pm L_z$$

$$\equiv L_z(L_x \pm \iota L_y) - (L_x \pm \iota L_y)L_z$$

$$\equiv L_z L_x \pm \iota L_z L_y - L_x L_z \mp \iota L_y L_z.$$

The first and third, and second and fourth, terms in this expression can be reduced to commutators:

$$[L_z, L_\pm] \equiv [L_z, L_x] \pm \iota [L_z, L_y].$$

From Equations (5) and (6) this reduces to

$$[L_z, L_\pm] \equiv \iota \hbar L_y \mp \iota(\iota \hbar L_x) \equiv \pm \hbar L_\pm, \tag{19}$$

where you should verify the algebra for yourself. Now, circular as it may seem, expand out the commutator on the left side of this result; this gives

$$L_z L_\pm - L_\pm L_z \equiv \pm \hbar L_\pm,$$

or

$$L_z L_\pm \equiv L_\pm(L_z \pm \hbar). \tag{20}$$

Now apply Equation (20) to some spherical harmonic $Y_{\ell, m}$:

$$L_z(L_\pm Y_{\ell, m}) = L_\pm\{(L_z \pm \hbar)Y_{\ell, m}\}.$$

From Equation (9), $L_z Y_{\ell, m} = m\hbar Y_{\ell, m}$, hence

$$L_z(L_\pm Y_{\ell, m}) = \hbar(m \pm 1)(L_\pm Y_{\ell, m}). \tag{21}$$

Study Equation (21) carefully. In words, it tells us that $L_\pm$ operates on $Y_{\ell, m}$ so as to yield a new function, $L_\pm Y_{\ell, m}$, whose z-component of angular momentum is, in units of $\hbar$, exactly one unit more (in the case of L_+) or one unit less (in the case of L_-) than that possessed by $Y_{\ell, m}$. *That is, L_+ and L_- respectively, act to raise or lower the state of the z-component of the angular momentum of $Y_{\ell, m}$ by one unit in terms of $\hbar$.*

You might wonder what effect the $L_\pm$ operators have on the ℓ-eigenvalue of $Y_{\ell, m}$. To see this, it is first helpful to compute the commutator of L^2 and $L_\pm$:

$$[L^2, L_\pm] \equiv L^2 L_\pm - L_\pm L^2$$

$$\equiv L^2(L_x \pm \iota L_y) - (L_x \pm \iota L_y)L^2$$

$$\equiv L^2 L_x \pm \iota L^2 L_y - L_x L^2 \mp \iota L_y L^2$$

$$\equiv [L^2, L_x] \pm \iota[L^2, L_y] \equiv 0, \tag{22}$$

where the last step follows from Equations (15) and (16). Applying this result to some spherical harmonic $Y_{\ell, m}$ tells us that

$$L^2(L_\pm Y_{\ell, m}) = L_\pm(L^2 Y_{\ell, m}). \tag{23}$$

However, from Equation (8) we know that $L^2 Y_{\ell, m} = \hbar^2 \ell(\ell + 1)Y_{\ell, m}$, hence

$$L^2(L_\pm Y_{\ell, m}) = \hbar^2 \ell(\ell + 1)(L_\pm Y_{\ell, m}). \tag{24}$$

Equation (24) indicates that when L^2 operates on $(L_\pm Y_{\ell, m})$, the result is $\hbar^2 \ell(\ell + 1)$, just as it is when L^2 operates on $Y_{\ell, m}$ alone. Hence, L_+ and L_- have *no effect* on the ℓ-eigenvalue of $Y_{\ell, m}$.

In Chapter 5 we saw that the harmonic oscillator raising and lowering operators do not return simply the next highest or lowest harmonic oscillator wavefunction. A like situation holds with L_+ and L_-, that is, $L_\pm Y_{\ell, m} \neq Y_{\ell, m\pm1}$. In general,

$$L_\pm Y_{\ell, m} = K_{\ell, m}^\pm Y_{\ell, m\pm1}, \tag{25}$$

where

$$K_{\ell, m}^\pm = \hbar\sqrt{\ell(\ell + 1) - m(m \pm 1)} = \hbar\sqrt{(\ell \mp m)(\ell \pm m + 1)}. \tag{26}$$

To prove this, it is helpful to first consider the operators L_+L_- and L_-L_+. We do L_+L_- in detail:

$$L_+L_- \equiv (L_x + \iota L_y)(L_x - \iota L_y) \equiv L_x^2 - \iota L_x L_y + \iota L_y L_x + L_y^2$$

$$\equiv L_x^2 + L_y^2 + \iota[L_y, L_x]. \tag{27}$$

From Problem 6-10, $[L_y, L_x] = -(\iota\hbar)L_z$, hence

$$L_+L_- \equiv L_x^2 + L_y^2 + \hbar L_z. \tag{28}$$

If a factor of L_z^2 had also appeared on the right side of this expression, we could write $L_x^2 + L_y^2 + L_z^2 = L^2$. We can make this so by adding and subtracting factors of L_z^2 on the right side and writing

$$L_+L_- \equiv L^2 + \hbar L_z - L_z^2. \tag{29}$$

By a similar development you can show that

$$L_-L_+ \equiv L^2 - \hbar L_z - L_z^2. \tag{30}$$

Equation (29) makes it easy to compute the expectation value of L_+L_- as it acts on some spherical harmonic $Y_{\ell, m}$:

$$\langle Y_{\ell, m}|L_+L_-|Y_{\ell, m}\rangle = \langle Y_{\ell, m}|L^2 + \hbar L_z - L_z^2|Y_{\ell, m}\rangle.$$

Recalling that $L^2 Y_{\ell, m} = \hbar^2 \ell(\ell + 1) Y_{\ell, m}$ and $L_z Y_{\ell, m} = m\hbar Y_{\ell, m}$, this evaluates as

$$\langle Y_{\ell, m}|L_+L_-|Y_{\ell, m}\rangle = \hbar^2\{\ell(\ell + 1) - m(m - 1)\}\langle Y_{\ell, m}|Y_{\ell, m}\rangle = \hbar^2\{\ell(\ell + 1) - m(m - 1)\}. \tag{31}$$

Similarly, Equation (30) gives

$$\langle Y_{\ell, m}|L_-L_+|Y_{\ell, m}\rangle = \hbar^2\{\ell(\ell + 1) - m(m + 1)\}\langle Y_{\ell, m}|Y_{\ell, m}\rangle = \hbar^2\{\ell(\ell + 1) - m(m + 1)\}. \tag{32}$$

Now suppose that we desire to evaluate the expectation value of L_+^2 as it acts on some spherical harmonic $Y_{\ell, m}$; that is, $\langle Y_{\ell, m}|L_+^2|Y_{\ell, m}\rangle$. Since L_+ acts to raise the m-state of $Y_{\ell, m}$ to $m + 1$, this calculation, involving two successive applications of L_+, would appear to lead to (neglecting constants) a result of the form $\langle Y_{\ell, m}|Y_{\ell, m+2}\rangle$, which should be zero in view of the orthogonality of the spherical harmonics. However, this neglects the fact that L_+ is a *complex* operator; we should really put $L_+^2 = L_+^* L_+$. Conveniently, L_+ and L_- are complex conjugates of each other; that is, $L_\pm^* = L_\mp$ (see Equation 18), so we can write

$$\langle Y_{\ell, m}|L_+^2|Y_{\ell, m}\rangle = \langle Y_{\ell, m}|L_+^* L_+|Y_{\ell, m}\rangle = \langle Y_{\ell, m}|L_- L_+|Y_{\ell, m}\rangle.$$

That is, $\langle L_+^2 \rangle$ would be the same as Equation (32). But now, work through the calculation assuming that L_+ and L_- operate as posited in Equation (25):

$$\langle Y_{\ell, m}|L_- L_+|Y_{\ell, m}\rangle = K_{\ell, m}^+ \langle Y_{\ell, m}|L_-|Y_{\ell, m+1}\rangle$$

$$= K_{\ell, m}^+ K_{\ell, m+1}^- \langle Y_{\ell, m}|Y_{\ell, m}\rangle = K_{\ell, m}^+ K_{\ell, m+1}^-. \tag{33}$$

Similarly, $\langle L_-^2 \rangle$ looks like Equation (31):

$$\langle Y_{\ell, m}|L_-^2|Y_{\ell, m}\rangle = \langle Y_{\ell, m}|L_-^* L_-|Y_{\ell, m}\rangle = \langle Y_{\ell, m}|L_+ L_-|Y_{\ell, m}\rangle$$

$$= K_{\ell, m}^- \langle Y_{\ell, m}|L_+|Y_{\ell, m-1}\rangle$$

$$= K_{\ell, m}^- K_{\ell, m-1}^+ \langle Y_{\ell, m}|Y_{\ell, m}\rangle = K_{\ell, m}^- K_{\ell, m-1}^+. \tag{34}$$

Hence, Equations (32) and (33) tell us that

$$K_{\ell, m}^+ K_{\ell, m+1}^- = \hbar^2 \{\ell(\ell + 1) - m(m + 1)\}, \tag{35}$$

whereas Equations (31) and (34) tell us that

$$K_{\ell, m}^- K_{\ell, m-1}^+ = \hbar^2 \{\ell(\ell + 1) - m(m - 1)\}. \tag{36}$$

Actually, Equations (35) and (36) are not independent: putting $m = m - 1$ in Equation (35) leads to Equation (36); equivalently, setting $m = m + 1$ in Equation (36) reproduces Equation (35). The only consistent way to satisfy these results is to set

$$K_{\ell, m}^\pm = \hbar\sqrt{\ell(\ell + 1) - m(m \pm 1)} = \hbar\sqrt{(\ell \mp m)(\ell \pm m + 1)}, \tag{37}$$

as claimed in Equation (26).

■ Section 8.1 Problems

8-1(E) Show that the angular momentum raising and lowering operators, when applied to the $Y_{2,1}$ spherical harmonic, give results in accordance with Equation (8.1.26).

8-2(I) For a given spherical harmonic $Y_{\ell,m}$, we must have $|m| \leq \ell$. Operating L_+ on $Y_{\ell,\ell}$ or L_- on $Y_{\ell,-\ell}$ should thus yield zero.

(a) Show that $Y_{\ell,\ell}(\theta, \phi) = \dfrac{(-1)^\ell}{2^\ell \ell!} \sqrt{\dfrac{(2\ell+1)(2\ell)!}{4\pi}} \, (\sin^\ell\theta) \, e^{i\ell\phi}.$

(b) Show that $L_+ Y_{\ell,\ell}(\theta,\phi) = 0.$

(c) Using the identity $Y_{\ell,-m} = (-1)^m (Y_{\ell,m}^*)$, show that $L_- Y_{\ell,-\ell}(\theta, \phi) = 0.$

■ 8.2   The Stern-Gerlach Experiment: Evidence for Quantized Angular Momentum and Electron Spin

The solution of the angular part of Schrödinger's equation for a central potential in Chapter 6 revealed that the z-component of the angular momentum of such systems is quantized in units of $\hbar$. To the extent of the development given in Chapters 6 and 7, however, this result does not manifest itself in any way in the energy eigenvalues of the system; energy quantization is solely the purview of the radial equation. Inasmuch as this effect is a unique prediction of wave mechanics, experimental verification of such effects would constitute a powerful argument in favor of Schrödinger's equation. This verification was realized in 1921 as the **Stern-Gerlach experiment**, *before* the development of wave mechanics [1].

Lying at the heart of the Stern-Gerlach experiment is the concept that atoms behave like tiny magnets. By virtue of its "orbital" motion around the nucleus, an electron creates an electric current i which gives rise to a magnetic field (see Problem 8-5). If such a circulating current encloses cross-sectional area A, then the atom acquires a vector magnetic moment of magnitude $\mu = iA$. $\boldsymbol{\mu}$ is directed in the sense of the angular momentum $\mathbf{L}$ of the electron according as the right-hand rule. [Note that we now use μ to designate magnetic dipole moment as opposed to a mass, as was the case in Chapters 6 and 7. In this section, masses will be represented by the symbol "m." No confusion with magnetic quantum number should arise.] Since a magnetic dipole immersed in an externally supplied magnetic field $\mathbf{B}$ will experience a torque given by $\boldsymbol{\tau} = \boldsymbol{\mu} \times \mathbf{B}$, an atom placed in a $\mathbf{B}$-field will experience a force. Since i can be expressed in terms of L, the magnitude of this force consequently depends on the ℓ-state of the orbiting electron(s). Where there are forces there will be accelerations;

roughly speaking, a stream of atoms (a so-called atomic beam) passed through a suitable **B**-field can then be expected to split into a number of components depending on the values of ℓ present. As we shall see, Stern and Gerlach did observe this effect, but in a way that revealed new information about electrons and their interactions.

A full wave-mechanical treatment of this effect lies well beyond the scope of this text [2]; the intention here is to use a brief semiclassical argument to develop a basic understanding of the Stern-Gerlach experiment and establish what orders of magnitude are involved. (More extensive details can be found in Chapter 10 of French and Taylor.)

We first need an expression for the magnetic dipole moment created by an orbiting electron. Consider an electron orbiting the nucleus in a circular orbit of speed v and radius r as in the Bohr model. If the orbit is counterclockwise as shown in Figure 8.1, then (classically) **L** is vertically upward, as shown in the figure.

The orbital motion of the electron is equivalent to an electric current i:

$$i = \frac{\text{charge}}{\text{time}} = \frac{\text{charge}}{\text{orbital period}} = \frac{e}{(2\pi r/v)} = \frac{ev}{2\pi r}, \tag{1}$$

The area enclosed by the orbit is πr^2. The dipole moment of this arrangement is then given by

$$\mu = iA = \left(\frac{ev}{2\pi r}\right)(\pi r^2) = \frac{evr}{2} = \frac{eL}{2m_e}, \tag{2}$$

where $L = m_e vr$ is the classical orbital angular momentum of the electron (mass m_e). To be precise, both μ and L are vector quantities; we should write

$$\boldsymbol{\mu} = \left(\frac{e}{2m_e}\right)\mathbf{L}. \tag{3}$$

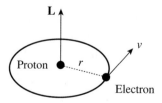

FIGURE 8.1   Electron Orbiting a Proton.

Now, if the magnitude of L is in fact quantized as $L = \hbar\sqrt{\ell(\ell + 1)}$, we can write the magnitude of μ as

$$\mu = \left(\frac{e\hbar}{2m_e}\right)\sqrt{\ell(\ell + 1)}. \qquad (4)$$

On an intuitive level, μ can be thought of as quantifying the strength of a bar magnet, with $\boldsymbol{\mu}$ conventionally represented as a vector from the south to the north pole of the magnet. The prefactor in Equation (4) is known as the **Bohr magneton** μ_B, and it serves as a natural unit of magnetic dipole moment for atomic systems:

$$\mu_B = \left(\frac{e\hbar}{2m_e}\right) = 9.2744 \times 10^{-24}\ amp - m^2. \qquad (5)$$

[A note on units: 1 $amp - m^2$ is equivalent to 1 Joule/Tesla. The Tesla is the MKS unit of magnetic field (also known as magnetic flux density); 1 Tesla = 1 (Newton/$amp - m$) = 1 (kg/C-sec). A historical unit of magnetic field that is still in use is the Gauss; 1 Tesla = 10^4 Gauss. The magnetic field of the Earth at its surface is about 0.5 Gauss. A good laboratory electromagnetic can create a field of a few Tesla.]

Now, it happens that if a stream of atoms possessing nonzero magnetic moments is directed to pass through a nonuniform magnetic field, the magnetic forces involved will split up the stream into a number of substreams, with one substream for each possible value of the z-component of μ (usually designated μ_z). Suppose for sake of simplicity that the atoms are all in the same ℓ state. If our interpretation of the angular part of Schrödinger's equation is correct, then for a given ℓ there can be $(2\ell + 1)$ possible values of the magnetic quantum number m (recall that $-\ell \le m \le + \ell$), hence $(2\ell + 1)$ possible values of μ_z. Whatever the value of ℓ, $(2\ell + 1)$ must be odd, so we should expect to see the beam split into an odd number of components on passing through the magnetic field. This is the essence of the Stern-Gerlach experiment, which is sketched in Figure 8.2. The essential setup is that atoms of mass m are emitted from an oven with speed v (a function of the oven temperature) and directed through a region of nonuniform magnetic field of linear extent x (the x-direction is to the right and the z-direction is upward in the figure). The entire apparatus is enclosed in a vacuum chamber to minimize collisions of the atoms with air molecules.

For atoms of mass m with z-components of μ given by μ_z, it can be shown that the vertical deflection W works out to

$$W = \frac{x}{mv^2}(R + x/2)\,\mu_z\left(\frac{dB}{dz}\right), \qquad (6)$$

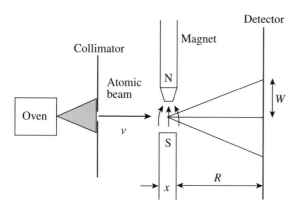

FIGURE 8.2   Schematic illustration of the Stern-Gerlach experiment. A stream of fast-moving atoms travels through an inhomogeneous magnetic field, which splits them into various beams according to their ℓ-values.

where the *field gradient* (dB/dz) is provided by machining suitably shaped magnet pole-pieces.

The deflections predicted by Equation (6) are not large but are detectable; see Problem 8-4. On performing this now-historic experiment with a beam of silver atoms, Stern and Gerlach observed *two* components, in contradiction to the preceding prediction. The same result was found a few years later for hydrogen [3]. These results seemed to show that angular momentum is quantized, but not in the way predicted by the preceding analysis.

Resolution of this evidence with the theoretical expectation was provided in the form of a postulate by Uhlenbeck and Goudsmit [4]. They suggested that in addition to their orbital angular momenta, electrons possess intrinsic spin angular momentum **S**. In analogy with the orbital angular momentum quantum number ℓ, Uhlenbeck and Goudsmit proposed the existence of an electron *spin quantum number "s"* restricted to magnitude 1/2 (in units of $\hbar$), and, in analogy to the $2\ell + 1$ possible z-projections of **L**, that there can be only $2s + 1 = 2$ possible z-projections of **S**. The magnitude of the spin angular momentum is then

$$|S| = \sqrt{s(s + 1)}\hbar = \sqrt{3/4}\hbar$$

and the possible z-projections are

$$s_z = s\hbar = \pm \hbar/2.$$

Uhlenbeck and Goudsmit's proposal was purely empirical: it worked. The classical analogy to electron spin is that of a planet spinning about its axis while orbiting the Sun. The word "spin" in the context of an electron is only a label, however: we cannot really conceive of a point particle spinning. The overall effect is to add a fourth quantum number $s = \pm 1/2$ to the already existing quantum numbers (n, ℓ, m), thereby doubling the number of possible electronic states. Possible states up to $n = 3$ are enumerated in Table 8.1.

The situation demonstrated by Stern and Gerlach's experiment can now be roughly elucidated. A neutral silver atom has 47 electrons—an odd number. If it is assumed that electrons "pair off" with equal and opposite spin angular momenta as much as possible, and that the remaining electron is in an $\ell = 0$ state, then the presence of two beams in the experiment can be explained since the lone unpaired electron will have $s_z = \pm 1/2$. A full understanding of this result and of how electrons fill up available states requires an appreciation of Hund's Rule, the Pauli Exclusion Principle, and the symmetry properties of multielectron atomic wavefunctions. Factors such as nuclear spin effects, non-Coulombic effects due to nonspherical nuclei, and mutual electron shielding complicate the situation further [5].

The existence of intrinsic electronic angular momentum was later found to be a natural consequence of reworking Schrödinger's equation to incorporate relativistic effects [6]. In some atoms, net nonzero orbital and spin angular momenta are present simultaneously, and the corresponding magnetic moments interact in such a way as to cause a slight splitting of energy levels: the energy of the system is slightly higher when they are parallel and slightly lower when antiparallel. This effect, known as spin-orbit coupling or L-S coupling, involves defining a total vector angular momentum $\mathbf{J}$ as $\mathbf{J} = \mathbf{L} + \mathbf{S}$, and is fundamental to our understanding of the details of the structure and spectra of multielectron atoms.

The splitting of spectral lines of atoms in the presence of a magnetic field is now known as the Zeeman effect, and a similar effect for electric fields is known as the Stark effect; examples of these effects are discussed in Chapter 9. Quantitative

Table 8.1   Electron States.

n	1	2		3		
ℓ	0	0	1	0	1	2
m	0	0	$-1\ \ 0\ \ 1$	0	$-1\ \ 0\ \ 1$	$-2\ -1\ \ 0\ \ 1\ \ 2$
s	$\pm 1/2$	$\pm 1/2$	$\pm 1/2$	$\pm 1/2$	$\pm 1/2$	$\pm 1/2$
States	2	2	6	2	6	10
Subshell	$1s$	$2s$	$2p$	$3s$	$3p$	$3d$
Shell	K	L		M		
Total states	2	8		18		

measurement of line splittings can be used, for example, to determine the strength of such fields in the Sun and other stars.

■ Section 8.2 Problems

8-3(E) It was remarked that a magnetic dipole μ immersed in an externally supplied magnetic field $\mathbf{B}$ will experience a torque given by $\tau = \mu \times \mathbf{B}$. Use this to show that the unit of magnetic field must be $N/(amp - m)$.

8-4(I) Silver-107 atoms have a mass of 106.905 mass units. You are setting up a Stern-Gerlach experiment where the atoms leave an oven at 1000 m/s, travel through an inhomogeneous magnetic field of extent 1 centimeter, and then travel 2 meters before being detected. For simplicity, take $\ell = 1$, and assume $\mu_z = \mu$. If you want to achieve a deflection of $W = 0.5$ mm, what field gradient dB/dz will you need? If your magnet can provide a field of up to several tens of Teslas, is this experiment possible?

8-5(I) A circular electric current i of radius r creates a magnetic field at its center of magnitude $B = (\mu_o i/2r)$. Consider an electron in a hydrogen atom. By using an argument like that at the start of this section, show that if the electron is orbiting in Bohr state "n," then the magnetic field created by the electron at the location of the proton is given by

$$B = \frac{\mu_o m_e^2 e^7}{256\pi^4 \epsilon_o^3 \hbar^5 n^5}.$$

Evaluate this numerically for $n = 1$. In nuclear physics, the *nuclear magneton* μ_K serves as a natural unit of magnetic field and is given by $\mu_K = (e\hbar/2m_p)$, where m_p is the mass of the proton. The magnetic moment of the proton is 2.793 μ_K. A magnetic dipole moment μ placed in a magnetic field B acquires a potential energy of magnitude $V = \mu B$. What is the value of this energy (in eV) for a proton in the field of an $n = 1$ electron and how does it compare to the orbital energy for the $n = 1$ state?

■ 8.3   Diatomic Molecules and Angular Momentum

One of the important applications of the theory of angular momentum is understanding the rotational energy states of diatomic molecules as revealed by microwave spectroscopy. In this section we develop a straightforward semiclassical analysis of such molecules.

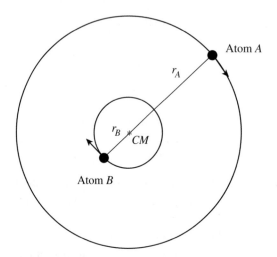

FIGURE 8.3   Diatomic Molecule.

Our model of a diatomic molecule is shown in Figure 8.3: two electrically neutral atoms (so, to a good approximation, no Coulomb potential to deal with) of masses m_A and m_B orbiting their common center of mass; r_A is the orbital radius of atom A and r_B that of atom B. To keep the situation simple, imagine the atoms to be on the ends of a massless, spinning, rigid rod. (The electrical forces in molecules are often modeled as harmonic oscillator-type potentials such as were examined in Chapter 5; these lead to the equally spaced *vibrational* energy levels of that chapter. Our concern here is with *rotational* energies.)

To keep the center of mass in a fixed location we must have

$$m_A r_A = m_B r_B, \tag{1}$$

a constraint we will make considerable use of shortly.

Imagine that the molecule is spinning about its center of mass with angular speed ω. Classically, the angular momentum of such an arrangement is $L = I\omega$, where I is the moment of inertia of the system as measured with respect to the rotational axis. If the atoms are uncharged, then the only energy in the system is the rotational kinetic energy $E = I\omega^2/2$. Putting $\omega = L/I$ gives

$$E = \frac{1}{2}I\omega^2 = \frac{L^2}{2I} = \frac{\hbar^2 \ell(\ell + 1)}{2I} = \frac{h^2 \ell(\ell + 1)}{8\pi^2 I}, \tag{2}$$

where we have assumed that angular momentum is quantized in accordance with $L = \hbar\sqrt{\ell(\ell + 1)}$.

Now consider such a system that undergoes a "rotational transition" $\ell \rightarrow \ell - 1$. The energy of the emitted photon will be

$$\Delta E = E_\ell - E_{\ell-1} = \frac{h^2}{4\pi^2 I}(\ell). \tag{3}$$

We can get an idea of the order of magnitude of ΔE via some simple approximations. Assume that the molecule consists of two equal-mass atoms, each of mass m and separated by distance r. Then $I = \Sigma m(r/2)^2 = mr^2/2$, and

$$\frac{h^2}{4\pi^2 I} = \frac{h^2}{2\pi^2 mr^2}.$$

For sake of explicitness, consider two hydrogen atoms ($m = 1.67 \times 10^{-27}$ kg) separated by $r = 1$ Å. Then

$$\frac{h^2}{2\pi^2 mr^2} = 1.33 \times 10^{-21}\,J = 0.008\,\text{eV}.$$

For two heavier (and/or more separated) atoms we would find an even smaller energy. We can infer that the energy spacings of the *rotational* levels in a spinning molecule are much smaller than either those of the *vibrational* levels of the molecule as a whole, or of the *electronic* levels within atoms themselves. Smaller energy spacing will mean photons of much lesser frequency, hence much higher wavelength. Analysis of the rotational characteristics of molecules is thus typically a matter of far-infrared or microwave spectroscopy.

Most molecules involve atoms of unequal mass, though. We can modify Equation (2) to accommodate this by looking in more detail at the moment of inertia of the system. From Figure 8.3 this will be

$$I = m_A r_A^2 + m_B r_B^2. \tag{4}$$

Eliminating r_A in this expression via Equation (1) leads to

$$I = m_B^2 r_B^2 \left[\frac{m_A + m_B}{m_A m_B} \right]. \tag{5}$$

Molecular spectroscopists prefer to speak in terms of the **bond length** $r = r_A + r_B$ of the system. Writing $r_B = r - r_A$ and again invoking Equation (1) to eliminate r_A gives

$$r_B = r \left[\frac{m_A}{m_A + m_B} \right]. \tag{6}$$

Substituting Equation (6) into Equation (5) gives the moment of inertia in terms of the bond length,

$$I = \mu r^2, \tag{7}$$

where μ is the **reduced mass** of the system, defined in the same way as in Chapter 7:

$$\mu = \left[\frac{m_A m_B}{m_A + m_B} \right]. \tag{8}$$

With this modification, the rotational energy levels are given by

$$E = \frac{h^2 \ell(\ell + 1)}{8\pi^2 \mu r^2}. \tag{9}$$

In research practice, spectroscopists use measured photon frequencies for a given species (hence known μ) to infer bond lengths. The relevant information is often tabulated in handbooks by listing what is known as the equilibrium rotation constant B_e of a given species. This is defined as

$$B_e = \frac{h}{8\pi^2 \mu r^2}. \tag{10}$$

B_e has units of reciprocal seconds; values are often tabulated in units of Hz, and, in testament to the precision achievable in such spectroscopy, are known to a remarkable number of significant digits. B_e values and bond lengths can be found in a number of reference books. For example, the 86th (2005–2006) edition of the *CRC Handbook of Chemistry and Physics* (Boca Raton: Taylor and Francis) lists B_e values and bond lengths for dozens of diatomic species (pp. 9–82 through 9–85).

EXAMPLE 8.1

The *CRC Handbook* lists the value of B_e for hydrogen chloride, HCl, as 3.175827×10^{11} Hz. Given that the isotopes involved are $^1_1$H and $^{35}_{17}$Cl, what is the bond length of this molecule?

A table of isotopes gives the atomic weights of these species as 1.0078250 and 34.968853 mass units. These numbers give a reduced mass of 0.979593 mass units, or 1.626652×10^{-27} kg. The bond length then follows from Equation (10) as

$$r = \sqrt{\frac{h}{8\pi^2 \mu B_e}} = \sqrt{\frac{(6.62607 \times 10^{-34} J - sec)}{8\pi^2 (1.626652 \times 10^{-27} kg)(3.175827 \times 10^{11} Hz)}}$$

$$= 1.275 \times 10^{-10} m = 1.275 \text{Å},$$

about the size one would expect for a molecule.

■ Section 8.3 Problems

8-6(E) Lithium fluoride ($^7_3$Li$^{19}_9$F) has an equilibrium rotation constant of 4.032983×10^{10} Hz. What is the bond length of this species?

8-7(E) The *CRC Handbook* lists the rotation constant and bond length of lithium oxide ($^7_3$Li$^{16}_8$O) as 3.63597×10^{10} Hz and 1.688 Å, respectively. What is the reduced mass of this species as indicated by these values? How does your result compare to the reduced mass calculated from the isotopic masses, 7.016004 and 15.994915 mass units?

■ 8.4   Identical Particles, Indistinguishability, and the Pauli Exclusion Principle

In this section we take up in a somewhat informal way a question similar to the center-of-mass and relative-coordinates separation of variables technique discussed in Chapter 7, but which has profound implications for the nature of particles and their wavefunctions.

The issue here concerns solutions of Schrödinger's equation for a system of two (or more) particles moving in the same potential, for example, two electrons in a helium atom. To keep the treatment simple, we shall assume that the electrons are *non-interacting*; that is, that they exert no forces on each other, or at least that interelectronic forces can be neglected in comparison with those that they experience from the nucleus. Suppose that the particles have masses m_1 and m_2, and respectively experience potentials $V_1(\mathbf{r}_1)$ and $V_2(\mathbf{r}_2)$ where $\mathbf{r}_1$ and $\mathbf{r}_2$ are their coordinates (see Figure 7.3). The potentials that they experience may be different even if they are moving within the same environment or even if $\mathbf{r}_1 = \mathbf{r}_2$: they might, for example, carry opposite electrical charges. The total Hamiltonian operator for the system will be the sum of the kinetic and potential energies of each:

$$H = -\frac{\hbar^2}{2m_1}\nabla_1^2 - \frac{\hbar^2}{2m_2}\nabla_2^2 + V_1(\mathbf{r}_1) + V_2(\mathbf{r}_2). \tag{1}$$

It is in writing the potential energy for each particle as a function of only that particle's position and not as a function involving the position of the other particle that we build in that the particles do not interact with each other.

Now presume that there is some solution $\Psi(\mathbf{r}_1,\mathbf{r}_2)$ of the SE for this system with some total energy E:

$$-\frac{\hbar^2}{2m_1}\nabla_1^2\Psi - \frac{\hbar^2}{2m_2}\nabla_2^2\Psi + V_1(\mathbf{r}_1)\Psi + V_2(\mathbf{r}_2)\Psi = E\Psi. \tag{2}$$

If the particles do not interact, it would seem reasonable to assume that Ψ can be written as a product of two functions, one for each particle: $\Psi(\mathbf{r}_1, \mathbf{r}_2) = \psi_A(\mathbf{r}_1)\,\psi_B(\mathbf{r}_2)$; this is in analogy to the center-of-mass and relative-coordinates separation posited in Section 7.4. The interpretation of Ψ is that Ψ^2 gives the "joint probability" that particle 1 will be found in state A within volume $d\tau_1$ of position $\mathbf{r}_1$, whereas particle number 2 is simultaneously to be found in state B within volume $d\tau_2$ of position $\mathbf{r}_2$. The subscripts A and B serve as a reminder that the two independent particles will in general be in *different* states. With this separability assumption the SE becomes

$$-\frac{\hbar^2}{2m_1}\nabla_1^2\psi_A\psi_B - \frac{\hbar^2}{2m_2}\nabla_2^2\psi_A\psi_B + V_1\psi_A\psi_B + V_2\psi_A\psi_B = E\psi_A\psi_B, \tag{3}$$

where we have dropped the understood coordinate dependences of the potentials. Now, the Laplacian operators ∇_1^2 and ∇_2^2 operate on only one set of coordinates each: $\mathbf{r}_1 = (x_1, y_1, z_1)$ for the former and similarly for the latter. With this in mind, Equation (3) can be factored into the form

$$\left\{-\frac{\hbar^2}{2m_1}\nabla_1^2\psi_A + V_1\psi_A\right\}\psi_B + \left\{-\frac{\hbar^2}{2m_2}\nabla_2^2\psi_B + V_2\psi_B\right\}\psi_A = E\psi_A\psi_B. \tag{4}$$

The form of Equation (4) suggests that we write the total energy E as the sum of energies for the individual-particle states: $E = E_A + E_B$. With this, as might be expected, Equation (4) separates neatly into two independent expressions:

$$-\frac{\hbar^2}{2m_1}\nabla_1^2\psi_A + V_1\psi_A = E_A\psi_A,$$ (5)

and

$$-\frac{\hbar^2}{2m_2}\nabla_2^2\psi_B + V_2\psi_B = E_B\psi_B.$$ (6)

You should be able to convince yourself that this procedure can be extended to any number of noninteracting particles. In a three-dimensional situation, Equations (5) and (6) would each separate into three subequations if the potentials are of separable form.

We come now to an important point. Imagine that the preceding argument is applied to two *identical particles*—perhaps two electrons in the vicinity of a nucleus. We have been assuming that it is legitimate to imagine "labeling" the electrons as numbers 1 and 2; that is, that we can imagine being able to *distinguish* them from each other. However, it has been known since the early days of statistical mechanics that in reality nature admits no such notion: identical particles are in principle *indistinguishable*: there is no way to tell them apart. (In classical mechanics, the notion of distinguishability can be gotten away with because the probability distributions of particles do not appreciably overlap. But at the atomic level, probability distributions intermingle, rendering it impossible to say that number 1 is *here* while number 2 is *there*.) Indistinguishability is a fundamental physical fact and must be accounted for in our calculations.

The fact of indistinguishability presents an awkward situation for our presumed product wavefunction

$$\Psi(\mathbf{r}_1, \mathbf{r}_2) = \psi_A(\mathbf{r}_1)\,\psi_B(\mathbf{r}_2),$$ (7)

namely, that Ψ does *not* respect the fact of indistinguishability! If the particles were "swapped," that is, if $\mathbf{r}_1$ is replaced by $\mathbf{r}_2$ and vice-versa, Ψ would be altered since the states A and B will in general be different. Indistinguishability means that Ψ should remain unchanged if we swap particle labels. Since it is probabilities that are the ultimately measurable quantities, this means that we must demand that Ψ must satisfy

$$\Psi^2(\mathbf{r}_1, \mathbf{r}_2) = \Psi^2(\mathbf{r}_2, \mathbf{r}_1).$$ (8)

By trying various combinations of states and coordinates, it quickly becomes apparent that only two forms for Ψ will satisfy Equation (8):

$$\Psi_{symm} = C[\psi_A(\mathbf{r}_1)\psi_B(\mathbf{r}_2) + \psi_A(\mathbf{r}_2)\psi_B(\mathbf{r}_1)] \tag{9}$$

and

$$\Psi_{anti} = C[\psi_A(\mathbf{r}_1)\psi_B(\mathbf{r}_2) - \psi_A(\mathbf{r}_2)\psi_B(\mathbf{r}_1)], \tag{10}$$

where the C's are normalization constants. Equation (9) is said to be the *symmetric* form of Ψ, since swapping $\mathbf{r}_1$ and $\mathbf{r}_2$ leaves Ψ unchanged; correspondingly, Equation (10) is called the *antisymmetric* form since the same swapping will result in negating the value of Ψ while still satisfying Equation (8).

At this point it is instructive to consider an actual example of Equations (9) and (10). For simplicity, we consider a one-dimensional case: two identical particles moving in the harmonic oscillator potential $V = kx^2/2$. We use the dimensionless ξ coordinates of Chapter 5, labeling them ξ_1 and ξ_2. Presume that the states involved are the lowest and first-excited harmonic-oscillator states

$$\psi_A = e^{-\xi^2/2} \tag{11}$$

and

$$\psi_B = \xi e^{-\xi^2/2}. \tag{12}$$

We can ignore normalization constants as they will not affect the following argument. Figures 8.4 and 8.5, respectively, show the absolute values of the corresponding symmetric and antisymmetric wavefunctions

$$\Psi_{symm}(\xi_1, \xi_2) = \psi_A(\xi_1)\psi_B(\xi_2) + \psi_A(\xi_2)\psi_B(\xi_1) = (\xi_2 + \xi_1)\exp[-(\xi_1^2 + \xi_2^2)] \tag{13}$$

and

$$\Psi_{anti}(\xi_1, \xi_2) = \psi_A(\xi_1)\psi_B(\xi_2) - \psi_A(\xi_2)\psi_B(\xi_1) = (\xi_2 - \xi_1)\exp[-(\xi_1^2 + \xi_2^2)]. \tag{14}$$

From Figure 8.4 it should be clear that, in the case of the symmetric wavefunction, locations where the joint probability tends to be high are characterized by coordinate values such that $\xi_1 \sim \xi_2$. Qualitatively, we can describe this by saying that particles that are described by symmetric joint wavefunctions will preferentially be found at locations close to each other. Conversely, in the antisymmetric case (Figure 8.5), locations where the joint probability tends to be high are characterized by coordinates such that $\xi_1 \neq \xi_2$; in fact, it is highest when $\xi_1 \sim -\xi_2$. Such particles thus

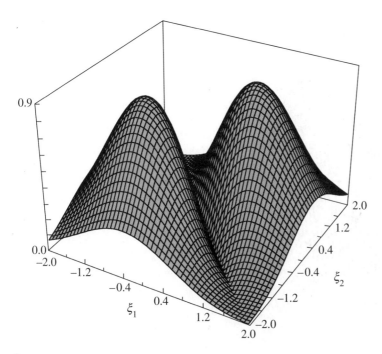

I FIGURE 8.4 |Ψ| for a Two-particle Symmetric Wavefunction for $n = 0$ and $n = 1$ Harmonic-oscillator States.

tend to avoid each other. (These conclusions can also be seen directly by looking at the forms of Equations 13 and 14.) These "approach/avoidance" behaviors are general features of such two-particle joint wavefunctions.

It is important to emphasize that this behavior is *not* a consequence of any interaction between the particles involved; indeed, we have assumed all along that they do not interact with each other. It is purely a consequence of the demand that Ψ must respect the fact that the particles are indistinguishable. It is remarkable that such a powerful conclusion can emerge from such a straightforward argument.

What dictates whether a given type of particle will be described by an overall symmetric or antisymmetric wavefunction? This issue cannot be resolved with the previous development. A full understanding of this question is quite involved, but we can give a qualitative description of the essential points. In Section 8.2 we saw how experiments conducted in the early 1920s revealed that particles possess intrinsic angular momentum, an attribute now known as *spin*. These experiments further revealed that all particles can be classed as one of two types: those whose spin is an odd half-integer multiple of $\hbar$ ("spin-1/2" particles) and those whose spins are full-integer (including zero) multiples of $\hbar$ ("spin-one" particles). The former are known as *fermions* in honor of Enrico Fermi; the latter are known as *bosons* in honor of

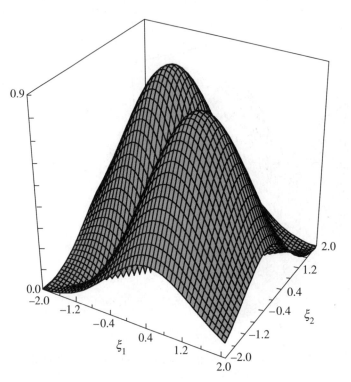

FIGURE 8.5 $|\Psi|$ for a Two-particle Antisymmetric Wavefunction for $n = 0$ and $n = 1$ Harmonic-oscillator States.

Indian physicist Satyendra Bose. [An interesting biographical article on Bose's life and work, "The man behind Bose statistics," by Wali, K., appears in *Physics Today* 2006; 59(10):46–52.] Fermions, which include electrons, protons, and neutrons, are described by antisymmetric overall wavefunctions whereas bosons (which include photons and other, more exotic particles) are of the symmetric kind. Hence, the presence of a boson in a particular state increases the probability that an identical particle will be found in the same state. The presence of a fermion in a particular state decreases the probability that an identical particle will be found in the same state. A composite structure, such as an entire atom, possesses the symmetry corresponding to the sum of its constituent spins. For example, normal helium ($_2^4$He) is a boson in view of its even number of spin-1/2 constituents (2 each of electrons, protons, and neutrons), whereas helium-3 ($_2^3$He) is a fermion (2 protons, 1 neutron, 2 electrons). Bosons, being characterized by symmetric wavefunctions, will presumably prefer to be found in the proximity of each other. This prediction has been verified experimentally via creating what is known as a *Bose-Einstein condensate* (BEC). A liquid-phase BEC was first achieved in 1908 by cooling liquid He-4 to near absolute-zero temperature; in this circumstance the helium acts as a *superfluid* with no resistance to motion. A gas-phase BEC was first achieved in 1988 with rubidium ($^{85}_{37}$Rb) atoms that had been cooled to a temperature of about 200 billionths of a degree above absolute zero; this work is described in "Gaseous Bose-Einstein condensate finally observed" by Collins, G.P., *Physics Today* 1998;51(8):9. A summary of experimental work on gas-phase BEC's to four years after their discovery appears in "Experimental studies of Bose-Einstein condensation" by Ketterle, W., *Physics Today* 1999;52(12):30–35 [See also *Physics Today* 1998;51(8):9, 1998;51(10):17–19, and 1999;52(8):9.] In such circumstances, all of the atoms involved are in the same (lowest) quantum state and collectively act as a single atom.

One important point remains. From Equation (10) it should be clear that, in the antisymmetric (fermion) case, if the two particles should find themselves in the same state ($A = B$), then $\Psi = 0$ everywhere. However, this would be inconsistent with the presumed presence of the particles in the first place. Consequently, we are forced to conclude that *no two electrons in the same atom can find themselves in the same quantum state*. This is the **Pauli exclusion principle**.

Ultimately, four quantum numbers are necessary to specify the state of an electron: the principle quantum number n, the angular momentum quantum number ℓ, the magnetic quantum number m, and its spin-state quantum number, $\pm 1/2$. In view of the spin quantum number, the total number of states for principle quantum number n is $2n^2$ (see Equation 7.4.48). For $n = 1, 2, 3, \ldots$, this amounts to 2, 8, 18, $\ldots$, states; these values correspond to the noble gases helium, neon, argon, and so on, which are said to possess "closed" (completely filled) electron shells. Elements with 3, 9, 19, $\ldots$, electrons will thus have their "last" electron being the lone occupant of $n = 2, 3, 4, \ldots$, states. Such elements are those in the first column of the periodic table; as one might expect, their lone electrons can be dissociated relatively easily, making these elements particularly reactive. A full treatment of the chemical nature of elements involves analysis of the order in which energy states are filled in view of the interaction between electron wavefunctions well as relativistic effects. Suffice it to say, the important concepts of wavefunction symmetry/antisymmetry and exclusion survive these issues.

■ Section 8.4 Problems

8-8(E) Classify the following neutral atoms in terms of whether they will be fermions or bosons: $^{29}_{14}$Si, $^{40}_{20}$Ca, $^{69}_{31}$Ga, $^{105}_{46}$Pd, $^{137}_{55}$Cs, $^{235}_{92}$U.

8-9(E) In Problem 4-16 it was remarked that early in the history of nuclear physics the electrically neutral mass of nuclei now attributed to neutrons was considered to arise from neutral particles composed of combinations of protons and electrons (as opposed to neutrons in their own right as fundamental particles). That problem explored the implications of the uncertainty principle for that theory. Here we have a look at the spin statistics of the situation. Consider a nitrogen-14 ($^{14}_{7}$N) nucleus. If the "protons + electrons" model were correct, would you predict N-14 to be a spin-1/2 or spin-1 system? What about in the case of the "protons + neutrons" model? Spectroscopic evidence indicates that N-14 is a spin-1 system. Which model does this support?

9 | Approximation Methods

In previous chapters we have explored solutions to Schrödinger's equation for a variety of potentials. In most cases these solutions were expressible in closed analytic forms. As you might imagine, however, the number of potentials for which Schrödinger's equation is soluble in closed form is very limited. For many potentials—even some remarkably simple ones (e.g., the linear potential of Problem 4-10)—it is impossible to develop closed-form analytic solutions.

How can we analyze such potentials within the framework of the knowledge of solutions of Schrödinger's equation that we have built up? The purpose of this chapter is to explore analytic methods of obtaining approximate solutions in such cases (numerical methods are discussed in Chapter 10). We consider three methods in particular. In Section 9.1 we examine the Wentzel-Kramers-Brillouin or **WKB method** [1], a scheme for determining approximate energy eigenvalues. In Sections 9.2 and 9.3 we develop **perturbation theory**, a powerful, quite general method for establishing approximate wavefunctions and energies for potentials that can be expressed as variants of potentials for which the SE can be solved exactly. In Sections 9.4 and 9.5 we examine how the **variational method** can be employed to generate approximate ground-state energies based on an educated guess at the form of the ground-state wavefunction. By applying these techniques to problems known to possess exact solutions, it is possible to get a sense of how accurate they can be. As before, our emphasis here is on obtaining *bound-state* solutions.

■ 9.1 The WKB Method

We have seen that for regions of space where the total energy of a particle exceeds the local potential energy—that is, $E > V(x)$—the de Broglie wavelength characterizing a particle of mass m is given by

$$\lambda(x) = \frac{h}{\sqrt{2m[E - V(x)]}}. \tag{1}$$

[We revert to the use of m to designate mass in this chapter. It will also sometimes be used as a summation index, but no confusion with mass or magnetic quantum number should arise.] In cases where $V(x)$ is constant (such as inside a finite or infinite rectangular potential well), λ will be constant. In such a situation the wavefunctions are mathematically identical in form to the standing-wave patterns of a vibrating string clamped at both ends, as illustrated in Figure 9.1. From elementary mechanics you may recall that such standing-wave patterns are defined by the requirement that an integral number of half-wavelengths fit between the clamped ends. The essence of the WKB method is to similarly assume that if ψ is characterized by a wavelength λ, then the particle's energy E must be such that an approximately half-integral number of de Broglie wavelengths fit between the classical turning points of the motion. The approximation in this method comes from neglecting the fact that, quantum mechanically, the particle can penetrate into regions of space where $E < V(x)$. In effect, this method is predicated on the idea that if penetration of the wave into the potential barrier is slight in comparison to the extent of the domain for which $E > V(x)$, then $\psi(x)$ approximately goes to zero where $E = V(x)$.

In general, however, $V(x)$ will not be constant and λ will be a function of position; it is consequently not justifiable to simply equate $n(\lambda/2)$ to the distance between the turning points. We can, however, build up an integral representation of Equation (1). A short interval of distance dx over which the potential $V(x)$ is effectively constant will contain a number of wavelengths given by

$$\frac{dx}{\lambda} = \frac{\sqrt{2m\left[E - V(x)\right]}}{h}dx. \tag{2}$$

The total number of wavelengths between the turning points is given by the integral of Equation (2) between those limits; if an integral number of half-wavelengths are to approximately fit between the turning points, then

$$\int \frac{dx}{\lambda} \sim \frac{n}{2}, \tag{3}$$

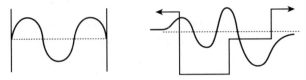

FIGURE 9.1 Left: A string vibrating in the $n = 3$ mode.
Right: A quantum wavefunction with $n = 4$.

or, on combining Equations (2) and (3),

$$2\sqrt{2m}\int\sqrt{E - V(x)}dx \sim nh. \tag{4}$$

Equation (4) is the WKB approximation. A more sophisticated derivation (Pauling and Wilson, Section 27b) renders the right side of Equation (4) as $(n + 1/2)h$, an expression that gives better results for low-n states, but this is a refinement with which we will not concern ourselves. With this result, one can estimate the energy corresponding to quantum level n for a particle of mass m under the influence of any potential function $V(x)$. In practice, the limits of integration are given by the positions at which some general energy E cuts the $V(x)$ curve; the result is an expression for $E(n)$.

Before illustrating use of the WKB method with some examples, it is instructive to look a little more closely at the conditions of its validity. The accuracy of Equation (3) depends on the quantum wavelength λ not varying too rapidly over short distances. What we are really demanding here is that any change $d\lambda$ in λ over distance dx be small:

$$\frac{d\lambda}{dx} \ll 1. \tag{5}$$

To compute actual numbers, it is more useful to express Equation (5) in terms of the energy eigenvalues and potential function $V(x)$. From the de Broglie relation the quantum-mechanical wavelength is given in terms of momentum by $\lambda = h/p$. Classically, we can write momentum as

$$p(x) = \sqrt{2m[E - V(x)]}. \tag{6}$$

Taking the derivative gives

$$\frac{d\lambda}{dx} = -\frac{h}{p^2}\frac{dp}{dx} = \frac{mh}{\{2m[E - V(x)]\}^{3/2}}\left(\frac{dV}{dx}\right).$$

That is, Equation (5) is equivalent to

$$\frac{mh}{\{2m[E - V(x)]\}^{3/2}}\left(\frac{dV}{dx}\right) \ll 1. \tag{7}$$

This is sometimes written with the absolute value of the gradient of the potential, $|dV/dx|$, to accommodate the fact that λ can either increase [or decrease] as $V(x)$ decreases [or increases.]

If dV/dx is small, the momentum is large, or both, Equation (7) is likely to be satisfied. The phrase "momentum is large" has a macroscopic ring to it, so we shall refer to Equation (7) as the **classical approximation** in this context. At locations where an energy level E cuts the $V(x)$ curve, or where $E \sim V(x)$—that is, at or near the classical turning points of the motion—Equation (7) will clearly not be satisfied. If such regimes form a substantial part of the domain of the problem at hand, the WKB approximation cannot be expected to be terribly accurate. An illustration of using Equations (4) and (7) is given in the following example.

EXAMPLE 9.1

Use the WKB approximation to determine approximate energy eigenvalues for a particle of mass m moving in the one-dimensional linear potential

$$V(x) = \begin{cases} \infty, & x \leq 0 \\ \alpha x, & 0 < x < \infty. \end{cases}$$

Consider some general energy E as shown in Figure 9.2.
If energy E cuts the $V(x)$ line at $x = a$, then $E = \alpha a$. From Equation (4) we have

$$2\sqrt{2m} \int_0^a \sqrt{E - \alpha x}\, dx \sim nh.$$

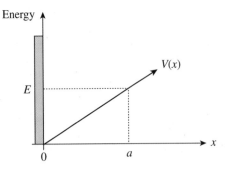

Energy

E

$V(x)$

0 a x

I FIGURE 9.2 Linear Potential.

Evaluating the integral gives

$$nh \sim 2\sqrt{2m}\left[-\frac{2}{3\alpha}\sqrt{(E-\alpha x)^3}\right]_0^a \sim -\frac{4\sqrt{2m}}{3\alpha}[(E-\alpha a)^{3/2}-E^{3/2}].$$

With $E = \alpha a$ we find

$$E_n \sim \left(\frac{3\alpha h}{4\sqrt{2m}}n\right)^{2/3} \sim \left(\frac{6\pi\alpha\hbar}{4\sqrt{2m}}n\right)^{2/3} \sim 2.811\left(\frac{\alpha\hbar}{\sqrt{2m}}n\right)^{2/3}.$$

This result is consistent with that in Problem 4-10; for an electron in such a potential with $\alpha = 1$ eV/Å, $E_1 \sim 4.39$ eV. An analytic solution to this problem involves an infinite polynomial known as an Airy function, the roots of which are related to the energy eigenvalues. The exact ground-state energy is of the form derived here but with a numerical factor of 2.338 as opposed to 2.811; that is, the WKB method overestimates the ground-state energy by about 20%. In Section 9.4 we will explore an alternate analytic method for estimating the ground-state energy corresponding to this potential. A direct numerical solution of Schrödinger's equation for this problem is detailed in Chapter 10.

To what extent is the classical approximation satisfied for this problem? To get a sense of this we evaluate the left side of Equation (7) at an x-position equal to halfway between $x = 0$ and where a general energy level E_n cuts the potential line $V(x)$. For convenience, write the previous result as $E_n = \beta n^{2/3}$, where $\beta = (3\pi\alpha\hbar/2\sqrt{2m})^{2/3}$. A given energy level E_n will cut the potential line $V(x) = \alpha x$ at the turning point $x_{turn} = \beta n^{2/3}/\alpha$. Evaluating the left side of Equation (7) at $x_{turn}/2$ gives

$$\frac{mh}{\{2m[E-V(x)]\}^{3/2}}\left(\frac{dV}{dx}\right) = \frac{mh\alpha}{\{2m[E_n-\alpha x_{turn}/2]\}^{3/2}} = \frac{h\alpha}{\sqrt{m}\beta^{3/2}n} = \frac{4\sqrt{2}}{3n}.$$

Equation (7) then demands

$$\frac{4\sqrt{2}}{3} \ll n \quad \Rightarrow \quad n \gg 1.886.$$

There is no hard-and-fast answer to the question, "For what values of n can this be considered to be satisfied?" It depends on your definition of "much greater than." In addition, the numbers can be made to change by evaluating Equation (7) at a different value of x. But "$n <$ at least a few" is likely to be unsatisfactory by any reasonable definition. It is perhaps somewhat surprising that the WKB method is in error by *only* 20% for the ground state.

EXAMPLE 9.2

Treat the hydrogen atom as a one-dimensional system in the radial coordinate r and use the WKB approximation to estimate the energy levels.

The situation is shown schematically in Figure 9.3, where a bound-state energy $-E$ cuts the Coulomb potential at $r = a$.

The WKB approximation in this case gives

$$2\sqrt{2m} \int_0^a \sqrt{E - V(r)}\, dr = 2\sqrt{2m} \int_0^a \sqrt{E + (e^2/4\pi\epsilon_o r)}\, dr \sim nh.$$

The upper limit of integration is given by

$$E = -\frac{e^2}{4\pi\epsilon_o a} \Rightarrow aE = -\frac{e^2}{4\pi\epsilon_o}.$$

Substituting this expression into the integral gives

$$2\sqrt{2m} \int_0^a \sqrt{E - \frac{aE}{r}}\, dr \sim nh.$$

To simplify this integral, it is helpful to remember that we are seeking bound states; that is, $E < 0$. Writing $E = -|E|$, we have

$$2\sqrt{2m|E|} \int_0^a \sqrt{\frac{a}{r} - 1}\, dr \sim nh.$$

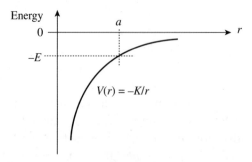

FIGURE 9.3 Coulomb Potential.

This integral is most easily solved by invoking the change of variable $r = a \sin^2\beta$ to yield

$$4a\sqrt{2m|E|} \int_0^{\pi/2} \cos^2\beta \, d\beta \sim nh.$$

This integral evaluates to $\pi/4$. The energy levels are then

$$|E| \sim \frac{n^2 h^2}{2m\pi^2 a^2} \sim \frac{n^2 h^2}{2m\pi^2} \frac{16\pi^2 \epsilon_o^2 E^2}{e^4},$$

or, on canceling a common factor of E from both sides,

$$|E_n^{\text{WKB}}| \sim \frac{me^4}{8\epsilon_o^2 h^2 n^2}.$$

Remarkably, the WKB method yields *exactly* the energy levels as given by the Bohr and Schrödinger models.

■ 9.2 The Superposition Theorem Revisited

In Chapter 4 we encountered the idea of constructing a superposition state by forming a linear sum of solutions to Schrödinger's equation for some potential $V(x)$. In this section we examine a closely related mathematical technique that lies at the heart of both the perturbation and variational methods developed later in this chapter.

An essential ingredient in developing the superposition theorem was the orthogonality theorem: that the family of solutions $\psi_n(x)$ to the SE for a given potential satisfies the relationship

$$\langle \psi_j | \psi_i \rangle = \delta_i^j, \tag{1}$$

where ψ_j and ψ_i are any of the ψ_n and where $\delta_i^j = 1$ if $i = j$, zero otherwise. (Review Section 4.2 for the angle-bracket notation and Section 4.6 for the δ_i^j notation.) This relationship will prove useful.

In developing the superposition theorem we had in mind the idea of a system in a sort of indeterminate state composed of contributions from individual states ψ_n with the contribution of any particular state dictated by a corresponding "expansion coefficient" a_n. In the present development we reverse the sense of the argument to ask:

Suppose that $\phi(x)$ is some continuous, but otherwise arbitrary function valid over the same domain as the $\psi_n(x)$. What values must the expansion coefficients take if we desire to write $\phi(x)$ as a linear sum of the $\psi_n(x)$; that is, if we wish to have

$$\phi(x) = \sum_n a_n \psi_n(x) ? \tag{2}$$

With both $\phi(x)$ and the $\psi_n(x)$ known, this seems a curious demand of no practical value. As we shall see, however, this sort of construction proves valuable indeed.

To establish the a_n it is helpful to use the orthogonality properties of the $\psi_n(x)$. To do this, begin by multiplying through Equation (2) by one of the $\psi(x)$, say $\psi_j(x)$. This gives

$$\psi_j(x)\phi(x) = \psi_j(x) \sum_n a_n \psi_n(x) = \sum_n a_n \psi_j(x)\psi_n(x). \tag{3}$$

Integrating both sides of Equation (3) [in practice, over the domain of the $\psi(x)$] gives

$$\langle \psi_j | \phi \rangle = \int \left\{ \sum_n a_n \psi_j(x)\psi_n(x) \right\} dx.$$

Inasmuch as the a_n are constants they can be brought out of the integral provided their positions within the sum are properly maintained:

$$\langle \psi_j | \phi \rangle = \sum_n a_n \langle \psi_j | \psi_n \rangle.$$

. From the orthogonality condition expressed in Equation (1), the integral on the right side reduces to δ_i^j. Hence

$$\langle \psi_j | \phi \rangle = \sum_n a_n \delta_j^n. \tag{4}$$

The sum in Equation (4) runs over all possible values of n. But since $\delta_j^n = 0$ when $n \neq j$, the only surviving term is that for which $n = j$, namely a_j. The result is a recipe for the jth expansion coefficient in terms of $\phi(x)$ and $\psi_j(x)$:

$$a_j = \langle \psi_j | \phi \rangle. \tag{5}$$

The critical step in this derivation was simplifying the integral in the equation preceding Equation (4): had the $\psi_n(x)$ not obeyed the orthogonality relation, Equation (5) would not have followed. It is worth emphasizing that $\phi(x)$ need not (and in general will not) be a solution to the SE.

The resulting expression for $\phi(x)$ will be valid only over the domain of the $\psi(x)$. If we desire in addition that $\phi(x)$ be normalized over this range, a constraint arises on the a_n. Normalization demands

$$\langle \phi^*|\phi \rangle = \int \left\{ \left(\sum_n a_n^* \psi_n^*(x) \right) \left(\sum_m a_m \psi_m(x) \right) \right\} dx = 1. \tag{6}$$

Note that two different dummy summation indices are used here to maintain generality. Equation (6) can be rearranged to read

$$\sum_n \sum_m a_n^* a_m \langle \psi_n^* | \psi_m \rangle = 1. \tag{7}$$

The integral in Equation (7) reduces to δ_n^m via Equation (1), leaving

$$\sum_n \sum_m a_n^* a_m \delta_n^m = 1. \tag{8}$$

Consider the inner sum in Equation (8): for some particular value of n, it runs over all possible values of m. The index n is then incremented and all possible values of m run through again. This process is continued until all of the possible values of n are exhausted. In each case, however, $\delta_n^m = 0$ unless $m = n$. The result is that in each run of the inner sum only one term, that for $m = n$, is nonzero:

$$\sum_n \sum_m a_n^* a_m \delta_n^m = \sum_n a_n^* a_n = \sum_n |a_n|^2 = 1. \tag{9}$$

The condition that $\phi(x)$ be normalized means that the sum of the squares of the absolute values of the expansion coefficients be unity. Conversely, if $\phi(x)$ is initially chosen such that it is normalized over the domain of the $\psi(x)$, this will happen automatically when the a_n are computed from Equation (5) as Equation (2) was assumed to represent an exact expression for $\phi(x)$.

EXAMPLE 9.3

Express the function $\phi(x) = x$ as a linear sum of infinite rectangular well wavefunctions.

The relevant wavefunctions are

$$\psi_n(x) = \sqrt{\frac{2}{L}} \sin\left(\frac{n\pi x}{L}\right).$$

From Equation (5) the expansion coefficients are given by

$$a_n = \langle \psi_n | \phi \rangle = \sqrt{\frac{2}{L}} \int_0^L x \sin\left(\frac{n\pi x}{L}\right) dx.$$

Defining $c = n\pi/L$ and evaluating the integral gives

$$a_n = \sqrt{\frac{2}{L}} \left[\frac{1}{c^2} \sin(cx) - \frac{x}{c} \cos(cx) \right]_0^L$$

$$= \sqrt{\frac{2}{L}} \left[-\frac{L^2}{n\pi} \cos(n\pi) \right] = (-1)^{n+1} \frac{\sqrt{2} L^{3/2}}{n\pi},$$

where we used the fact that $\cos(n\pi) = (-1)^n$. Note that the expansion coefficients are functions of n; this is a regular occurrence. Hence our expression for $\phi(x)$ is

$$\phi(x) = x = \sum_n a_n \psi_n(x) = \frac{2L}{\pi} \sum_n \frac{(-1)^{n+1}}{n} \sin\left(\frac{n\pi x}{L}\right).$$

Readers familiar with Fourier series will recognize the nature of this example: that any function can be reproduced by adding together an infinite number of sinusoidal functions. For computational purposes it is not practical to sum an infinite number of terms; however, the "n" in the denominator of the sum ensures that the high-n terms in the sum will make relatively little contribution. This is demonstrated in Figure 9.4, where $\phi(x)$ is plotted for the case of $L = 1.0$. The two curves

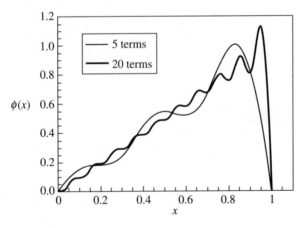

FIGURE 9.4 Approximating a Straight Line as a Sum of Rectangular-well Wavefunctions.

correspond to including terms up to $n = 5$ and $n = 20$. Both curves collapse to zero at x = 1.0 because the infinite-well wavefunctions vanish there; an infinite number of terms would need to be incorporated to reproduce a straight line up to $x = 1$.

■ 9.3 Perturbation Theory

Sometimes we encounter problems that we have not solved *per se* but which bear a strong resemblance to others that we have previously met. Almost intuitively, accumulated wisdom of such past experience begins to suggest strategies for attacking the new problem. Perturbation theory systematizes this strategy by specifying a recipe for constructing an approximate solution to Schrödinger's equation for a potential that cannot be solved exactly in terms of the eigenfunctions and eigenvalues of a similar problem that can. The "modification" required to cast the exactly soluble problem into the desired one is known as a "perturbation."

Figure 9.5 shows an example: an infinite one-dimensional potential well with a tilted floor described by $V(x) = \alpha x$. The SE for this potential is not soluble in closed form (see Problem 5-9); however, we know that if $\alpha = 0$ the solution is trivial. Hypothesizing a sort of continuity of nature, it would seem reasonable to presume that if α is small (say, such that αL is small in comparison with the lowest energy level of the unperturbed well), then the wavefunctions and energy levels of the perturbed well will probably not be much different from their $\alpha = 0$ counterparts. The essence of perturbation theory is to work out correction factors to be added to the unperturbed solutions to approximate the solution of the perturbed problem.

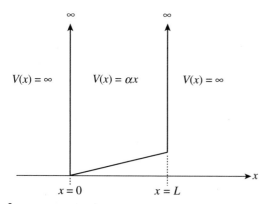

I FIGURE 9.5 Perturbed Infinite Rectangular Well.

Developing perturbation theory is a somewhat lengthy task that hinges on the superposition theorem developed in the preceding section. While the physical concept underlying it—that the solution to the SE for the perturbed potential can be expressed as a sum over solutions to a closely similar "unperturbed" potential—is intuitively appealing, the mathematics can be daunting at first glance, and so are worked out in some detail.

As in the previous section, an important aspect of what follows is again the orthogonality theorem of Chapter 4. Here, however, we invoke it in its full form: that for two wavefunctions ψ_k and ψ_n that satisfy the same potential, the energies and wavefunctions must satisfy

$$(E_n - E_k)\langle \psi_k^*|\psi_n \rangle = 0.$$

If ψ_k and ψ_n should happen to be degenerate, then $E_n = E_k$ and no conclusion can be made about the orthogonality of ψ_k and ψ_n: $\langle \psi_k^*|\psi_n \rangle$ *might* be zero, but this cannot be assumed. In what follows, no assumptions are made regarding orthogonality (or not) of wavefunctions unless it is clear that they refer to the different energies; as a consequence, the derivation is equally valid for both nondegenerate and degenerate systems. We do, however, restrict the discussion to bound-state, time-independent problems.

In developing perturbation theory it is convenient to introduce some simplifying notation. Suppose that we wish to solve the SE for the wavefunctions $\psi(\mathbf{r})$ and energies E corresponding to some potential $V(\mathbf{r})$; we put $\mathbf{r}$-dependences for ψ and V as a reminder that we may be dealing with a system of more than one dimension. We write the SE in the usual form:

$$H\psi(\mathbf{r}) = E\psi(\mathbf{r}), \quad \boldsymbol{H} = -\frac{\hbar^2}{2m}\nabla^2 + V(\mathbf{r}) \tag{1}$$

where $\boldsymbol{H}$ is the Hamiltonian operator. $V(\mathbf{r})$ is presumed to be such that a closed analytic solution to the SE is difficult or impossible to obtain. Suppose further that there is some similar potential $V^0(\mathbf{r})$ for which we can solve the SE exactly. Designate the wavefunctions and energies corresponding to this potential as $\psi_n^0(\mathbf{r})$ and E_n^0. *Superscript 0 refers to the unperturbed problem.* In this case the SE can be expressed as

$$H^0\psi_n^0(\mathbf{r}) = E_n^0\psi_n^0(\mathbf{r}), \quad \boldsymbol{H}^0 = -\frac{\hbar^2}{2m}\nabla^2 + V^0(\mathbf{r}). \tag{2}$$

These unperturbed states may be infinite in number. Irrespective of whether or not some of them may be degenerate, the numbering scheme $n = 1, 2, 3, \ldots$, can proceed arbitrarily; for practical computational purposes we will have to assume some upper limit N on the index n. [There is an exception to this, as discussed at the end of the subsection on first-order perturbation theory following Equation (15), but don't worry about this for now.] The boundary conditions for the perturbed and unperturbed potentials are assumed to be the same.

Comparing Equations (1) and (2) shows that we can write the perturbed Hamiltonian in terms of the unperturbed Hamiltonian as

$$H = H^0 + [V(\mathbf{r}) - V^0(\mathbf{r})] = H^0 + V'(\mathbf{r}). \tag{3}$$

$V'(\mathbf{r})$ is defined as the difference (in the sense perturbed minus unperturbed) between the perturbed and unperturbed potentials. In the spirit of the superposition process of Section 4.7, we assume that a solution for the perturbed potential can in general be written as a linear sum over all of the solutions of the unperturbed potential:

$$\psi(\mathbf{r}) = \sum_m C_m \psi_m^0(\mathbf{r}), \tag{4}$$

where the C's are dimensionless expansion coefficients and the index of summation $m = 1, 2, 3, \ldots, N$.

Now substitute Equations (3) and (4) into Schrödinger's equation for the perturbed problem, Equation (1). Dropping the understood dependences of the potential and wavefunctions on $\mathbf{r}$, this gives

$$(H^0 + V') \sum_m C_m \psi_m^0 = E \sum_m C_m \psi_m^0.$$

On expanding out the left side of this equation, the unperturbed Hamiltonian can be taken within the summation, yielding

$$\sum_m C_m E_m^0 \psi_m^0 + \sum_m C_m (V' \psi_m^0) = E \sum_m C_m \psi_m^0, \tag{5}$$

where we have used $H^0 \psi_m^0 = E_m^0 \psi_m^0$.

Now multiply through Equation (5) by one of the unperturbed wavefunctions, say ψ_j^0 (or, if ψ_j^0 is complex, by its complex conjugate) and integrate over the range of the potential. This gives

$$\sum_m C_m E_m^0 \langle \psi_j^0 | \psi_m^0 \rangle + \sum_m C_m \langle \psi_j^0 | V' | \psi_m^0 \rangle = E \sum_m C_m \langle \psi_j^0 | \psi_m^0 \rangle,$$

or

$$\sum_m C_m \{ (E_m^0 - E) \langle \psi_j^0 | \psi_m^0 \rangle + \langle \psi_j^0 | V' | \psi_m^0 \rangle \} = 0. \tag{6}$$

We can cast Equation (6) into the more compact form

$$\sum_m C_m V_{jm} = 0 \tag{7}$$

by defining matrix elements

$$V_{jm} = \{(E_m^0 - E)\langle\psi_j^0|\psi_m^0\rangle + \langle\psi_j^0|V'|\psi_m^0\rangle\}. \tag{8}$$

If the summation in Equation (4) runs from $m = 1$ to N, then Equations (7) and (8) can be expressed as

$$
\begin{bmatrix}
V_{11} & \cdots & V_{1k} & \cdots & V_{1r} & \cdots & V_{1N} \\
\vdots & \ddots & \vdots & & \vdots & & \vdots \\
V_{k1} & \cdots & V_{kk} & \cdots & V_{kr} & \cdots & V_{kN} \\
\vdots & & \vdots & \ddots & \vdots & & \vdots \\
V_{r1} & \cdots & V_{rk} & \cdots & V_{rr} & \cdots & V_{rN} \\
\vdots & & \vdots & & \vdots & \ddots & \vdots \\
V_{N1} & \cdots & V_{Nk} & \cdots & V_{Nr} & \cdots & V_{NN}
\end{bmatrix}
\begin{bmatrix}
C_1 \\
\vdots \\
C_k \\
\vdots \\
C_r \\
\vdots \\
C_N
\end{bmatrix}
= 0. \tag{9}
$$

The only way to satisfy Equation (9) is to require that the determinant of the large square matrix, hereafter abbreviated $[V]$, be zero. To determine the energy eigenvalues of the perturbed potential one must search, usually by trial and error, for those values of E that yield $\det[V] = 0$. Since we have an N-by-N matrix, there will be N independent (although not necessarily different) solutions for E.

Once the perturbed energies have been established we can go back to solve for the expansion coefficients C corresponding to each of them. It is important to bear in mind that there will be a perturbed wavefunction $\psi(E)$ corresponding to *each* value of E and that *each* E must be treated separately. To do this, split up one of the elements of $[V]$ with the help of Equation (8), say the (r, k)th element (mnemonic: *r*ow, *k*olumn), and then recast Equation (9) as

$$
\begin{bmatrix}
V_{11} & \cdots & V_{1k} & \cdots & V_{1r} & \cdots & V_{1N} \\
\vdots & \ddots & \vdots & & \vdots & & \vdots \\
V_{k1} & \cdots & V_{kk} & \cdots & V_{kr} & \cdots & V_{kN} \\
\vdots & & \vdots & \ddots & \vdots & & \vdots \\
V_{r1} & \cdots & \langle\psi_r^0|V'|\psi_k^0\rangle & \cdots & V_{rr} & \cdots & V_{rN} \\
\vdots & & \vdots & & \vdots & \ddots & \vdots \\
V_{N1} & \cdots & V_{Nk} & \cdots & V_{Nr} & \cdots & V_{NN}
\end{bmatrix}
\begin{bmatrix}
C_1 \\
\vdots \\
C_k \\
\vdots \\
C_r \\
\vdots \\
C_N
\end{bmatrix}
=
\begin{bmatrix}
0 \\
\vdots \\
C_k(E - E_k^0)\langle\psi_r^0|\psi_k^0\rangle \\
\vdots \\
0 \\
\vdots \\
0
\end{bmatrix}. \tag{10}
$$

In doing this rearrangement it is crucial to choose an element (r, k) such that $(E - E_k^0) \langle \psi_r^0 | V' | \psi_k^0 \rangle$ is nonzero; otherwise, the large matrix of Equation (10) will not be different from that of Equation (9) and the determinant would still be zero, rendering it impossible to proceed from this point.

A general expansion coefficient C_i can be obtained by inverting Equation (10),

$$C_i = C_k \{ V_{ik}^* (E - E_k^0) \langle \psi_r^0 | \psi_k^0 \rangle \}, \ (i = 1, N) \tag{11}$$

where V_{ik}^* designates the (i, k)th element of the inverse of the square matrix in Equation (10), *not* the complex conjugate of V_{ik}. Coefficient C_k itself is established by demanding that the perturbed wavefunction be normalized:

$$\langle \psi | \psi \rangle = 1 \Rightarrow \langle \sum C_n \psi_n^0 | \sum C_m \psi_m^0 \rangle = 1 \Rightarrow \sum_n \sum_m C_n C_m \langle \psi_n^0 | \psi_m^0 \rangle = 1. \tag{12}$$

With Equation (11) this reduces to

$$C_k^2 (E - E_k^0)^2 \langle \psi_r^0 | \psi_k^0 \rangle^2 \sum_n \sum_m \{ (V_{nk}^*) (V_{mk}^*) \langle \psi_n^0 | \psi_m^0 \rangle \} = 1,$$

or

$$C_k = \frac{1}{(E - E_k^0) \langle \psi_r^0 | \psi_k^0 \rangle \sqrt{\sum_n \sum_m \{ (V_{nk}^*) (V_{mk}^*) \langle \psi_n^0 | \psi_m^0 \rangle \}}}. \tag{13}$$

Equation (13), in combination with Equation (11), gives, finally,

$$C_i = \frac{V_{ik}^*}{\sqrt{\sum_n \sum_m \{ (V_{nk}^*) (V_{mk}^*) \langle \psi_n^0 | \psi_m^0 \rangle \}}}. \tag{14}$$

If the unperturbed wavefunctions are nondegenerate, then $\langle \psi_n^0 | \psi_m^0 \rangle = \delta_n^m$, and only $m = n$ survives the innermost sum:

$$C_i = \frac{V_{ik}^*}{\sqrt{\sum_n (V_{nk}^*)^2}} \quad \text{(nondegenerate only).} \tag{15}$$

Nondegenerate First-Order Perturbation Theory

The development just described indicates that the calculations involved in a perturbation problem could rapidly escalate to a daunting degree. In the event that the unperturbed states are nondegenerate, however, considerable simplification can be had.

Consider the matrix elements of Equation (8):

$$V_{jm} = \{(E_m^0 - E)\langle \psi_j^0 | \psi_m^0 \rangle + \langle \psi_j^0 | V' | \psi_m^0 \rangle\}. \tag{8}$$

If the unperturbed states are nondegenerate, we must have $\langle \psi_j^0 | \psi_m^0 \rangle = \delta_j^m$ from the orthogonality theorem. That is, the first term within the curly brackets is zero unless $m = j$. As to the remaining term, $\langle \psi_j^0 | V' | \psi_m^0 \rangle$, if the perturbing potential V' is small (a condition that can be quantified only after the fact), then $\langle \psi_j^0 | V' | \psi_m^0 \rangle$ will likely be small *except* perhaps when $j = m$. If we accept this approximation, then the only elements of V that would be significantly different from zero are the diagonal ones:

$$V_{mm} \sim \{(E_m^0 - E) + \langle \psi_m^0 | V' | \psi_m^0 \rangle\}. \tag{16}$$

In this case the determinant of V reduces to

$$\det[\mathbf{V}] \sim \prod_m \{(E_m^0 - E) + \langle \psi_m^0 | V' | \psi_m^0 \rangle\}, \tag{17}$$

which means that the only way in which Equation (9) can be satisfied is if

$$E \sim E_m^0 + \langle \psi_m^0 | V' | \psi_m^0 \rangle, \quad (m = 1, 2, 3, ...). \tag{18}$$

This result indicates that every state of the unperturbed system will give rise to a perturbed state whose energy is just that of the unperturbed state plus the expectation value of the perturbing potential acting on that unperturbed state. This result *only* applies when the unperturbed states are nondegenerate.

To establish the expansion coefficients in this case, it is easiest to return to Equation (5):

$$\sum C_m E_m^0 \psi_m^0 + \sum C_m (V' \psi_m^0) = E \sum C_m \psi_m^0. \tag{5}$$

There will be a set of expansion coefficients corresponding to each possible perturbed energy of Equation (18). Let us find those corresponding to the perturbed state that develops from some general unperturbed state, say the nth one:

$$E \sim E_n^0 + \langle \psi_n^0 | V' | \psi_n^0 \rangle. \tag{19}$$

Substitute Equation (19) into Equation (5), breaking out the $m = n$ terms in the sums explicitly. The result is, after some rearranging,

$$-C_n \psi_n^0 \langle \psi_n^0 | V' | \psi_n^0 \rangle + \sum_{m \neq n} C_m \{ E_m^0 - E_n^0 - \langle \psi_n^0 | V' | \psi_n^0 \rangle \} \psi_m^0$$

$$+ \sum_{m \neq n} C_m (V' \psi_m^0) + C_n (V' \psi_n^0) = 0. \tag{20}$$

Now multiply through Equation (20) by one of the unperturbed wavefunctions, say ψ_k^0 ($k \neq n$), and integrate over the domain of the potential, invoking the orthogonality theorem where appropriate. The result is

$$C_k \{ E_k^0 - E_n^0 - \langle \psi_n^0 | V' | \psi_n^0 \rangle \} + \sum_{m \neq n} C_m \langle \psi_k^0 | V' | \psi_m^0 \rangle + C_n \langle \psi_k^0 | V' | \psi_n^0 \rangle = 0. \tag{21}$$

Study Equation (21) carefully. If V' is small and the unperturbed wavefunctions are orthogonal, all terms in the summation are likely to be negligible with the possible exception of $m = k$; that is, we can approximate Equation (21) as

$$C_k \{ E_k^0 - E_n^0 - \langle \psi_n^0 | V' | \psi_n^0 \rangle + \langle \psi_k^0 | V' | \psi_k^0 \rangle \} + C_n \langle \psi_k^0 | V' | \psi_n^0 \rangle \sim 0,$$

or

$$C_k \sim \frac{-C_n \langle \psi_k^0 | V' | \psi_n^0 \rangle}{\{ E_k^0 - E_n^0 - \langle \psi_n^0 | V' | \psi_n^0 \rangle + \langle \psi_k^0 | V' | \psi_k^0 \rangle \}}. \tag{22}$$

In Equation (22), $\langle \psi_n^0 | V' | \psi_n^0 \rangle$ and $\langle \psi_k^0 | V' | \psi_k^0 \rangle$ are likely to be small in comparison to E_k^0 and E_n^0. Further, since ψ_n^0 can probably be expected to make the dominant contribution to the perturbed wavefunction that arises from the unperturbed energy E_n^0, we are likely safe in setting $C_n \sim 1$. Hence we have

$$C_k \sim -\frac{\langle \psi_k^0 | V' | \psi_n^0 \rangle}{(E_k^0 - E_n^0)} \qquad (k \neq n), \tag{23}$$

which, in combination with Equation (4), gives us an approximate expression for the perturbed wavefunction:

$$\psi_n \sim \psi_n^0 - \sum_{k \neq n} \frac{\psi_k^0 \langle \psi_k^0 | V' | \psi_n^0 \rangle}{(E_k^0 - E_n^0)}. \tag{24}$$

The notation ψ_n serves as a reminder that this result has evolved from a perturbation to the unperturbed state ψ_n^0. In principle, the sum in Equation (24) runs over an infinite number of states. However, only those values of E_k^0 that are close to E_n^0 will yield significant contributions, so there is some hope that it will converge quickly.

Equations (19) and (24) constitute what is known as time-independent, nondegenerate *first-order* perturbation theory; if one is dealing with a nondegenerate system, and if the perturbations $\langle \psi_n^0 | V' | \psi_n^0 \rangle$ caused by V to the unperturbed energies E_n^0 are small in comparison to E_n^0, this first-order approach is usually adequate. Otherwise, the full matrix approach must be invoked. In dealing with the perturbed energy states in first-order perturbation theory one can (in theory at least) handle an infinite number of states since only the mth-state eigenfunction and eigenvalue appears in the correction term for the mth energy state in Equation (18). The perturbed eigenfunction for state m (Equation 24) still requires a summation over an infinite number of states in principle, however.

EXAMPLE 9.4

To a first order approximation, what are the energy levels and wavefunctions for the perturbed infinite rectangular well depicted in Figure 9.5?

This is a one-dimensional, nondegenerate problem, so we can use Equations (19) and (24). The unperturbed energies and wavefunctions are given by

$$E_n^0 = \frac{n^2 h^2}{8mL^2},$$

and

$$\psi_n^0(x) = \sqrt{\frac{2}{L}} \sin\left(\frac{n\pi x}{L}\right).$$

The perturbing potential is $V' = \alpha x$. We first compute the perturbed energy levels. From Equation (19),

$$\langle \psi_n^0 |V'|\psi_n^0\rangle = \frac{2\alpha}{L} \int\limits_0^L x\sin^2\left(\frac{n\pi x}{L}\right) dx.$$

The integral is of the form

$$\int\limits_0^L x\sin^2(ax)\, dx = \left[\frac{x^2}{4} - \frac{x\sin(2ax)}{4a} - \frac{\cos(2ax)}{8a^2}\right]_0^L,$$

where $a = (n\pi/L)$. Substituting for the limits gives

$$\langle \psi_n^0 |V'|\psi_n^0\rangle = \frac{2\alpha}{L}\left\{\left[\frac{L^2}{4} - \frac{L\sin(2n\pi)}{4a} - \frac{\cos(2n\pi)}{8a^2}\right] - \left[0 - 0 - \frac{\cos(0)}{8a^2}\right]\right\}$$

$$= \frac{2\alpha}{L}\left\{\left[\frac{L^2}{4} - \frac{1}{8a^2}\right] + \frac{1}{8a^2}\right\} = \frac{\alpha L}{2}.$$

Therefore, to first order, the energy levels of the perturbed well are

$$E_n \sim E_n^0 + \alpha L/2.$$

Each level is perturbed upward by the average value of the perturbing potential across the well. Note that if $\alpha \to 0$, the result reduces to the energy levels of the unperturbed well; this is always a useful way of checking the validity of a perturbation calculation.

The perturbed wavefunction corresponding to any perturbed energy E_n is more involved. From Equation (24) we have

$$\langle \psi_k^0 |V'|\psi_n^0\rangle = \frac{2\alpha}{L} \int\limits_0^L \sin\left(\frac{k\pi x}{L}\right) x\sin\left(\frac{n\pi x}{L}\right) dx.$$

Using the trigonometric identity

$$\sin(ax)\sin(bx) = (1/2)\,\{\cos[(a - b)x] - \cos[(a + b)x]\},$$

this integral can be simplified to

$$\langle \psi_k^0 |V'|\psi_n^0\rangle = \frac{\alpha}{L}\left\{\int\limits_0^L x\cos\left[\frac{(k - n)\pi x}{L}\right] dx - \int\limits_0^L x\cos\left[\frac{(k + n)\pi x}{L}\right] dx\right\}.$$

Designate the first integral as $I1$ and the second as $I2$. Both are of the form

$$\int x \cos(ax)\,dx = \frac{\cos(ax)}{a^2} + \frac{x\sin(ax)}{a}.$$

Consider $I1$. Defining $m = k - n$, we have

$$I1 = \left[\frac{\cos(m\pi x/L)}{(m\pi/L)^2} + \frac{x\sin(m\pi x/L)}{(m\pi/L)} \right]_0^L.$$

Clearly, m must be an integer; since $\sin(m\pi) = 0$ for all m, the second term vanishes at both limits. The remaining term yields

$$I1 = \frac{L^2}{m^2\pi^2}[\cos(m\pi) - 1].$$

Now, if m is even, $\cos(m\pi) = 1$ and $I1$ vanishes. If m is odd, $\cos(m\pi) = -1$ and the term in square brackets evaluates to -2. Therefore,

$$I1 = \begin{cases} 0, & (k-n)\ even \\ -\dfrac{2L^2}{(k-n)^2\pi^2}, & (k-n)\ odd. \end{cases}$$

Similarly,

$$I2 = \begin{cases} 0, & (k+n)\ even \\ -\dfrac{2L^2}{(k+n)^2\pi^2}, & (k+n)\ odd. \end{cases}$$

Now, if $(k - n)$ is even, $(k + n)$ will be as well; similarly, $(k - n)$ odd implies $(k + n)$ odd. Therefore,

$$\langle \psi_k^0|V'|\psi_n^0\rangle = \frac{\alpha}{L}(I1 + I2) = \frac{2\alpha L}{\pi^2}\left[\frac{1}{(k+n)^2} - \frac{1}{(k-n)^2} \right], \quad (k-n)\ odd.$$

This result indicates that in the sum over unperturbed states in Equation (24), only those terms with $(k - n)$ odd make a contribution. Bringing the preceding expression to a common denominator gives

$$\langle \psi_k^0 | V' | \psi_n^0 \rangle = -\frac{8\alpha L}{\pi^2}\left[\frac{nk}{(k + n)^2(k - n)^2}\right], \quad (k - n) \text{ odd.}$$

In the denominator of Equation (24) we have

$$E_k^0 - E_n^0 = \frac{\pi^2\hbar^2}{2mL^2}(k^2 - n^2),$$

hence,

$$\psi_n(x) \sim \psi_n^0(x) - \sum_{\substack{k \neq n \\ (k-n)\,\text{odd}}} \frac{\left[\sqrt{\dfrac{2}{L}}\sin\left(\dfrac{k\pi x}{L}\right)\right]\left[-\dfrac{8\alpha L}{\pi^2}\left(\dfrac{nk}{\left(k+n\right)^2\left(k-n\right)^2}\right)\right]}{\dfrac{\pi^2\hbar^2}{2mL^2}\left(k^2 - n^2\right)},$$

or, after some simplification,

$$\psi_n(x) \sim \psi_n^0(x) + \frac{16\sqrt{2}\alpha mL^{5/2}}{\hbar^2\pi^4} \sum_{\substack{k \neq n \\ (k-n)\,\text{odd}}} \frac{nk\sin\left(k\pi x / L\right)}{\left(k^2 - n^2\right)^3}.$$

Note again that if $\alpha \to 0$, we recover the unperturbed rectangular-well wavefunctions. This result is plotted in Figure 9.6 for the case of an electron in the $n = 1$ state of an infinite well with $L = 1$ Å and $\alpha = 100$ eV/Å; terms up to $k = 25$ were included ($\psi/10^5$ is plotted for convenience of scale). Notice how the perturbation "pushes" the particle preferentially to the left side of the well, a result consistent with the precepts for sketching wavefunctions developed in Section 3.6.

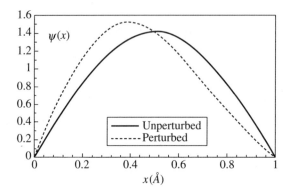

| FIGURE 9.6   Perturbed and Unperturbed $n = 1$ States of an Infinite Rectangular Well.

EXAMPLE 9.5

Determine first-order expressions for the ground-state energy and wavefunction of a particle of mass m moving in the perturbed harmonic-oscillator potential

$$V(x) = kx^2/2 + \beta x \quad (\beta > 0, \; -\infty \leq x \leq \infty).$$

Again we have a nondegenerate problem; the perturbing potential is $V'(x) = \beta x$. As sketched in Figure 9.7, the effect of this perturbation is to lower the potential well for $x < 0$ while raising it for $x > 0$. This has the effect of destroying the symmetry of the well; we can expect as a consequence that the perturbed wavefunction will be asymmetric.

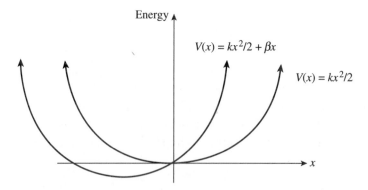

| FIGURE 9.7   Perturbed Harmonic Potential.

The ground-state of a harmonic oscillator is

$$\psi_0^0(x) = A_0 \exp(-\alpha^2 x^2/2),$$

where

$$A_0 = \sqrt{\alpha}/\pi^{1/4}$$

and

$$\alpha^4 = mk/\hbar^2.$$

The perturbed ground state energy is then

$$\langle \psi_0^0|V'|\psi_0^0 \rangle = \beta A_0^2 \int_{-\infty}^{\infty} x \exp(-\alpha^2 x^2)\, dx.$$

Since the integrand is an antisymmetric function, this integral evaluates to zero. To first order, a linear potential perturbing a harmonic oscillator causes no change to the ground state energy. The same result will clearly hold for any odd-powered perturbation. (Why?)

As to determining the perturbed ground-state wavefunction, we need to recall from Chapter 5 the general expression for the harmonic-oscillator wavefunction for any level k:

$$\psi_k^0(x) = A_k H_k(\alpha x)\exp(-\alpha^2 x^2/2), \quad k = 0, 1, 2, \ldots,$$

$$A_k = \sqrt{\alpha}/\sqrt{\pi\, 2^k k!}.$$

Therefore,

$$\langle \psi_k^0|V'|\psi_0^0 \rangle = \beta A_k A_0 \int_{-\infty}^{\infty} x \exp(-\alpha^2 x^2)\, H_k(\alpha x) H_0(\alpha x)\, dx,$$

or, on defining $\xi = \alpha x$,

$$\langle \psi_k^0|V'|\psi_0^0 \rangle = \frac{\beta A_k A_0}{\alpha^2} \int_{-\infty}^{\infty} \xi \exp(-\xi^2)\, H_k(\xi) H_0(\xi)\, d\xi.$$

Now, it is a property of Hermite polynomials (Weber and Arfken, Chapter 13) that

$$\int_{-\infty}^{\infty} \xi \exp(-\xi^2) H_n(\xi) H_m(\xi) d\xi = \sqrt{\pi} [2^{n-1} n! \, \delta_m^{n-1} + 2^n (n+1)! \, \delta_m^{n+1}]. \quad (1)$$

This property of the Hermite polynomials has an interesting consequence for the perturbed ground-state wavefunction. We have, with $n = k$ and $m = 0$ in Equation (24),

$$\psi_0 \sim \psi_0^0 - \frac{\beta \sqrt{\pi} A_0}{\alpha^2} \sum_{k \neq 0} \frac{A_k \psi_k^0 [2^{k-1} k! \, \delta_0^{k-1} + 2^k (k+1)! \, \delta_0^{k+1}]}{(E_k^0 - E_0^0)}.$$

The sum in this expression runs over all values of k, excluding $k = 0$. The first Kronecker delta, δ_0^{k-1}, is zero except when $k - 1 = 0$; that is, when $k = 1$. The second will be zero except when $k + 1 = 0$; that is, $k = -1$. But the series runs from $k = 1$ upward, so the second Kronecker delta makes no contribution at all to the sum. The only surviving term is that for $k = 1$, which gives

$$\psi_0 \sim \psi_0^0 - \frac{\beta \sqrt{\pi} A_0 A_1}{\alpha^2} \frac{\psi_1^0}{(E_1^0 - E_0^0)}.$$

On substituting explicit expressions for A_1, ψ_1^0, E_1^0, and E_0^0, we have

$$\psi_0 \sim A_0 e^{-\alpha^2 x^2/2} \left(1 - \frac{\beta}{\hbar \omega} x\right).$$

If β vanishes we recover the unperturbed ground-state solution. To a first-order approximation the perturbation causes no change to the ground-state energy level, but it does destroy the symmetry of the wavefunction. The forms of the perturbed and unperturbed ground-state wavefunctions are sketched in Figure 9.8. First-order perturbation theory predicts that, at $x = 0$, the perturbed and unperturbed wavefunctions will have the same value.

A closer look at the results of this example reveals a disturbing feature: the perturbed wavefunction possesses two extrema. How can this be for a ground state? The resolution of this question serves as a cautionary tale for users of perturbation theory.

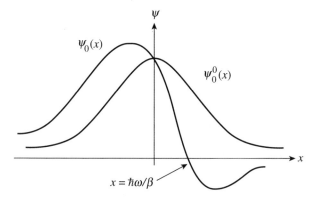

| **FIGURE 9.8** Unperturbed and Approximate Perturbed Ground-state Harmonic-oscillator Wavefunctions.

It is possible to solve this example exactly and so glean some insight as to the limits of perturbation theory. First, on completing the square, the perturbed potential can be written as

$$V(x) = \left(\sqrt{\frac{k}{2}}x + \frac{\beta}{\sqrt{2k}}\right)^2 - \frac{\beta^2}{2k}.$$

On defining a new coordinate given by $\xi = \gamma(Ax + B)$ where $\gamma^4 = 2m/\hbar^2 A^2$, $A = \sqrt{k/2}$, and $B = \beta/\sqrt{2k}$, Schrödinger's equation for this potential can be written in the form

$$\frac{d^2\psi}{d\xi^2} + (\lambda - \xi^2)\psi = 0,$$

where $\lambda = \gamma^2(E + \beta^2/2k)$. This is identical to the form of the SE for the unperturbed harmonic oscillator, Equation (5.1.5). The ground state energy corresponds to $\lambda = 1$ (see Equation (5.3.20) with $n = 0$),

$$E^{exact}_{ground} = \frac{\hbar\omega}{2} - \frac{\beta^2}{2k},$$

where $\omega = \sqrt{k/m}$ as usual. Contrary to the conclusion of first-order perturbation theory, the exact solution shows that the ground state energy is less than for the unperturbed case. The essential behavior of the exact ground-state wavefunction is then

$$\psi_{\text{ground}}^{\text{exact}} \sim e^{-\xi^2/2} \sim e^{-[\gamma(Ax+B)^2]}$$

$$\sim \left[e^{-\alpha^2 x^2/2}\right]\left[e^{-(\beta/\hbar\omega)x}\right]\left[e^{-\beta^2/2\hbar\omega k}\right],$$

where α is as we defined in Chapter 5. As expected for a ground state, this solution has no nodes other than at $x = 0$ and $x = \infty$. The first factor on the right side is the normal harmonic oscillator ground state, whereas the third factor is a constant. The middle factor on the right side is a new x-dependent term; if $\beta \rightarrow 0$, we recover the unperturbed case. The interesting thing about this new term is that if one expands it to first order in x,

$$e^{-(\beta/\hbar\omega)x} \approx 1 - \frac{\beta}{\hbar\omega}x + \ldots,$$

we arrive at an expression identical to that given by first-order perturbation theory! The result yielded by first-order perturbation theory is thus but the first term of an exponential function. For $x > 0$, the exact solution is asymmetric and has only one extremum.

The point of this example should be clear: perturbation theory yields only an *approximation* to a true solution, and one must be careful when interpreting the results.

EXAMPLE 9.6

A collection of hydrogen atoms is subject to a uniform external electric field in the z-direction of strength λ Volt/meter. Determine the perturbations to the electronic energy levels.

The effect of an external electric field on the energy levels of an atom is known as the *Stark effect*, after German physicist Johannes Stark (1874–1957). Stark won the 1919 Nobel prize for Physics for its discovery. Here we must use the full machinery of degenerate perturbation theory. The electrical potential corresponding to this field is $V = -\lambda z = -\lambda r \cos\theta$ [recall $\mathbf{E} = -\nabla V$]. An electron of charge $-e$ will then experience a perturbing potential energy $V' = qE$:

$$V' = (-e)(-\lambda r \cos\theta) = +e\lambda r \cos\theta.$$

To keep the calculations involved with the matrix of Equation (9.3.9) tractable, we limit the number of states considered to those of the first two hydrogenic energy levels; that is, to those of fundamental quantum numbers $n = 1$ and $n = 2$. In writing the matrix elements (9.3.8), we label these states from 1 to 5, with states (1, 2, 3, 4, 5) corresponding to hydrogenic states $(n, \ell, m) = (1, 0, 0)$, (2, 0, 0), (2, 1, 0), (2, 1, 1), and (2, 1, −1), respectively. Also, we shall concern ourselves only with the perturbed energies as opposed to the expansion coefficients. Table 7.2 gives the relevant unperturbed wavefunctions. Since some of these functions are explicitly complex, it must be remembered to use the complex conjugates of the ψ_j^0 in computing the matrix elements.

Tedious, if straightforward, calculations (which the reader should verify) show that most of the elements of the matrix in Equation (9.3.9) vanish. The matrix finally appears as

$$
\begin{bmatrix}
(E_1 - E) & 0 & 256\lambda a_o e/243\sqrt{2} & 0 & 0 \\
0 & (E_1/4 - E) & 3\lambda a_o e & 0 & 0 \\
256\lambda a_o e/243\sqrt{2} & 3\lambda a_o e & (E_1/4 - E) & 0 & 0 \\
0 & 0 & 0 & (E_1/4 - E) & 0 \\
0 & 0 & 0 & 0 & (E_1/4 - E)
\end{bmatrix},
$$

where a_o is the Bohr radius and E_1 is the hydrogen ground-state energy. After further algebra, the determinant of this matrix emerges as

$$B^2(AB^2 - AD^2 - C^2B) = 0,$$

where $A = E_1 - E$, $B = E_1/4 - E$, $C = 256\lambda a_o e/243\sqrt{2}$, and $D = 3\lambda a_o e$. Writing this out explicitly gives

$$(E_1/4 - E)^2 \{E^3 - (3E_1/2)E^2 + (9E_1^2/16 - D^2 - C^2)E$$
$$+ (E_1 D^2 + E_1 C^2/4 - E_1^3/16)\} = 0.$$

From the prefactor of $(E_1/4 - E)^2$ in the determinant, we can infer that there is a double root of $E = E_1/4$. This means that, to this level of approximation, two of the four $n = 2$ states remain unperturbed. The energies of the other three solutions are obtained by solving the cubic equation in E that resides within the curly brackets. Because this is algebraically messy, we content ourselves with a numerical example.

To aid in examining this cubic equation it is helpful to cast it into a dimensionless form. This can be accomplished by expressing the electric field strength λ as a multiple (say, λ^*) of some field strength that could be regarded as natural for the problem at hand. To this end, we use the strength of the electric field of the proton at a distance of one Bohr radius:

$$\lambda = \lambda^*\left(\frac{e}{4\pi\epsilon_o a_o^2}\right).$$

Hence

$$\lambda e a_o = \lambda^*\left(\frac{e^2}{4\pi\epsilon_o a_o}\right) = \lambda^*\left(\frac{e^2}{4\pi\epsilon_o}\right)\left(\frac{\pi m_e e^2}{\epsilon_o h^2}\right) = -2\lambda^* E_1.$$

With this result we can put

$$C = -\gamma E_1, \qquad \gamma = \lambda^*(256/243\sqrt{2})$$

and

$$D = -\delta E_1, \qquad \delta = 6\lambda^*.$$

With these, the cubic in E becomes

$$(E/E_1)^3 - (3/2)(E/E_1)^2 + (9/16 - \delta^2 - \gamma^2)(E/E_1) + (\delta^2 + \gamma^2/4 - 1/16) = 0.$$

Parenthetically, the strength of the proton's electric field at a_o is about 5×10^{11} N/C; a pulsed laser system can briefly create fields of about this strength.

Taking $\lambda^* = 0.01$ as an example, three solutions emerge for (E/E_1): $\sim 0.1899, 0.3099$, and 1.0002. The first two of these represent not-quite-symmetrically perturbed $n = 2$ hydrogenic states (normally at $(E/E_1) = 0.25$); the last represents a very slightly perturbed $n = 1$ state. This example illustrates a situation where the original degeneracy is said to be *partially lifted* since two degenerate states at energy $E_1/4$ remain.

A word of warning is appropriate here: If λ^* is chosen too large ($\lambda^* = 0.25$, for example), you will find that one of the roots for E/E_1 emerges as a negative number, which would have to be interpreted as an unbound state. (Recall that all of the hydrogenic states have $E_n < 0$.) This is because the perturbing potential energy that an $n = 2$ electron would experience in such a situation, on the order of $-2\lambda^* E_1$, is greater in magnitude than its initial energy $E_1/4$. The level of approximation used here would not be adequate in such circumstances; more unperturbed states would have to be allowed to contribute to the solution. Perturbation theory is intended for use when the perturbing effect is small compared to the initial condition of what is being perturbed.

■ 9.4   The Variational Method

The variational method is a technique for estimating ground-state energies of potentials where one can make an educated guess at the mathematical form of the ground-state wavefunction. The only requirement is a normalized trial wavefunction that satisfies the boundary conditions of the problem; it need not satisfy the SE. We will first show how an estimate on the ground-state energy can be obtained, then address some strategies for establishing a trial wavefunction.

If $\phi(x)$ is the trial ground-state wavefunction, then the predicted ground-state energy E is

$$E = \langle \phi^* | H | \phi \rangle, \tag{1}$$

where H is the Hamiltonian operator

$$H = -\frac{\hbar^2}{2m} \frac{d^2}{dx^2} + V(x), \tag{2}$$

presuming that we are working in one dimension.

Now, the SE for the potential under consideration will in principle possess some family of exact solutions; call these $\psi_n(x)$ and label their corresponding energies E_n. If we knew the $\psi_n(x)$ we could expand $\phi(x)$ in terms of them along the lines of the development of the superposition theorem of Section 9.2:

$$\phi(x) = \sum_n a_n \psi_n(x), \tag{3}$$

where

$$a_j = \langle \psi_j | \phi \rangle. \tag{4}$$

In reality, the idea is that we do not know the $\psi_n(x)$: if we did there would be no sense in trying to establish an approximate solution! The important point for the moment is that if we did know them we could in principle expand out Equation (3) explicitly.

If $\phi(x)$ is to be plausible as a trial wavefunction, it must satisfy two physical criteria: (i) it must satisfy the boundary conditions of the problem at hand, and (ii) it must be normalized. In practice, condition (i) is ensured by a judicious choice of $\phi(x)$, as will be discussed shortly. Condition (ii) was explored in Section 9.2, where we found that the constraint

$$\sum |a_n|^2 = 1 \tag{5}$$

will ensure normalization of $\phi(x)$. Although this result plays a central role in the development that follows, we will see that in practice the a_n need not be explicitly computed.

Substitute Equation (3) into Equation (1). This gives

$$\langle \phi^*|H|\phi\rangle = \int \left(\sum_n a_n^* \psi_n^* \right) H \left(\sum_m a_m \psi_m \right) dx$$

$$= \sum_n \sum_m a_n^* a_m \int \psi_n^* (H\psi_m) \, dx = \sum_n \sum_m a_n^* a_m \int \psi_n^* E_m \psi_m \, dx$$

$$= \sum_n \sum_m a_n^* a_m E_m \int \psi_n^* \psi_m \, dx$$

$$= \sum_n \sum_m a_n^* a_m E_m \delta_n^m. \tag{6}$$

Because of the δ_n^m the inner sum (over m) vanishes for all terms except when $m = n$, leaving

$$E = \sum_n a_n^* a_n E_n = \sum_n |a_n|^2 E_n. \tag{7}$$

Consider the right side of Equation (7). Designate the true ground state energy as E_0; since all of the other states must have $E_n \geq E_0$, then

$$\sum_n |a_n|^2 E_n \geq \sum_n |a_n|^2 E_0,$$

or, since E_0 is a constant,

$$\sum_n |a_n|^2 E_n \geq E_0 \sum_n |a_n|^2.$$

The sum on the right side is just 1, however (Equation 5), so,

$$\sum_n |a_n|^2 E_n \geq E_0. \tag{8}$$

Comparing Equations (7) and (8) shows that

$$E \geq E_0. \tag{9}$$

The essential result here is that if $\phi(x)$ is a normalized trial wavefunction for the ground state of a system, $\langle \phi^*|H|\phi \rangle$ sets an upper limit to the ground-state energy. In practical use, one starts with a trial wavefunction that obeys the relevant boundary conditions, and which contains some parameter(s), and then varies the parameter(s) to minimize $\langle \phi^*|H|\phi \rangle$. In the next section we will examine how this scheme can be modified to give a lower limit on E_0 as well.

How does one make a "judicious" choice for the trial wavefunction? A potential that supports bound states can ultimately be conceived of as some sort of potential well, in which case we know that $\psi \to 0$ as $x \to \infty$. From prior experience (finite rectangular well, harmonic oscillator, hydrogen atom) we also know that such states are often characterized by exponential-decay functions. If the domain of the potential runs over $-\infty \leq x \leq +\infty$, a function of the form $\phi(x) = Ae^{-\beta x^2}$ will both satisfy the boundary conditions and be normalizable over the domain. Note that ϕ contains two constants, A and β. A is a normalization constant; on computing $\int \phi^2(x)\,dx$ it will emerge in terms of β. When the energy estimate E is computed from Equations (1) and (2), it too will emerge in terms of β; the resulting expression can then be differentiated with respect to β and minimized in order to yield the lowest possible estimate of E. β is thus the *variational* parameter. [Parenthetically, if the domain is $-\infty \leq x \leq +\infty$, any even-powered exponential would do. (Why?) Similarly, if the domain is restricted to $0 \leq x \leq +\infty$ then an odd-powered exponential such as $Ae^{-\beta x}$ or $Ae^{-\beta x^3}$ could be used. (Why?)] If your potential contains an infinite wall at, say, $x = 0$ (but otherwise runs over $0 \leq x \leq +\infty$), such an exponential function will be fine as $x \to \infty$ but unsatisfactory at $x = 0$, as it does not respect the boundary condition there. In such a case we could modify $\phi(x)$ to, say, the form $\phi(x) = Axe^{-\beta x^2}$. If you are ambitious you could try a function of the form $\phi(x) = Af(x)e^{-\beta x^2}$ where $f(x)$ is a function containing yet more variational parameters; you would then face a multiparameter minimization problem. An approach for a two-parameter function might be $\phi(x) = Ae^{-\beta x^n}$ where the power "n" in the exponential is considered a variational parameter along with β. This sort of extreme measure is usually not required for the level of problems intended here, however.

Although it has been emphasized that this method yields an upper limit on the ground-state energy, there is no explicit requirement in the derivation that $\phi(x)$ actually look anything like a ground-state wavefunction; indeed *all* states, ground and excited alike, have to satisfy the boundary conditions and be normalizable. The variational theorem tells you only that the energy corresponding to $\phi(x)$ must be greater than or equal to that of the ground state. If you choose $\phi(x) = Af(x)e^{-\beta x^2}$ with $f(x)$ as a polynomial, for example, you might actually be choosing a function that does a better job of mimicking an excited state rather than the ground state, in which case the resulting value of E will likely be a very poor estimate of the ground state energy. Simplicity is a virtue when choosing trial wavefunctions.

EXAMPLE 9.7

Use the variational method to set an upper limit on the ground-state energy of the linear potential

$$V(x) = \begin{cases} \infty & (x < 0) \\ \alpha x & (x \geq 0). \end{cases}$$

This problem was addressed with the uncertainty principle in Problem 4-10 and with the WKB method in Example 9.1; it will be interesting to compare the merits of these approximation schemes.

First we need a plausible trial wavefunction $\phi(x)$. From Chapter 3, we know that the ground state wavefunction will have one maximum. We also know that it must go to zero at $x = 0$ and decay exponentially at large x. These features are sketched in Figure 9.9.

As suggested by the previous discussion, a simple function that satisfies these requirements is

$$\phi(x) = Axe^{-\beta x},$$

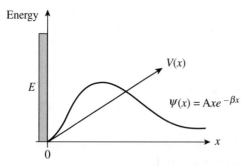

FIGURE 9.9 Hypothetical Linear Potential Ground State.

where A is the normalization constant and β the variational parameter. Normalization demands

$$A^2 \int_0^\infty x^2 e^{-2\beta x} dx = 1,$$

that is, $2A^2/(2\beta)^3 = 1$, or $A^2 = 4\beta^3$.

It is always necessary to compute $d^2\phi/dx^2$ in order to compute $H\phi$:

$$\frac{d^2\phi}{dx^2} = A(\beta^2 x - 2\beta)e^{-\beta x},$$

hence

$$H\phi = -\frac{\hbar^2}{2m}\frac{d^2\phi}{dx^2} + V(x)\phi = Ae^{-\beta x}(2\beta\epsilon - \beta^2\epsilon x + \alpha x^2),$$

where

$$\epsilon = \hbar^2/2m.$$

The expectation value of the Hamiltonian is then

$$\langle\phi|H|\phi\rangle = A^2\left\{2\beta\epsilon\int_0^\infty xe^{-2\beta x}dx - \beta^2\epsilon\int_0^\infty x^2 e^{-2\beta x}dx + \alpha\int_0^\infty x^3 e^{-2\beta x}dx\right\}.$$

These integrals evaluate to $1/(4\beta^2)$, $1/(4\beta^3)$, and $3/(8\beta^4)$, respectively, and in combination with the expression for A give

$$E = \epsilon\beta^2 + (3\alpha/2\beta).$$

To set the strictest possible limit on E_0 we need to minimize E with respect to β. Computing $dE/d\beta$, setting the result to zero, and solving for β gives

$$\beta_{min} = (3\alpha/4\epsilon)^{1/3}.$$

Back-substituting this result into the expression for E gives

$$E_{min} = \epsilon(3\alpha/4\epsilon)^{2/3} + (3\alpha/2)(3\alpha/4\epsilon)^{-1/3} = 2.476\alpha^{2/3}\epsilon^{1/3}.$$

Therefore, the ground state energy must satisfy $E_0 \leq 2.476\alpha^{2/3}\epsilon^{1/3}$. This is consistent with the results yielded by the uncertainty principle and the WKB method: $E_0/(\alpha^{2/3}\epsilon^{1/3}) > 1.191$ and ~ 2.811, respectively. The exact solution is $2.338\alpha^{2/3}\epsilon^{1/3}$. Our variational upper limit exceeds the correct result by only about 6%.

The power of the variational method is that any trial wavefunction will do as long as it respects the boundary conditions of the problem. It need not (and in general will not) satisfy the SE for the potential at hand. The closer one's guess for the trial wavefunction is to the actual ground-state wavefunction, the more accurate will be the result.

EXAMPLE 9.8

This example is somewhat abstract; you might want to come back to it after first working a few of the end-of-chapter problems on the variational technique.

In this example we apply the variational theorem in spherical coordinates to determine an upper limit for the ground-state energy for a particle of mass m moving in the attractive central potential (ACP)

$$V(r) = -K E_1 \left(\frac{a_o}{r}\right)^n \quad (0 \leq r \leq \infty), \tag{1}$$

where K is a dimensionless strength parameter, a_o is the Bohr radius, and E_1 is the absolute value of the ground-state energy of the hydrogen atom. Both K and n are assumed to be positive; bound states will have $E < 0$.

As a trial wavefunction, we use a function of the form of the hydrogenic ground-state:

$$\phi(r) = A\exp(-\beta r/2) \quad (0 \leq r \leq \infty),$$

where β is the variational parameter. Normalizing this function demands

$$4\pi A^2 \int_0^\infty r^2 e^{-\beta r}\, dr = 1,$$

where the factor of 4π arises from integrating over θ and ϕ. The integrals reduce to $2/\beta^3$, so our trial wavefunction is

$$\phi(r) = \sqrt{\frac{\beta^3}{8\pi}} \exp(-\beta r/2) \qquad (0 \le r \le \infty). \tag{2}$$

The value of using this particular trial wavefunction is that when $n = 1$ and $K = 2$ we should recover the exact ground-state energy for hydrogen, thus providing a check on our calculations.

Since both the potential and the trial wavefunction have only radial dependencies, we can write the Hamiltonian operator as

$$H = -\frac{\hbar^2}{2m}\nabla^2 + V(r) \equiv -\frac{\hbar^2}{2m}\frac{1}{r^2}\frac{d}{dr}\left(r^2\frac{d}{dr}\right) + V(r). \tag{3}$$

The expectation value for the energy is

$$E = 4\pi \int_0^\infty \phi\,(H\phi)\,r^2 dr, \tag{4}$$

where the factor of 4π comes from integrating over the volume element in spherical coordinates $(0 \le \theta \le \pi;\ 0 \le \phi \le 2\pi)$.

The Laplacian of the trial wavefunction is

$$\nabla^2\phi = -\frac{\beta^{5/2}}{2\sqrt{8\pi}}\left(\frac{2}{r} - \frac{\beta}{2}\right)e^{-\beta r/2},$$

leading to

$$E = \frac{\hbar^2\beta^4}{8m}\int_0^\infty (2r - \beta r^2/2)\,e^{-\beta r}\,dr - \frac{KE_1 a_o^n \beta^3}{2}\int_0^\infty r^{2-n}e^{-\beta r}\,dr.$$

Evaluating the integrals gives, after some algebra,

$$E = \frac{\hbar^2\beta^2}{8m} - \frac{KE_1\,a_o^n\,\beta^n\,\Gamma(3-n)}{2}, \quad (n < 3) \tag{5}$$

where $\Gamma(x)$ denotes a gamma function (see Appendix C). The solution of the second integral in the expression for E leads to a constraint on the value of n.

Minimizing E with respect to β gives

$$\beta = \left\{ \frac{\hbar^2}{2mn\,K\,E_1\,a_o^n\,\Gamma(3-n)} \right\}^{\frac{1}{n-2}} \quad (n < 3). \tag{6}$$

The reader should verify that for $n = 1$, $K = 2$, and $m = m_e$ this expression gives $\beta = 2/a_o$, and that Equation (2) consequently reduces to exactly the hydrogenic ground-state wavefunction. Back-substituting this result into the expression above for E yields

$$\frac{E}{(E_1/\mu)} = \frac{1}{4\,[(K\mu)n\,\Gamma(3-n)]^{2/(n-2)}} \left\{ 1 - \frac{2}{n} \right\}, \tag{7}$$

where μ is the ratio of the mass of the particle to that of the electron: $\mu = (m/m_e)$.

A key point here is that the variational method is predicated on minimizing E; on computing the second derivative of E with respect to β from Equation (5), one finds that it yields a minimum only for $n < 2$.

Clearly, the ground-state energies of ACPs depend on n and the combination $(K\mu)$ of the dimensionless parameters K and μ. Figure 9.10 illustrates ground-state upper limits for ACPs of various $(K\mu)$ as a function of n; the quantity plotted on the vertical axis is the dimensionless energy $W = E/(E_1/\mu)$. A number of conclusions follow directly:

(i) Negative-energy bound states are possible for ACPs with $0 < n < 2$.

(ii) The prediction of Equation (7) for the Coulomb potential, $(K, n, \mu) = (2, 1, 1)$, is $W = -1$, the exact value. This is to be expected on the basis that the trial wavefunction is the exact solution of Schrödinger's equation in this case.

(iii) The most striking feature of Figure 9.10 is that for $(K\mu) > 0.5$ (see below) there exists a *least-bound* ground state of an ACP; as $(K\mu)$ increases, both the value of n at which the maximum energy occurs and the energy of the ground state both decrease; that is, the ground state becomes more tightly bound. Interestingly, the ground state of the Coulomb potential is about as unbound as it could possibly be. Numerical solutions of the radial Schrödinger equation (Chapter 10) verify the presence of the maxima seen in the figure. Equation (7) actually proves to yield fairly stringent upper

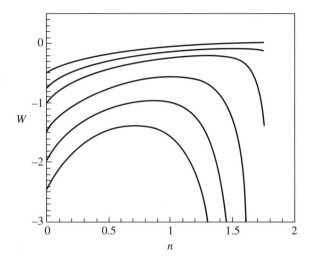

FIGURE 9.10   Upper limits for ground-state energies of attractive central potentials. From top to bottom, the curves correspond to $K\mu = 0.5, 0.75, 1, 1.5, 2$, and 2.5.

limits: for $(K\mu) = 1$, for example, it predicts $-W = (0.435, 0.250, 0.260)$ for $n = (0.5, 1.0, 1.5)$, whereas the true solutions are $-W \sim (0.438, 0.250, 0.292)$; the variational calculation overestimates the true energies by about $(0.7, 0, 11)$ percent.

How does the value $K\mu = 0.5$ come to be critical for determining whether or not an ACP will exhibit a least-bound ground state? To answer this, it is instructive to study the behavior of E as $n \rightarrow 2$. In this limit, $\Gamma(3 - n)$ approaches unity from above, in which case Equation (7) reduces to

$$\left[\frac{E}{(E_1/\mu)}\right]_{n \to 2} \Rightarrow \frac{1}{4}(2K\mu)^\infty (1 - 2/n). \tag{8}$$

Two fates are possible for E when $0 < n < 2$: if $(K\mu) \leq 0.5$, then $E \rightarrow 0$ from below, whereas if $(K\mu) > 0.5$, $E \rightarrow -\infty$. An exact solution of Schrödinger's equation for this potential reveals that the critical value of $(K\mu)$ that discriminates between these two behaviors is $(K\mu) = 1/4$. That the present result for the critical value of $(K\mu)$ differs from this is not surprising in view of the fact that we have utilized a trial wavefunction that is approximate except when $n = 1$.

■ 9.5   Improving the Variational Method (Optional)

The variational method is somewhat unsatisfying in that it gives no indication of how far the true ground state energy E_0 may be from the upper limit E that it provides. In this section we take up a modification of the variational technique that gives both upper and lower limits on E_0.

Again, let $\phi(x)$ be a normalized trial ground-state wavefunction, and let E be defined as before by

$$E = \langle \phi^* | H | \phi \rangle. \tag{1}$$

Now define a new quantity D given by

$$D = \int (H\phi)^* (H\phi) \, dx. \tag{2}$$

D will have units of (energy)^2. Expanding $\phi(x)$ in terms of the exact solutions $\psi_n(x)$ to the problem, we can write

$$D = \int \left(H \sum_n a_n \psi_n \right)^* \left(H \sum_m a_m \psi_m \right) dx.$$

Recalling that $H\psi_j = E_j \psi_j$, we have

$$D = \int \left(H \sum_n a_n \psi_n \right)^* \left(H \sum_m a_m \psi_m \right) dx = \sum_n \sum_m \left\{ a_n^* a_m E_n E_m \int \psi_n^* \psi_m \, dx \right\}$$

$$= \sum_n \sum_m \left\{ a_n^* a_m E_n E_m \delta_m^n \right\} = \sum_n a_n^* a_n E_n^2,$$

or,

$$D = \sum_n |a_n|^2 E_n^2. \tag{3}$$

Now consider the quantity Δ defined as

$$\Delta = \sum_n |a_n|^2 (E_n - E)^2, \tag{4}$$

where E is defined in Equation (1). Expanding the binomial in this definition gives

$$\Delta = \sum_n |a_n|^2 (E_n^2 - 2E_n E + E^2)$$

$$= \sum_n |a_n|^2 E_n^2 - 2E \left(\sum_n |a_n|^2 E_n \right) + E^2 \sum_n |a_n|^2.$$

The first term in this expression is D (Equation 3), the bracketed term is E (Equation 9.4.7), and the sum in the last term is equal to 1 (Equation 9.4.5), hence

$$\Delta = D - 2E(E) + E^2 = D - E^2. \tag{5}$$

Again, the ground-state energy E_0 must be less than (or at most equal to) all of the higher energy levels: $E_0 \le E_n$. Therefore

$$(E_0 - E)^2 \le (E_n - E)^2,$$

or,

$$\sum_n |a_n|^2 (E_0 - E)^2 \le \sum_n |a_n|^2 (E_n - E)^2.$$

The right side of this last expression is just Δ; in the left side, $(E_0 - E)^2$ is a constant and can be brought in front of the sum to give

$$(E_0 - E)^2 \sum_n |a_n|^2 \le \Delta.$$

But the sum of the $|a_n|^2$ is just 1, so

$$\Delta \ge (E_0 - E)^2, \tag{6}$$

or

$$\sqrt{\Delta} \ge \pm (E_0 - E). \tag{7}$$

Now, Equation (9.4.9) tells us that $E \geq E_0$, or $(E_0 - E) \leq 0$. Considering the lower-sign case in Equation (7), we have

$$\sqrt{\Delta} \geq E - E_0,$$

or,

$$E_0 \geq E - \sqrt{\Delta}.$$

Recalling the $\Delta = D - E^2$ (Equation 5), we can combine this result with Equation (9.4.9) to give a revised statement of the variational method that provides both upper and lower limits on E_0:

$$E \geq E_0 \geq E - \sqrt{D - E^2}. \tag{8}$$

In practice, one sets up a trial function with variational parameters and varies these parameters until $D - E^2$ is minimized; this ensures the most stringent possible limits on E_0 consistent with how well the trial wavefunction matches the true ground-state wavefunction. Selection of the upper sign in Equation (7) leads to a weaker upper limit on E_0 than is already available from Equation (9.4.9).

EXAMPLE 9.9

Rework Example 9.7 with the improved variational method.
From Example 9.7 we had

$$H\phi = -\epsilon\frac{d^2\phi}{dx^2} + V(x)\phi = A e^{-\beta x}(2\beta\epsilon - \beta^2\epsilon x + \alpha x^2),$$

where

$$A^2 = 4\beta^3,$$

and

$$E = \epsilon\beta^2 + (3\alpha/2\beta).$$

From Equation (2) and the result for $(H\phi)$, we find

$$D = \int (H\phi)^*(H\phi)\,dx = 4A^2\beta^2\epsilon^2 \int_0^\infty e^{-2\beta x}\,dx - 4A^2\beta^3\epsilon^2 \int_0^\infty xe^{-2\beta x}\,dx$$

$$+ (4A^2\beta\epsilon\alpha + A^2\beta^4\epsilon^2) \int_0^\infty x^2 e^{-2\beta x}\,dx - 2A^2\beta^2\epsilon\alpha \int_0^\infty x^3 e^{-2\beta x}\,dx$$

$$+ A^2\alpha^2 \int_0^\infty x^4 e^{-2\beta x}\,dx.$$

These integrals are all standard; after some algebra one finds

$$D = 5\beta^4\epsilon^2 + \beta\epsilon\alpha + 3\alpha^2/\beta^2.$$

Combining this result with our previous result for E gives

$$(D - E^2) = 4\beta^4\epsilon^2 - 2\beta\epsilon\alpha + 3\alpha^2/4\beta^2.$$

Minimizing $(D - E^2)$ with respect to β results in a quadratic equation in β^3:

$$16\epsilon^2(\beta^3)^2 - 2\epsilon\alpha(\beta^3) - (3\alpha^2/2) = 0.$$

Solving the quadratic gives

$$\beta_{min}^3 = \frac{3\alpha}{8\epsilon} \quad \text{or} \quad -\frac{\alpha}{4\epsilon}.$$

The second root implies an imaginary value for β. This would lead to an imaginary estimate for E, which we reject as unphysical. Note that the remaining root, $\beta_{min}^3 = 3\alpha/8\epsilon$, is different from the result obtained in Example 9.7 ($\beta_{min}^3 = 3\alpha/4\epsilon$) when only E alone was minimized. Back-substituting this root into the expression for $(D - E^2)$ results in

$$(D - E^2)_{min} = [4(3/8)^{4/3}](\alpha^{4/3}\epsilon^{2/3}),$$

or,

$$\sqrt{(D - E^2)_{min}} = 1.040\,(\alpha^{2/3}\epsilon^{1/3}).$$

In the expression for E alone, this root gives

$$E_{min} = [5(3/8)^{2/3}](\alpha^{2/3}\epsilon^{1/3}) = 2.600\,(\alpha^{2/3}\epsilon^{1/3}),$$

and hence

$$E - \sqrt{(D - E^2)_{min}} = 1.560\,(\alpha^{2/3}\epsilon^{1/3}).$$

Consistent with the remarks following Equation (8), this result for E_{min} is slightly greater than the one we obtained by minimizing E alone in Example 9.7. Combining the results from both methods gives

$$2.476 \geq (E_0/\alpha^{2/3}\epsilon^{1/3}) \geq 1.560.$$

These limits bracket the exact value of 2.338.
    An improved version of the trial wavefunction for this problem is

$$\psi(x) = Ax\exp(-\beta x^n),$$

where n is taken to be a second variational parameter that is held constant through the variational calculation. The result is an expression for $\beta(n)$ that sets maximum and minimum limits on the ground state energy according to Equation (8); n can then be varied until the most restrictive limits are found, which can be shown to be $2.298 \leq (E_0/\alpha^{2/3}\epsilon^{1/3}) \leq 2.378$ when $n = 1.773$. These limits bracket the exact result to better than 2% [2].

■ Summary

This chapter explores three methods of obtaining approximate energies and/or wavefunctions corresponding to potentials for which one cannot solve Schrödinger's equation exactly.
    The WKB approximation says that the energy E corresponding to principal quantum number n of a particle of mass m moving in a potential $V(x)$ satisfies

$$2\sqrt{2m}\int\sqrt{E - V(x)}\,dx \sim nh.$$

This approximation is valid where

$$\frac{mh}{\{2m[E - V(x)]\}^{3/2}}\left(\frac{dV}{dx}\right) \ll 1.$$

The development of perturbation theory hinges on the superposition theorem: that any function $\phi(x)$ can be represented as a linear sum over all of the $\psi_n(x)$ that satisfy the SE for some potential:

$$\phi(x) = \sum_n a_n \psi_n(x),$$

where the expansion coefficients are in general given by

$$a_n = \langle \psi_j(x)|\phi(x)\rangle.$$

In notation where superscript 0 designates the energies and wavefunctions corresponding to a potential for which one can solve the SE exactly, the energies and wavefunctions corresponding to a perturbation V' are given by those values of E that render the determinant

$$\begin{vmatrix} V_{11} & \cdots & V_{1k} & \cdots & V_{1r} & \cdots & V_{1N} \\ \vdots & \ddots & \vdots & \vdots & \vdots & \vdots & \vdots \\ V_{k1} & \cdots & V_{kk} & \cdots & V_{kr} & \cdots & V_{kN} \\ \vdots & \vdots & \vdots & \ddots & \vdots & \vdots & \vdots \\ V_{r1} & \cdots & V_{rk} & \cdots & V_{rr} & \cdots & V_{rN} \\ \vdots & \vdots & \vdots & \vdots & \vdots & \ddots & \vdots \\ V_{N1} & \cdots & V_{Nk} & \cdots & V_{Nr} & \cdots & V_{NN} \end{vmatrix}$$

equal to zero, where the elements are given by

$$V_{jm} = \{(E_m^0 - E)\langle \psi_j^0|\psi_m^0\rangle + \langle \psi_j^0|V'|\psi_m^0\rangle\}.$$

If a solution for the perturbed potential is written as a linear sum of N of the solutions of the unperturbed potential,

$$\psi(\mathbf{r}) = \sum_{m=1}^{N} C_m \psi_m^0(\mathbf{r}),$$

then the expansion coefficients are given by

$$C_i = \frac{V_{ik}^*}{\sqrt{\sum_n \sum_m \{(V_{nk}^*)(V_{mk}^*)\langle \psi_n^0 | \psi_m^0 \rangle\}}}, \quad (i = 1, N)$$

where V_{ik}^* designates the (i, k)th element of the inverse of the square matrix

$$\begin{bmatrix} V_{11} & \cdots & V_{1k} & \cdots & V_{1r} & \cdots & V_{1N} \\ \vdots & \ddots & \vdots & & \vdots & \vdots & \vdots \\ V_{k1} & \cdots & V_{kk} & \cdots & V_{kr} & \cdots & V_{kN} \\ \vdots & \vdots & \vdots & \ddots & \vdots & \vdots & \vdots \\ V_{r1} & \cdots & \langle \psi_r^0 | V' | \psi_k^0 \rangle & \cdots & V_{rr} & \cdots & V_{rN} \\ \vdots & \vdots & \vdots & \vdots & \ddots & \vdots \\ V_{N1} & \cdots & V_{Nk} & \cdots & V_{Nr} & \cdots & V_{NN} \end{bmatrix},$$

not the complex conjugate of V_{ik}. First-order expressions for the energies and wavefunctions corresponding to a perturbation V' are much easier to deal with, being given by

$$E \sim E_m^0 + \langle \psi_m^0 | V' | \psi_m^0 \rangle$$

and

$$\psi_n \sim \psi_n^0 - \sum_{k \neq n} \frac{\psi_k^0 \langle \psi_k^0 | V' | \psi_n^0 \rangle}{(E_k^0 - E_n^0)}.$$

The variational method is a powerful technique for estimating ground state energies when one can formulate a trial ground-state wavefunction. The trial function need not satisfy the SE for the potential at hand, only the boundary conditions of the problem. In the simplest form of this method, if $\phi(x)$ is a normalized trial function, then the ground-state energy E_0 is constrained by

$$E_0 \leq \langle \phi^* | H | \phi \rangle$$

where H is the Hamiltonian operator.

Problems

9-1(I) Expand the function $\phi(x) = x^2$ in terms of the infinite rectangular well wave-functions. Take $L = 1$; plot your result for terms in the sum up to (a) $n = 5$, and (b) $n = 20$.

9-2(I) Expand the function $\phi(x) = e^{ax}$ in terms of the infinite rectangular well wavefunctions. Take $L = 1$ and $a = 3$; plot your result for terms in the sum up to (a) $n = 5$, and (b) $n = 20$.

9-3(I) Using the WKB approximation, determine the energy eigenvalues for a particle of mass m moving in a potential given by $V(x) = \alpha|x|$, $(-\infty \leq x \leq \infty)$.

9-4(I) In Example 9.2 it was shown that the WKB method predicts the energy levels of the hydrogen atom exactly. Following the approach of Example 9.1, investigate the application of the classical approximation to this system at the point $r_{turn}/2$ for a general energy level E_n.

9-5(I) Show that application of the WKB method to the harmonic-oscillator potential $V(x) = kx^2/2$ leads to $E_n \sim n\hbar\omega$. Investigate the application of the classical approximation to this system at the point $x_{turn}/2$ for a general energy level E_n.

9-6(I) Set up the WKB expression for the energy levels of a potential given by

$$V(x) = \begin{cases} \infty & x \leq 0 \\ A\sin^2(x/\alpha) & 0 \leq (x/\alpha) \leq \pi/2 \\ 0 & \text{otherwise.} \end{cases}$$

If an electron were trapped in such a potential with $A = 24\ eV$ and $\alpha = 6$ Å at an energy of 12 eV, approximately what quantum state would it be in?

NOTE: $\displaystyle\int_0^{\pi/4} \sqrt{1 - 2\sin^2 y}\, dy = 0.5991.$

9-7(I) Set up the WKB integral for the potential

$$V(x) = \begin{cases} \infty & (x < 0) \\ V_0(e^{\alpha x} - 1) & (0 \leq x \leq \ln 2/\alpha) \\ V_0 & (x > \ln 2/\alpha). \end{cases}$$

If there is an energy level with $n = 4$ at $E = 7$ eV when $V_0 = 28$ eV, determine the value of α.

9-8(A) Consider the family of potential wells defined by

$$V(x) = \alpha|x|^q, \qquad (-\infty \le x \le \infty); q > 0.$$

(a) Show that the WKB integral for this potential can be put in the form

$$\frac{4\sqrt{2m}}{q\alpha^{1/q}} E^{(q+2)/2q} \int_0^1 y^{1/q-1}\sqrt{1 - y}\,dy \sim nh,$$

where $y = (\alpha/E)x^q$.

(b) An integral of this form is related to a so-called *Beta function*, which can be expressed in terms of Gamma functions:

$$\int_0^1 x^{m-1}(1 - x)^{n-1}dx = \frac{\Gamma(m)\Gamma(n)}{\Gamma(m + n)}.$$

Two properties of the Gamma function, $\Gamma(x + 1) = x! = x\Gamma(x)$ and $\Gamma(1/2) = \sqrt{\pi}$ are helpful here. Hence show that the energy levels are given approximately by

$$E_n \sim \left\{\frac{nh\alpha^{1/q}\Gamma(3/2 + 1/q)}{2\sqrt{2\pi m}\Gamma(1 + 1/q)}\right\}^{2q/(p+2)}.$$

Check this result in the case of the harmonic oscillator: $q = 2$ and $\alpha = k/2$. For further treatment of this problem, see Sukhatme, U.P., *American Journal of Physics* 1973;41:1015.

9-9(I) An infinite rectangular potential well is subject to a perturbing potential $V(x) = \alpha x^2$, $(0 \le x \le L)$. Determine a first order approximation for the energy for any state $\psi_n(x)$.

9-10(A) An infinite rectangular potential well is subject to a perturbing potential $V(x) - V^0(x) = -V_0$, $(0 \le x \le L/2)$; see the accompanying diagram.

Determine, to a first order approximation, the energy and wavefunction for any state $\psi_n(x)$.

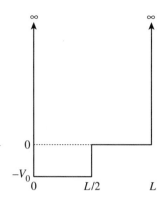

| FIGURE P9.10

9-11(A) A particle of mass m with $\ell = 0$ is trapped in an infinite spherical well of radius a (see Chapter 7). The well is subjected to a perturbing potential $V(r) = \beta r^2$, $(0 \le r \le a)$. Derive expressions for the first order corrections to the energy and wavefunction for any state n.

9-12(I) As the previous problem but with $V(r) = Ar^2 \sin \theta$; derive an expression for the first order correction to the energy for state n.

9-13(A) A ground-state $(n = 0)$ harmonic oscillator is subject to a perturbing potential $V' = \beta x^4$.

(a) Determine the first-order perturbation to the ground-state energy.

(b) Derive an expression for the perturbed ground-state wavefunction. Note that Hermite polynomials satisfy the identity

$$\int_{-\infty}^{\infty} \xi^r e^{-\xi^2} H_n(\xi) H_{n+p}(\xi) \, d\xi = \begin{cases} 0, & (p > r) \\ 2^n (n + r)! \sqrt{\pi}, & (p = r). \end{cases}$$

Hint: The parity properties of Hermite polynomials are useful in eliminating some of the integrals not covered by this identity. Leave your answer in terms of $H_2(\xi)$ and $H_4(\xi)$.

9-14(A) As a consequence of some process within its nuclear proton, the electron in a hydrogen atom finds itself subject to a perturbing potential $V' = \lambda r$. Using Example 9.6 as a model, derive an expression for the determinant to be solved for the perturbed energies. Include contributions from the $n = 1$ and $n = 2$ hydrogenic states. In computing the matrix elements, the following identity for spherical harmonics is helpful:

$$\int\int Y_{\ell_1 m_1} Y_{\ell_2 m_2} \sin\theta\, d\theta\, d\phi = \delta_{\ell_1}^{\ell_2} \delta_{m_1}^{m_2}.$$

Also, the result of Problem 7-18 for $\langle r \rangle$ may be helpful.

9-15(I) A hydrogen atom in the ground state is subject to the perturbing potential $V'(r) = \beta r$. Use nondegenerate first-order perturbation theory to determine the perturbation to the ground-state energy. If it is desired that the perturbation amount be no more than $E_1/10$ (E_1 being the usual hydrogenic ground-state energy), what is the maximum tolerable value of β? Express your results in units of eV and Å.

9-16(E) In Chapter 8 it was shown that an electron orbiting a nucleus with orbital angular momentum **L** gives rise to a (vector) magnetic dipole moment $\boldsymbol{\mu} = (e/2m_e)\mathbf{L}$. A magnetic dipole moment placed in a magnetic field **B** acquires a potential energy given by $V = -\boldsymbol{\mu} \cdot \mathbf{B}$. Consider hydrogen atoms in general (n, ℓ, m) states suddenly subjected to a magnetic field $\mathbf{B} = B\mathbf{z}$ where $\mathbf{z}$ denotes the usual Cartesian-coordinate unit vector in the z-direction. Use nondegenerate first-order perturbation theory to show that the hydrogenic states will be perturbed by an amount $\Delta E = -\mu_B mB$ where μ_B is the Bohr magneton, $\mu_B = (e\hbar/2m_e)$. What does this result imply for the normally fourfold-degenerate $n = 2$ states? Within sunspots, magnetic fields can be as strong as $B = 0.3$ T. In the unperturbed Bohr model, $3 \rightarrow 2$ transitions usually give rise to photons of wavelength 6564 Å. What alteration in the photon wavelength would you expect to observe in the vicinity of such a sunspot? The perturbation of atomic energy levels by an external magnetic field is known as the *Zeeman effect* after Dutch physicist Pieter Zeeman (1865–1943), who shared the 1902 Nobel prize for physics with Hendrik Lorentz for its discovery. A fuller analysis of this effect takes into account both the orbital and spin angular momenta of electrons; some details are given in Chapter 14 of French and Taylor.

9-17(E) In Example 9.6, the term $C = 256\lambda a_o e/243\sqrt{2}$ actually plays a fairly small role in the solution of the cubic equation for the perturbed energy levels. If it is assumed that $C \rightarrow 0$, then the solution for the perturbed energies reduces to $AB^2(B + D)(B - D) = 0$ in the notation of that example. Hence, the result is an unperturbed $n = 1$ level at energy E_1 (the A term), two unperturbed

$n = 2$ levels at energy $E_1/4$ (the B^2 term), and two perturbed $n = 2$ levels at $E = E_1/4 \pm 3\lambda a_o e$ (the $B \pm D$ terms). For a field of strength $\lambda^* = 0.01$, what is the value of the perturbation term $3\lambda a_o e$ expressed as a wavelength; that is, what would be the wavelength of a photon arising from an electron tran-siting from a perturbed $n = 2$ level to an unperturbed $n = 2$ level? Stark-effect spectroscopy is usually carried out in the *microwave* region of the electromagnetic spectrum.

9-18(A) A one-dimensional potential is given by

$$V(x) = \begin{cases} \infty & (x < 0) \\ -A\sqrt{x}e^{-\alpha x^2} & (0 \le x \le \infty). \end{cases}$$

Analyze this potential by the variational method of Section 9.4 with the trial wavefunction $\phi(x) = Bxe^{-\beta x^2}$, where B is a normalization constant and β is the variational parameter. Develop an expression for the value of β that minimizes the system energy for a particle of mass m; you will not be able to solve this expression analytically for β. For the case of an electron mov-ing in this potential with $A = 100$ eV $\text{Å}^{-1/2}$ and $\alpha = 1.75$ Å^{-2}, solve for the value of β that minimizes the energy, and so determine an upper-limit on the ground-state energy.

9-19(A) Analyze the potential $V(x) = -Ae^{-\alpha x^2}$ $(-\infty \le x \le \infty)$ by the variational method with the trial wavefunction $\phi(x) = Be^{-\beta x^2}$ $(-\infty \le x \le \infty)$, where B is a normalization constant and β is the variational parameter. You will not be able to solve the energy-minimization condition analytically for β. In the case of an electron moving in such a potential with $A = 10$ eV and $\alpha = 5$ Å^{-2}, what is the resulting upper-limit on the ground-state energy?

9-20(A) In the theory of nuclear forces a modification of the Coulomb potential known as the *Yukawa potential* is sometimes utilized. This is a purely radial potential given by

$$V(r) = -\left(\frac{\kappa}{r}\right)e^{-(\alpha/a_o)r},$$

where a_o is the Bohr radius, $\kappa = e^2/4\pi\epsilon_o$ (as in the Coulomb potential), and where $\alpha > 0$. Carry out a variational analysis for an electron moving in this potential using as the trial wavefunction $\phi(r) = Ce^{-(\beta/a_o)r}$, where C is a normalization constant and β is the variational parameter; show that the ground-state energy satisfies

$$E_0 \le -E_1 \left\{ \beta^2 - \frac{8\beta^3}{(\alpha + 2\beta)^2} \right\},$$

where E_1 is the hydrogenic ground-state energy. For $\alpha = 0$ the Yukawa potential reduces to the standard hydrogen-atom potential. Since the trial wavefunction is of the form of that for the hydrogenic ground state, then for $\alpha = 0$ we should recover the *exact* solution for the hydrogen ground state; verify that this is so. For $\alpha = 0.5$, determine the value of β that minimizes the expression for E_0 and hence determine an upper limit on the ground state energy in this case.

9-21(I) Consider the following potential, which is a one-dimensional analog of the hydrogen atom:

$$V(x) = \begin{cases} -\dfrac{\kappa}{x}, & x \ge 0 \\ \infty, & x \le 0. \end{cases}$$

Carry out a variational analysis for a particle of mass m moving in this potential, taking as the trial wavefunction

$$\phi(x) = Cxe^{-\beta x} \quad (x \ge 0; \, \phi(x) = 0 \text{ otherwise}),$$

where C is the normalization constant and β is the variational parameter. If $\kappa = e^2/4\pi\epsilon_o$ as in the Coulomb potential, how does your estimate of the ground-state energy (for an electron) compare with that for the usual Coulomb potential?

9-22(I) Use the variational method with the trial wavefunction $\phi(x) = A(\lambda^2 - x^2)$, $|x| \le \lambda$ (ϕ = zero otherwise) to estimate the ground-state energy of the harmonic-oscillator potential $V(x) = kx^2/2$. A is a normalization constant; λ is the variational parameter. Compare your result to the true ground-state energy.

9-23(A) Consider a potential well defined by

$$V(x) = \begin{cases} \infty & x \le 0 \\ \alpha x^n & 0 \le x \le \infty. \end{cases}$$

Using as a trial wavefunction $\phi(x) = Axe^{-\beta x}$, where A is a normalization constant and β a variational parameter, use the variational method to derive an expression for the ground-state energy for $V(x)$. Check your result against Example 9.7 for $n = 1$.

9-24(A) Use the trial wavefunction $C \exp(-\beta r^2)$ to estimate the ground-state energy of the hydrogen atom. Compare your result to the true ground-state energy.

9-25(I) Consider two potentials $V_1(x)$ and $V_2(x)$, which run over the same domain. For a mass m moving in each, you are given that their ground-state solutions are (ψ_1, E_1) and (ψ_2, E_2). Now form a new potential by summing them: $V = V_1 + V_2$. By using the trial wavefunction $\psi(x) = A\psi_1(x)\psi_2(x)$, where A is a normalization constant, show by using the variational theorem that the ground state of the new potential must satisfy

$$E \leq E_1 + E_2 - \frac{A^2\hbar^2}{m}\int \psi_1\psi_2(\nabla\psi_1\nabla\psi_2)\,dx.$$

(The fact that the trial wavefunction has no variational parameter does not render it invalid for use in the variational theorem: there is no requirement that a trial function has to be a particularly good choice.) If $V_1 = V_2$, what does this result indicate for E in comparison to $E_1 + E_2$? Can you make any general statement about how E compares to $E_1 + E_2$?

9-26(E) In the analysis of the attractive central potential (ACP), it was remarked that $K = 2$ and $n = 1$ would cause that example to reduce to the Coulomb potential. Verify this statement.

10 Numerical Solution of Schrödinger's Equation

All of the solutions to Schrödinger's equation that we have considered so far, whether exact or approximate, have been expressible analytically. In many cases, however, the algebra attending these solutions was extremely tedious unless the potential was particularly simple. Based on this experience it is not hard to imagine that even a slight change to an otherwise soluble potential could result in an intractable problem, and that attempting to solve the SE exactly for many potentials will likely be difficult if not impossible.

Through the use of computers, however, it is possible to solve Schrödinger's equation even for complicated potentials via **numerical integration**. For most modern researchers this is the method of choice. Numerical solution not only shifts much drudgery from human to computer, but has the additional advantage that once one has constructed a working program, investigating a different potential becomes as easy as changing a few statements in a subroutine or spreadsheet call. The drawback of a numerical approach is that the eigenstates of a system have to be found specifically one at a time, as opposed to an exact analytic solution where the full spectrum of solutions is captured in one expression. But sometimes one has no choice in the matter.

Numerical solution of differential equations is an active, complex subdiscipline of mathematics and computing science. In this chapter we discuss a straightforward method for solving the one-dimensional Schrödinger equation numerically. It is suitable for use on any personal computer. The method we use is by no means the most elegant or efficient, but it is straightforward and reasonably accurate. The point here is not so much computational elegance as to explore how physical insight and computational power can be used in tandem to explore problems effectively. As in most other cases we have considered, the focus here is on solving for the eigenvalues of *bound* states.

■ 10.1 Atomic Units

Before plunging into details, some practical considerations need to be addressed. The one-dimensional Schrödinger equation can be written as

$$\frac{d^2\psi}{dx^2} = -\beta[E - V(x)]\psi(x),$$ (1)

where

$$\beta = 2m/\hbar^2.$$ (2)

For an electron, $\beta \sim 1.6 \times 10^{38}$ in MKS units. Given that numerical integration of a differential equation is likely to involve thousands of repetitive calculations—each accompanied by possible overflows, underflows, and accumulating round-off errors—numbers of such magnitude are inconvenient at best and catastrophic at worst. In computer work it is best to keep all quantities of order unity to maintain maximum accuracy.

There are two ways of circumventing the magnitude of β: either (i) cast the SE into a dimensionless form (as we have often done) and worry later about restoring proper units and conversion factors into the results, or (ii) work from the outset in a system of units appropriate to atomic-scale problems. To keep the physics of the situation in view, we choose the latter approach.

In setting up any system of units, one must adopt definitions for three fundamental quantities, usually chosen to be length, mass, and time. If you are dealing with problems involving electromagnetism, a fourth fundamental quantity has to be added to this list: electric charge. (The charge on the electron is a useful practical standard.) Units for all other quantities can then be *derived* from the fundamental units—for example [momentum] = [mass][length]/[time], or [energy] = [mass][length]^2/[time]^2—where square brackets denote "dimensions of." From previous experience we know that atomic-scale problems are characterized by lengths on the order of Ångstroms and energies on the order of eV. Let us construct a system of units from these quantities and the mass of the electron as the defined units:

[length] = 1 Å = 1.0000 × 10^{-10} meter. (3)

[mass] = 1 m_e = 9.1094 × 10^{-31} kg. (4)

[energy] = 1 eV = 1.6022 × 10^{-19} Joule. (5)

While it is of no direct use here, the unit of time in this system is a derived quantity:

$$[\text{time}] = \sqrt{\frac{[\text{mass}][\text{length}]^2}{[\text{energy}]}} = 2.3844 \times 10^{-16} \sec.$$

Now,

$$\hbar = 1.0546 \times 10^{-34} Joule - sec.$$

The units of β in Equation (2) are $(Jm^2)^{-1}$. With the preceding definitions, we can construct a conversion factor to atomic units:

$$1 \, (Jm^2)^{-1} = 1.6022 \times 10^{-39} (\text{eV\AA}^2)^{-1}. \tag{6}$$

For an electron, then,

$$\beta_e = 2m_e/\hbar^2 = 1.6831 \times 10^{38} (Jm^2)^{-1} = 0.26246 \, (\text{eV\AA}^2)^{-1}. \tag{7}$$

If we agree to specify mass (m) in terms of electron masses, lengths in Å, and energies in eV, we can then write Schrödinger's equation as

$$\frac{d^2\psi}{dx^2} = -0.26246 \, m [E - V(x)]\psi(x). \tag{8}$$

This system of units is in no way special. One could, for example, choose the unit of length to be the Bohr radius and the unit of energy to be the ionization energy of hydrogen from the $n = 1$ orbit. In a problem involving nuclear physics one might choose [length] $= 10^{-15}$ meter and [energy] $= 1$ MeV. The point is to build a system such that any numerical factors appearing in Schrödinger's equation for the problem(s) you want to solve are of order unity.

We are now ready to look at an approach to numerically solving Equation (8).

◼ 10.2   A Straightforward Numerical Integration Method

In essence, all methods of numerically integrating differential equations boil down to the following: the domain involved (x, in our case) is divided up into a number of equally spaced discrete points separated by a stepsize Δx. Starting from a specified value of the dependent variable $y(x)$ [here, $\psi(x)$] at some initial point, say x_o, one boot-straps along increasing x by adding small increments to $y(x)$ based on derivatives multiplied by stepsizes. As implied earlier, a vast technical literature exists in this area. We will utilize a very straightforward approach. (For readers interested in exploring more sophisticated techniques, Section 8.7 of Weber and Arfken is a good starting place and contains a number of valuable references; see also Chapter 15 of Press et al.)

To motivate this approach, we need three expressions. The first is Schrödinger's equation written in atomic units:

$$\frac{d^2\psi}{dx^2} = 0.26246\, m\, [V(x) - E]\psi(x). \tag{1}$$

The second expression we need is the definition of the second derivative of ψ at some position, say x_o,

$$\left(\frac{d^2\psi}{dx^2}\right)_{x_o} = \frac{\left[\left(\frac{d\psi}{dx}\right)_{x_o+\Delta x} - \left(\frac{d\psi}{dx}\right)_{x_o}\right]}{\Delta x}.$$

(Formally, we should define the second derivative as the limit of this expression as $\Delta x \to 0$, but in actual practice Δx will be finite.) We rearrange this expression to the form

$$\left(\frac{d\psi}{dx}\right)_{x_o+\Delta x} = \left(\frac{d^2\psi}{dx^2}\right)_{x_o} \Delta x + \left(\frac{d\psi}{dx}\right)_{x_o}. \tag{2}$$

Finally, we need the (truncated) expression for the Taylor-series expansion of $\psi(x)$:

$$\psi(x_o + \Delta x) = \psi(x_o) + \left(\frac{d\psi}{dx}\right)_{x_o} \Delta x + \left(\frac{d^2\psi}{dx^2}\right)_{x_o} \frac{\Delta x^2}{2} + \ldots. \tag{3}$$

The procedure for numerically integrating $\psi(x)$ can be summarized as follows.

(i) Specify $V(x)$, the stepsize Δx, the initial position x_o, and the values of ψ and $(d\psi/dx)$ at x_o.

(ii) Make a trial guess at the energy eigenvalue E.

(iii) A new integration "cycle" begins by using Equation (1) to compute $(d^2\psi/dx^2)_{x_o}$.

(iv) From the values for ψ and $(d\psi/dx)$ at x_o and the result from step (iii), use Equation (3) to compute $\psi(x_o + \Delta x)$.

(v) From the value of $(d\psi/dx)$ at x_o and the result from step (iii), use Equation (2) to compute $(d\psi/dx)_{x_o + \Delta x}$.

(vii) Now loop back to step (iii) and start a new cycle beginning with computing the second derivative of ψ at $(x_o + \Delta x)$. Step (iv) will then give the value of ψ at $(x_o + 2\Delta x)$, step (v) the value of $(d\psi/dx)_{x_o + 2\Delta x}$, and so forth. Proceed until x reaches some appropriate upper limit, plotting or printing out ψ as you go. A correct eigenvalue will be one that makes $\psi \rightarrow 0$ as $x \rightarrow \infty$. If this doesn't happen, begin again at step (ii). A crucial qualification here is that even if you are numerically analyzing a problem known to possess an exact analytic solution you will actually *never* be able to make your solution behave as $\psi \rightarrow 0$ as $x \rightarrow \infty$ even if E is chosen to be one of the exactly known eigenvalues. This is because all computers operate with finite numerical accuracy; accumulation of small round-off errors is ultimately unavoidable, with the result that the computed run of ψ will eventually diverge to $\pm\infty$. As we will see by example, the practical issue becomes one of isolating limits on guesses for E between which ψ "wags" between positive and negative divergences. Understandably, this method is sometimes known as a "shooting" approach (as in shooting various values of E into Schrödinger's equation in the hope of getting close to a correct eigenvalue) or a "wag the tail" approach.

This procedure is ideally suited for a spreadsheet: successive rows of the spreadsheet hold successive values of x while columns can be used to hold the values of V, ψ, and derivatives of the latter. One advantage of using a spreadsheet is that you can plot $\psi(x)$ as the computation proceeds and so directly see the effect of changing your estimate for E.

Some operational questions remain. Where do initial values for ψ and $(d\psi/dx)$ come from? What is an appropriate stepsize? How far should the calculation be carried? These questions require some physical judgment on the part of the operator. For example, if $V(x)$ possesses an infinite wall at $x = 0$, then we immediately know that $\psi = 0$ there. If $V(x)$ is symmetric about $x = 0$ and we seek an even-parity wavefunction, then set $\psi(0) \neq 0$ and $(d\psi/dx)_0 = 0$. If you already have an odd-parity solution for a symmetric potential with $(d\psi/dx)_{x_o} < 0$, then the next-higher-energy odd-parity solution must have $(d\psi/dx)_{x_o} > 0$. In the case of a potential possessing no symmetries, the sign of the value you choose for $(d\psi/dx)_{x_o}$ is irrelevant, as only $|\psi|^2$ has any physical meaning. As to the magnitude of Δx, some quick numerical estimates can serve as a guide. If you are dealing with a potential-well type problem, for example, you can esti-mate at what values of x your guess for E cuts the walls of the well and then divide the range into a sensibly large number of intervals, say 1000. Carrying the calculation out to a distance of three or four times the cut position should be sufficient to see if ψ is "reasonably" approaching zero as x gets large. But beware: no computer represents numbers exactly to an infinite number of decimal places, so even if your problem pos-sesses exactly known eigenvalues your numerical solution will never truly go to zero as $x \to \infty$. It will always eventually diverge. If you have doubts as to the accuracy of an energy eigenvalue, try dividing Δx by 2 and repeating the calculation: if the result is the same or closely similar, then Δx was small enough. More accuracy can general-ly be squeezed out of the solution by decreasing Δx, but this will eventually run up against issues of machine roundoff errors and simple practicability.

One physical point remains: what of the normalization of ψ, which has nowhere been demanded in the integration scheme? This apparent oversight is actually an advantage in that it allows some flexibility in specifying initial conditions. Consider a potential well with an infinite wall at $x = 0$. Suppose you set $\psi = 0$ and $(d\psi/dx) = 0.01$ at $x = 0$, and experiment with different values of E until an eigenvalue, say E_1, is found. If you then take $(d\psi/dx) = 0.05$, you will find that E_1 is still an eigenvalue; indeed, it is possible to show that the choice of $(d\psi/dx)_{x_o}$ affects only the amplitude of $\psi(x)$ but not its shape, leaving the energy eigenvalues unaltered (Problem 10-8). Consequently, normalization can be taken care of later by multiplying the computed wavefunction by a factor C defined such that

$$C \sum_{x_j} |\psi(x_j)|^2 \Delta x = 1.$$

For practical purposes, however, one is usually not interested in normalizing the wavefunction: energy eigenvalues are the physically measurable quantities.

EXAMPLE 10.1

Use the numerical integration scheme just outlined to find the first two energy eigenvalues for an electron moving in the linear potential

$$V(x) = \begin{cases} \infty & x \le 0 \\ \alpha x & x > 0, \end{cases}$$

with $\alpha = 1$ eV/Å.

This problem was treated with the uncertainty principle in Problem 4-10, by the WKB method in Example 9.1, and by the variational method in Examples 9.7 and 9.9. The energy eigenvalue for quantum state n in this potential was found to be of the form $E_n = \eta_n \alpha^{2/3} \epsilon^{1/3}$ where η_n is a dimensionless numerical coefficient and where $\epsilon = \hbar^2/2m$. Table 10.1 lists the values of η_1 yielded by these various methods. The exact value is taken from Abramowitz and Stegun [1]. Parenthetically, you might wonder why we work this example as opposed to a case where we know exact results in advance, such as an infinite square well or harmonic oscillator. The reason is that if we have only approximate estimates of the ground state energy on hand—those in Table 10.1—then we are forced to use them as a guide to informing an initial estimate for E, thus getting a taste of how the algorithm is actually applied in most cases. One is often not even lucky enough to have an approximate starting estimate for the energy.

For the case specified here, $\alpha^{2/3} \epsilon^{1/3}$ evaluates as

$$\alpha^{2/3} \epsilon^{1/3} = (1 \text{ eV/Å})^{2/3} \left(\frac{\hbar^2}{2m_e} \right)^{1/3} = (1.6022 \times 10^{-9} J/m)^{2/3} \left[\frac{(1.0546 \times 10^{-34} J - \sec)^2}{2 \, (9.1094 \times 10^{-31} kg)} \right]^{1/3}$$

$$= 2.5024 \times 10^{-19} J = 1.5619 \text{ eV},$$

that is, $E_n/\eta_n = 1.5619$ eV.

Because $V(0) = \infty$, we know that $\psi(0) = 0$. From the discussion in Section 3.6 we can infer that the ground and first excited state wavefunctions must possess one and two maxima, respectively, and asymptotically approach zero as $x \to \infty$. Plausible forms for such functions are sketched in Figure 10.1.

From the numbers given in Table 10.1 we might estimate $\eta \sim 1.8$ for the ground state, equivalent to $E \sim (1.8)(1.5619 \text{ eV}) \sim 2.8$ eV. As a sensible first trial guess for E we can round this off to 3 eV. This proposed energy level would cut the potential both at $x = 0$ Å and $x = 3$Å.

Table 10.1   **Linear potential ground-state numerical coefficient.**

Method	η_1
Uncertainty Principle	> 1.191
WKB Approximation	2.811
Variational	< 2.476
Improved Variational	1.560 − 2.476
Exact	2.338107

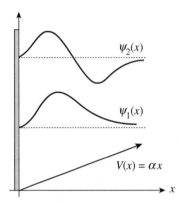

I FIGURE 10.1   Possible Linear Potential Wavefunctions..

Most of the action for ψ will lie between these limits; if we want, say, 1000 intervals between these limits we then adopt $\Delta x = 0.003$ Å. To be consistent with the infinite wall at $x = 0$ we take $\psi_0 = 0$. $(d\psi/dx)_0$ can be chosen arbitrarily; we take it to be 0.1.

Figure 10.2 shows a screenshot of the first few rows of a Microsoft Excel spreadsheet set up to integrate this problem. The values of E (3 eV) and Δx (0.003 Å) are defined in cells G1 and G2. Columns A through E, respectively, hold the values of x, $V(x)$, $\psi(x)$, $d\psi/dx$, and $d^2\psi/dx^2$. The values for x, V, ψ, and $(d\psi/dx)$ at $x = 0$ are entered manually (row 4). Subsequent values for x and $V(x)$ are based on formulae for their respective columns, whereas all of the other values for ψ and its derivatives are computed through formulae based on the algorithm

	A	B	C	D	E	F	G	H	I	J	K
						Example10-1.xls					
	x	V(x)	y	dy/dx	d^2y/dx^2	E =	3				
1						Delta-X	0.003				
2											
3											
4	0	0	0	0.1	0						
5	0.003	0.003	0.0003	0.1	-0.00023598						
6	0.006	0.006	0.0006	0.099999	-0.00047148						
7	0.009	0.009	0.0009	0.099998	-0.00070651						
8	0.012	0.012	0.0012	0.099996	-0.00094106	0.5					
9	0.015	0.015	0.0015	0.099993	-0.00117514		y				
10	0.018	0.018	0.0018	0.099989	-0.00140873	0.4					
11	0.021	0.021	0.0021	0.099985	-0.00164185						
12	0.024	0.024	0.0024	0.09998	-0.00187448	0.3					
13	0.027	0.027	0.0027	0.099975	-0.00210662						
14	0.03	0.03	0.003	0.099968	-0.00233828	0.2					
15	0.033	0.033	0.0033	0.099961	-0.00256946						
16	0.036	0.036	0.0036	0.099954	-0.00280014	0.1					
17	0.039	0.039	0.0039	0.099945	-0.00303033						
18	0.042	0.042	0.0042	0.099936	-0.00326003	0					
19	0.045	0.045	0.0045	0.099926	-0.00348923	0	2	4	6	8	10
20	0.048	0.048	0.0048	0.099916	-0.00371794						
21	0.051	0.051	0.0051	0.099905	-0.00394615						
22	0.054	0.054	0.0054	0.099893	-0.00417386						
23	0.057	0.057	0.0057	0.09988	-0.00440108						

FIGURE 10.2   Computed wavefunction for the linear potential $V(x) = \alpha x$ ($\alpha = 1$ eV/Å) for $E = 3$ eV. The divergence of the wavefunction indicates that this energy cannot be an eigenvalue.

outlined previously. For example, $(d^2\psi/dx^2)$ at $x = 0$ (cell E4) is defined as 0.26246 times (cell B4-E) times cell C4; when this formula is copied and pasted into the subsequent rows of column E, Excel automatically updates the cell references for $V(x)$ and $\psi(x)$. Similarly, $(d\psi/dx)$ at $x = 0.003$Å (cell D5) is defined as cell D4 plus cell E4 times Δx, and cell C5, the value of ψ at $x = 0.003$Å, as cell C4 + (cell D4)Δx + 0.5 (cell E4)Δx^2 with like copy and paste operations for both columns.

In what follows, the numbers for the first three cycles of the algorithm are worked through in detail to four decimal places (your computer will keep more significant figures than this). Work through these steps with your calculator, referring to Figure 10.2 as needed. For convenience, we denote derivatives with primes and use subscripts to designate x-values; for example, $\psi''_{0.003}$ denotes the value of $d^2\psi/dx^2$ at $x = 0.003$ Å.

Begin the first cycle. The values for steps (i) and (ii) were described earlier. For step (iii), Equation (1) with $m = 1$ for an electron gives

$$\psi''_{0.000} = 0.26246\left[V(x) - E\right]\psi_{0.000} = 0,$$

since $\psi_{0.000} = 0$. This result appears in cell E4. Proceeding to step (iv), we invoke Equation (3) to compute the value of ψ at $x = 0.003$ Å:

$$\psi_{0.003} = \psi_{0.000} + \psi'_{0.000}\Delta x + \psi''_{0.000}(\Delta x^2/2)$$
$$= 0 + (0.1)(0.003) + (0)(0.003)^2/2 = 3.0000 \times 10^{-4},$$

which appears in cell C5. Step (v) then provides the value of $d\psi/dx$ at $x = 0.003$ Å:

$$\psi'_{0.003} = \psi''_{0.000}\Delta x + \psi'_{0.000}$$
$$= 0(0.003) + 0.1 = 0.1000,$$

cell D5 in Figure 10.2. Step (vi) sends us back to step (iii) and the start of the second cycle. Now commence the second cycle of the algorithm at step (iii). From Equation (1),

$$\psi''_{0.003} = 0.26246\left[V(0.003) - E\right]\psi_{0.003}$$
$$= 0.26246\left[0.003 - 3\right](3 \times 10^{-4}) = -2.3598 \times 10^{-4}.$$

This result appears in cell E5; note that it depends upon the value of $\psi_{0.003}$ computed in step (iv) of cycle 1. Proceeding to step (iv) of this cycle gives

$$\psi_{0.006} = \psi_{0.003} + \psi'_{0.003}\Delta x + \psi''_{0.003}(\Delta x^2/2)$$
$$= (3 \times 10^{-4}) + (0.1)(0.003) + (-2.3598 \times 10^{-4})(0.003)^2/2$$
$$= 6.0000 \times 10^{-4},$$

where, to an accuracy of four decimal places, the Δx^2 term makes no contribution. This result appears in cell C6. Step (v) now gives

$$\psi'_{0.006} = \psi''_{0.003}\Delta x + \psi'_{0.003}$$

$$= (-2.3598 \times 10^{-4})(0.003) + 0.1 = 9.9999 \times 10^{-2},$$

cell D6. This brings us to the end of cycle 2. Note that $d\psi/dx$ has decreased slightly from its value in cycle 1.

Cycle 3 proceeds likewise. Looping back to step (iii) fills in cell E6 as

$$\psi''_{0.006} = 0.26246[V(0.006) - E]\psi_{0.006}$$

$$= 0.26246[0.006 - 3](6 \times 10^{-4}) = -4.7148 \times 10^{-4}.$$

Step (iv) advances us to $x = 0.009$ Å:

$$\psi_{0.009} = \psi_{0.006} + \psi'_{0.006}\Delta x + \psi''_{0.006}(\Delta x^2/2)$$

$$= (6 \times 10^{-4}) + (9.9999 \times 10^{-2})(0.003) + (-4.7148 \times 10^{-4})(0.003)^2/2$$

$$= 8.9999 \times 10^{-4},$$

cell C7. Step (v) of this cycle fills in cell D7:

$$\psi'_{0.009} = \psi''_{0.006}\Delta x + \psi'_{0.006}$$

$$= (-4.7148 \times 10^{-4})(0.003) + 9.9999 \times 10^{-2} = 9.9998 \times 10^{-2}.$$

$d\psi/dx$ has again decreased slightly from its previous value. At this point we again loop back to the fourth cycle at step (iii) again; you should find $\psi''_{0.009} = -7.0651 \times 10^{-4}$ (cell E7), and so on.

The graph in Figure 10.2 shows that the computed run of ψ for $E = 3$ eV begins to strongly diverge at $x \sim 6$ Å. Increasing the guess for E slightly (say, 3.1 eV) pushes the divergence to a slightly greater value of x. You should find that curve wags from a positive to a negative divergence between $E = 3.6$ and 3.7 eV. Narrowing it down, the wag is found to occur between 3.6510 and 3.6511 eV, corresponding to $\eta \sim 3.6510/1.5619 = 2.3375$, about 0.24% low in comparison to the exact value of 2.3381. The sensitivity of the solution to a slight change in E is stunning. Figure 10.3 shows the numerical solution for $E = 3.6510$ eV. Try experimenting with a different initial value of $(d\psi/dx)$; does the eigenvalue change significantly?

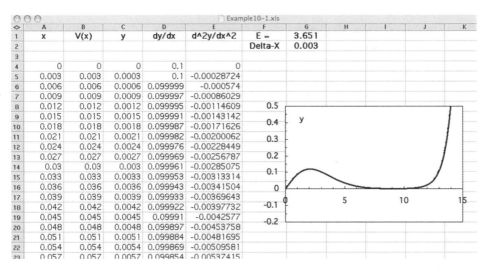

	A	B	C	D	E	F	G	H	I	J	K
1	x	V(x)	y	dy/dx	d^2y/dx^2	E =	3.651				
2						Delta-X	0.003				
3											
4	0	0	0	0.1	0						
5	0.003	0.003	0.0003	0.1	-0.00028724						
6	0.006	0.006	0.0006	0.099999	-0.000574						
7	0.009	0.009	0.0009	0.099997	-0.00086029						
8	0.012	0.012	0.0012	0.099995	-0.00114609						
9	0.015	0.015	0.0015	0.099991	-0.00143142						
10	0.018	0.018	0.0018	0.099987	-0.00171626						
11	0.021	0.021	0.0021	0.099982	-0.00200062						
12	0.024	0.024	0.0024	0.099976	-0.00228449						
13	0.027	0.027	0.0027	0.099969	-0.00256787						
14	0.03	0.03	0.003	0.099961	-0.00285075						
15	0.033	0.033	0.0033	0.099953	-0.00313314						
16	0.036	0.036	0.0036	0.099943	-0.00341504						
17	0.039	0.039	0.0039	0.099933	-0.00369643						
18	0.042	0.042	0.0042	0.099922	-0.00397732						
19	0.045	0.045	0.0045	0.09991	-0.0042577						
20	0.048	0.048	0.0048	0.099897	-0.00453758						
21	0.051	0.051	0.0051	0.099884	-0.00481695						
22	0.054	0.054	0.0054	0.099869	-0.00509581						
23	0.057	0.057	0.0057	0.099854	-0.00537415						

I FIGURE 10.3   Example 10.1 with $E = 3.651$ eV.

On proceeding to E_2 we find that the divergence wags between 6.3841 and 6.3842 eV, corresponding to $\eta_2 \sim 4.0874$. This is about 0.01% low compared to exact value, which is known to be 4.087949. The computed run of ψ for $E = 6.3841$ eV is shown in Figure 10.4. Note that ψ has two extrema, characteristic of an $n = 2$ wavefunction: it first passes through a positive-valued maximum, turns over, goes through zero, reaches a minimum, and finally turns back to the x-axis.

EXAMPLE 10.2

The *Pöschl-Teller* potential is given by

$$V(x) = -\frac{\hbar^2 \alpha^2 \lambda(\lambda - 1)}{2m \ \cosh^2(\alpha x)} \qquad (-\infty \leq x \leq \infty),$$

where α and λ are parameters, both assumed positive. α has dimension (length)$^{-1}$ while λ is dimensionless. $\cosh(\alpha x)$ denotes the hyperbolic cosine function of argument αx; if you are unfamiliar with this function, it is defined by

$$\cosh(\xi) = \frac{1}{2}(e^\xi + e^{-\xi}).$$

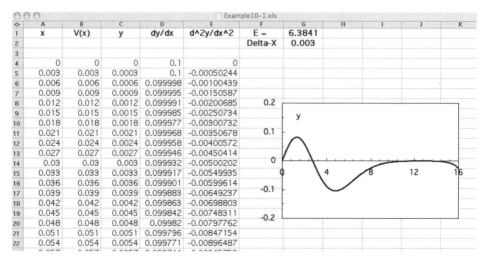

	A	B	C	D	E	F	G	H	I	J	K
1	x	V(x)	y	dy/dx	d^2y/dx^2	E =	6.3841				
2						Delta-X	0.003				
3											
4	0	0	0	0.1	0						
5	0.003	0.003	0.0003	0.1	-0.00050244						
6	0.006	0.006	0.0006	0.099998	-0.00100439						
7	0.009	0.009	0.0009	0.099995	-0.00150587						
8	0.012	0.012	0.0012	0.099991	-0.00200685	0.2					
9	0.015	0.015	0.0015	0.099985	-0.00250734						
10	0.018	0.018	0.0018	0.099977	-0.00300732						
11	0.021	0.021	0.0021	0.099968	-0.00350678	0.1					
12	0.024	0.024	0.0024	0.099958	-0.00400572						
13	0.027	0.027	0.0027	0.099946	-0.00450414						
14	0.03	0.03	0.003	0.099932	-0.00500202	0					
15	0.033	0.033	0.0033	0.099917	-0.00549935						
16	0.036	0.036	0.0036	0.099901	-0.00599614						
17	0.039	0.039	0.0039	0.099883	-0.00649237	-0.1					
18	0.042	0.042	0.0042	0.099863	-0.00698803						
19	0.045	0.045	0.0045	0.099842	-0.00748311						
20	0.048	0.048	0.0048	0.09982	-0.00797762	-0.2					
21	0.051	0.051	0.0051	0.099796	-0.00847154						
22	0.054	0.054	0.0054	0.099771	-0.00896487						

FIGURE 10.4   Example 10.1 with $E = 6.3841$ eV.

In this example we determine the first two bound states for an electron moving in this potential with $\alpha = 0.3$ Å^{-1} and $\lambda = 5$. Surprisingly, this potential can be solved analytically; the bound states are given by [2]

$$E = -\frac{\hbar^2\alpha^2}{2m}(\lambda - 1 - n)^2 \qquad (n \leq \lambda - 1; n = 0, 1, 2, \dots .)$$

This problem differs from Example 10.1 in that we have to deal with the coordinate "x" being both positive and negative. A good place to start is by casting the potential into our system of atomic units and then plotting it. From the discussion in Section 10.1, for a particle of mass "m" electron masses, $(2m/\hbar^2) = 0.26246 m$ (eV Å^2)$^{-1}$. If α is specified in units of Å^{-1}, we then have

$$V(x) = -\frac{\alpha^2\lambda(\lambda - 1)}{(0.26246 m)\cosh^2(\alpha x)} \qquad (eV).$$

Figure 10.5 shows a plot of this function ($m = 1$, $\alpha = 0.3$ Å^{-1}, $\lambda = 5$). This potential is symmetric about $x = 0$ (where $V = -\hbar^2\alpha^2\lambda(\lambda - 1)/2m = -6.858$ eV) and approaches 0 from below as $x \to \pm\infty$ due to the behavior of the cosh function. We can immediately conclude that any bound state must have $-6.858 \leq E \leq 0$ eV. The plot also shows that by $x = \pm 10$ Å, $V(x)$ is very close to zero (about

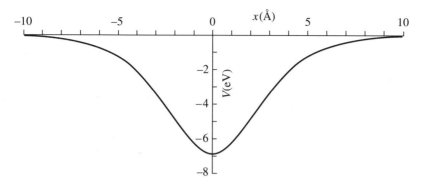

FIGURE 10.5 Pöschl-Teller Potential for $\alpha = 0.3$ Å^{-1} and $\lambda = 5$.

-0.07 eV); we take these extremes as our limits of numerical integration. But for its large-x behavior, this potential is reminiscent of the harmonic-oscillator potential of Chapter 5: for the ground state we should expect to find a solution for ψ with a single maximum at $x = 0$.

The spreadsheet developed for Example 10.1 can be used for this example upon changing the definition of $V(x)$ and setting the initial value of x to be -10 Å. To determine the ground state it is easiest to work upward from $E = -6.85$ and seek values of E between which divergent "wagging" occurs; the first such behavior is found to occur in the vicinity of $E \sim -5.4$ eV. Narrowing the estimate yields $E \sim -5.48655$ eV, precisely what the exact solution predicts. Figure 10.6 shows

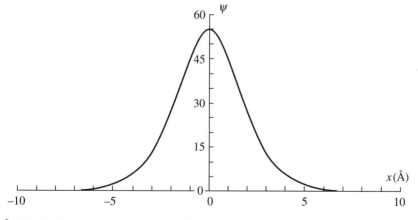

FIGURE 10.6 Computed Ground-state Wavefunction for Potential of Figure 10.5; $E = -5.48655$ eV.

the computed ground-state wavefunction for this energy based on choosing $\psi =$ 0.01 and $d\psi/dx = 0.001$ at $x = -10$ Å with $\Delta x = 0.002$. As expected, ψ is symmetric about $x = 0$ with one maximum there.

Proceeding to higher guesses for E, another wagging is observed to occur at about $E = -3.1$ eV; refining it gives $E = -3.0862$ eV, again in excellent agreement with the exact solution. The corresponding wavefunction is plotted in Figure 10.7. That this energy corresponds to the first excited state ($n = 1$) can be seen by the presence of two maxima in the wavefunction; note that $\psi(0) = 0$ as we would expect for a symmetric potential.

The second excited state for this potential proves to lie at $E \sim -1.373$ eV.

A working numerical integration program gives one a powerful, flexible tool for investigating a variety of problems. The method outlined here can be applied as well to the general central-potential radial equation (7.1.1), as only one coordinate is involved (see Problem 10-4).

Finally, a word of caution. As stated in the introduction to this chapter, numerical solution of differential equations is an active, highly specialized area of mathematical and computational research. The speed, accuracy, and stability of an algorithm can depend on how it is coded and the operating characteristics of the machine on which it is running. The algorithm developed here has been deliberately kept very straightforward in order to keep the physics of the situation as clear as possible. However, a number of much more sophisticated techniques are available. (An excellent reference

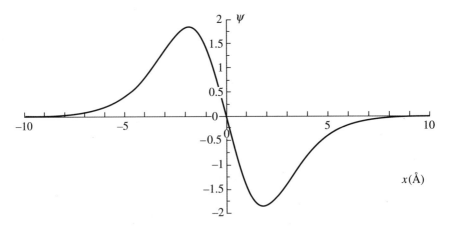

FIGURE 10.7   Computed first excited-state wavefunction for potential of Figure 10.5; $E = -3.0862$ eV. Note change in vertical scale from Figure 10.6.

for numerical computation issues in general is Press, W.H., Teukolsky, S.A., Vetterling, W.T., and Flannery, B.P., *Numerical Recipes in C++: The Art of Scientific Computing*. New York: Cambridge University Press, 1992.)

■ Problems

Note: Results of numerical integrations will vary slightly depending on the program/spreadsheet and operating system used; do not be alarmed if your results differ slightly from those given in Appendix B. All problems in this chapter should be considered to be of intermediate difficulty.

10-1 Write a program or set up a spreadsheet to numerically integrate the one-dimensional Schrödinger equation. Test your program by reproducing the results for the linear potential treated in Example 10-1. What is the energy of an electron in the $n = 3$ state of this potential?

10-2 A potential is given by

$$V(x) = \begin{cases} \infty, & x \le 0 \\ \alpha x^3 & x > 0, \end{cases}$$

where $\alpha = 5$ eV/Å³. Determine the energy of the ground and first excited states for an electron moving in this potential.

10-3 Consider a potential defined by

$$V(x) = \begin{cases} \infty, & x \le 0 \\ -Axe^{-\alpha x^2} & x > 0. \end{cases}$$

(a) Show (analytically) that the position x_o at which this potential reaches a minimum corresponds to $x_o = \sqrt{1/2\alpha}$. Show in addition that $V(x_o) = -Ax_o/\sqrt{e}$.

(b) Consider an electron moving in a potential of this form with $x_o = 1$ Å and $V(x_o) = -10$ eV. Determine its ground state energy.

10-4 In atomic units the radial equation for a central potential can be written as

$$\frac{d^2R}{dr^2} = \ell(\ell + 1)\frac{R}{r^2} - \frac{2}{r}\frac{dR}{dr} - \beta[E - V(r)]R,$$

where $\beta = (0.26246)$ m.

(a) Write a program or set up a spreadsheet to integrate the radial equation numerically for any value of ℓ.

(b) Show that in atomic units the potential function for the hydrogen atom is given by $V(r) = -14.3993/r$.

(c) Test your program for a few $\ell = 0$ and 1 hydrogen atom states. Use the form of the radial wavefunctions given in Table 7.1 to guide estimates for initial values.

(d) Consider a potential given by $V(r) = \alpha r^2$, where $\alpha = 5$ eV/Å². Use your program to deduce the two lowest energy levels for an electron moving in this potential for each of $\ell = 0$ and 1. Hint: Take $R(0) = 1$ and $R(0) = 0$ for $\ell = 0$ and $\ell \neq 0$, respectively.

(e) This potential is the spherical analog of the one-dimensional harmonic oscillator treated in Chapter 5. The radial equation can be solved analytically and yields energy eigenvalues given by

$$E = \hbar\sqrt{\frac{2\alpha}{m}}(2n + \ell + 3/2), \quad n = 0, 1, 2, \ldots .$$

Compare the energies predicted by this formula to those determined numerically.

10-5 Apply the program developed in Problem 10-4 to the general attractive central potential $\ell = 0$ discussed in Example 9.8. Check your program by applying it to the hydrogen atom, $(K, m, n) = (2, 1, 1)$. Verify the exact values claimed in the example for $(K\mu) = 1$ for $n = 0.5, 1.0$, and 1.5. For what value of the power n is the ground state energy a minimum when $K = 2$?

10-6 In Problem 9-18, the potential

$$V(x) = \begin{cases} \infty & (x < 0) \\ -A\sqrt{x}e^{-\alpha x^2} & (0 \leq x \leq \infty) \end{cases}$$

was investigated by the variational method, with the case of $A = 100$ eV Å$^{-1/2}$ and $\alpha = 1.75$ Å^{-2} examined in detail. Solve this potential numerically. How does your variational solution for the ground state compare to the result of a numerical integration?

10-7 Set up a program to numerically integrate Schrödinger's equation for the case of a finite rectangular well as treated in Section 3.3. Have your program track the wavefunction to $|x| = 2L$. How closely do your numerically determined energies match the results of Example 3.2?

10-8 It was remarked in Section 10.2 that the magnitude of the input value for $(d\psi/dx)_{x_o}$ affects only the amplitude of the resulting ψ but not its shape or the energy eigenvalues. Prove this. Hint: Assume that your guess for $(d\psi/dx)_{x_o}$ is replaced by a different one, say $k(d\psi/dx)_{x_o}$ where k is a pure number.

10-9 Use your program from Problem 10-4 to investigate the linear radial potential $V(r) = kr$. Set $k = 1$ eV/Å. How do the lowest three energy levels for $\ell = 0$ compare with those of Example 10-1? See Problem 7-8 for a limited analytic treatment of this potential.

10-10 Use your program from Problem 10-4 to investigate the exponential radial potential $V(r) = Ae^{kr}$. Set $A = 5$ eV and $k = 0.2$ Å^{-1}. What are the lowest three energy levels for $\ell = 0$ and 1?

10-11 Use your program from problem 10-4 to determine the lowest three energy levels for $\ell = 0$ and 1 for the Wood-Saxon potential,

$$V(r) = -\frac{A}{1 + e^{(r-b)/d}}.$$

Take $A = 100$ eV, $b = 2$ Å, and $d = 0.03$ Å.

10-12 In Problem 7-24 you explored the case of a mass μ trapped in a cylindrical potential well. Now suppose that you have a more general potential function $V(\rho)$, but with $V = \infty$ for $z \leq 0$ and $z \geq L$ as in that problem. Show that in this case Schrödinger's equation for the radial function $R(\rho)$ has the form (atomic units)

$$\frac{d^2R}{d\rho^2} = -\frac{1}{\rho}\frac{dR}{d\rho} - \left\{-0.26246\mu[E - V(\rho)] - \frac{n_z^2\pi^2}{L^2} - \frac{m^2}{\rho^2}\right\}R \quad (0 \leq z \leq L)$$

where n_z and m are the same quantum numbers that arose in Problem 7-24. If $V(\rho) = 0$, then this is just Bessel's equation with "m" playing the role of the order of the equation. Prepare a program or spreadsheet to numerically integrate this equation for any desired $V(\rho)$. Check your program for the case of an electron trapped in the infinite cylindrical potential of height 50 Å and radius 10 Å of Problem 7-24. Use your program to compute the energy eigenvalues (in eV) for the three lowest states corresponding to $m = 0$, 1, and 2 when $n_z = 1$. How do your results compare with those determined from the analytic solution of Problem 7-24? Hints: The results given in Appendix B are based on an integration starting at $\rho = 0.002$ (to avoid divergences) with $\Delta\rho = 0.002$ and $(dR/d\rho)_{0.002} = 0.1$. Bessel functions have $R(0) = 1$ for $m = 0$ and $R(0) = 0$ for $m \geq 1$. For $m = 0$, 1, and 2 the three lowest zeros of the Bessel functions are respectively (2.4048, 5.5201, 8.6537), (3.8317, 7.0156, 10.1735), and (5.1356, 8.4172, 11.6198). To incorporate the boundary condition for the edge of the well you need only find energies that yield $R(10 \text{ Å}) = 0$; your program may go beyond this limit in ρ but this is of no concern. (Why?)

10-13 Use the program you developed in the preceding problem to determine the energy states for $m = 0$, 1, and 2 (in eV) for an electron trapped in a (cylindrical) potential defined by $V(\rho) = A\rho^2$ $(0 \leq \rho \leq \infty)$ with $V = \infty$ for $z \leq 0$ and $z \geq L$. Take $A = 0.5$ eV/Å², $L = 50$ Å, and $n_z = 0$. The results given in Appendix B are based on an integration starting at $\rho = 0.002$ (to avoid divergences) with $\Delta\rho = 0.002$ and $(dR/d\rho)_{0.002} = 1.0$. Note that since $V(\rho) \neq 0$ the solutions to this problem are *not* Bessel functions.

10-14 The *Lennard-Jones 6-12 potential* is a semiempirical potential used in the study of intermolecular forces. This potential has the form

$$V(x) = A\left[\left(\frac{\alpha}{x}\right)^{12} - 2\left(\frac{\alpha}{x}\right)^6\right] \qquad (0 \leq x \leq \infty),$$

with $V(x) = \infty$ for $x \leq 0$. Plot this potential for $A = 100$ eV and $\alpha = 2$ Å. For an electron moving in this potential (with these values of A and α), how many bound states does it support and what are their energies?

11 A Sampling of Results from Time-Dependent Quantum Mechanics: Transition Rates and Probabilities

It was remarked in Chapter 2 that while the primary emphasis in this book is on solutions of the time-independent Schrödinger equation, understanding time-dependent problems is important as it is via interactions *between* stationary states that the characteristics of quantum systems are experimentally deduced. The purpose of this chapter is to give readers a taste of some of the results of time-dependent quantum theory. Specifically, we will look at three very practical, related issues: (i) how frequently we can expect a system to transit between two given quantum states, (ii) whether or not there are any restrictions on what transitions can in principle occur and, (iii) if a system currently in state "*m*" undergoes a sudden change of some sort (say an alpha decay or the like), what is the probability of it ending up in state "*n*" of the altered system? Deriving expressions for predicting such things requires a knowledge of time-dependent solutions to Schrödinger's equation, time-dependent perturbation theory, and radiation theory. Consequently, we will content ourselves with quoting some useful results and illustrating their application with some simple examples. Readers interested in more detailed treatments are urged to consult Section 40 of Pauling and Wilson and Chapters 8 and 14 of French and Taylor.

In discussing transition phenomena, it is important to bear in mind that the results have meaning only in a statistical sense. A conclusion to the effect that "the number of transitions from state m to state n for atomic species Z is 1000 per second" means, for practical purposes, that if we start with a large number of atoms of type Z all initially in state "*m*," then *on average* we will find 1000 in state "*n*" one second later. A given experiment might reveal 1027 or 945 atoms in state "*n*" after one second, but the average over a great many experiments will be 1000. Quantum mechanics provides exact answers to some questions but probabilities to most.

■ 11.1 Transition Frequencies

Suppose that you are given a large number of identical systems (electrons in infinite rectangular wells, for example), all initially in the same quantum state m. How many of these systems will, on average, have spontaneously "decayed" or "transited" to a lower-energy state n (accompanied, presumably, by the emission of a photon) after one second has elapsed? This quantity, known as the **Einstein coefficient of spontaneous emission**, is designated as A_{mn} and is given approximately by

$$A_{mn} = \frac{16\pi^3 q^2}{3\epsilon_o c^3 h^4}(E_m - E_n)^3 |\langle \psi_n^* |x| \psi_m \rangle|^2, \quad (m > n). \tag{1}$$

(E_m, ψ_m) and (E_n, ψ_n) are the energies and wavefunctions corresponding to states m and n, respectively, and q is the electrical charge of the system constituent (usually an electron) undergoing the transition. This expression results from an analysis of the effects of perturbing incident radiation on a system initially in state "m"; the charge and position factors in Equation (1) arise from the response of the system's electric dipole moment to the perturbing field (see Sections 39 and 40 of Pauling and Wilson). The units of Equation (1) are reciprocal seconds; that is, transitions/sec. The reciprocal of A_{mn} thus gives the **lifetime** of state m for transitions to state n. The "x" in the Dirac bracket implies a one-dimensional problem; in three-dimensions, one sums the absolute squares of three such integrals, one for each of x, y, and z, integrated over the volume of space appropriate to the system's wavefunction (see Example 11.2). Analogous equations concerning *induced* emission and absorption can also be derived; however, we will consider only spontaneous emission in this simple treatment.

EXAMPLE 11.1

A particle of mass equal to that of a hydrogen atom and possessing charge e (= 1 electron charge) is moving in the harmonic potential $V(x) = kx^2/2$. Determine the transition frequency between states n and $n - 1$.

The harmonic oscillator wavefunctions are given in Chapter 5. We have

$$\langle \psi_n^* |x| \psi_{n-1} \rangle = A_n A_{n-1} \int_{-\infty}^{\infty} x e^{-\alpha^2 x^2} H_n(\alpha x) H_{n-1}(\alpha x) \, dx$$

where A_n and A_{n-1} are normalization constants given in Equation (5.4.2); do not confuse them with the Einstein coefficient $A_{n, n-1}$. On making the usual change of variable $\xi = \alpha x$ with $\alpha = (mk/\hbar^2)^{1/4}$, we have

$$\langle \psi_n^* | x | \psi_{n-1} \rangle = \frac{A_n A_{n-1}}{\alpha^2} \int_{-\infty}^{\infty} \xi e^{-\xi^2} H_n(\xi) H_{n-1}(\xi) \, d\xi.$$

This integral was discussed in Example 9.5. In general, Hermite polynomials satisfy

$$\int_{-\infty}^{\infty} \xi e^{-\xi^2} H_n(\xi) H_m(\xi) \, d\xi = \sqrt{\pi} \left[2^{n-1} n! \, \delta_m^{n-1} + 2^n (n+1)! \, \delta_m^{n+1} \right].$$

We have $m = n - 1$, so only the first Kronecker delta in this identity survives, leaving

$$\langle \psi_n^* | x | \psi_{n-1} \rangle = \frac{2^n n! \sqrt{\pi} A_n A_{n-1}}{\alpha^2}.$$

On substituting for the normalization factors and α, this reduces to $\langle \psi_n^* | x | \psi_{n-1} \rangle = \sqrt{n}/(\sqrt{2}\alpha)$. Then putting $E_n - E_{n-1} = \hbar\sqrt{k/m}$ gives, after some algebra,

$$A_{n, n-1} = \frac{e^2 k}{6\pi \epsilon_o c^3 m^2} n.$$

From Problem 5-7, we can put $k \sim 500$ N/m; setting $n = 2$ and using the mass of a hydrogen atom gives

$$A_{n, n-1} \sim 2.05 \times 10^3 \ \text{sec}^{-1}.$$

The number of transitions per second is small compared to the frequency of the radiation emitted during a transition, about 10^{15} Hz.

EXAMPLE 11.2

Determine the transition frequency from the (2, 1, 0) to the (1, 0, 0) state of hydrogen. The wavefunctions are

$$\psi_{210} = \frac{1}{4\sqrt{2\pi}\, a_o^{5/2}} r e^{-r/2a_o} \cos\theta$$

and

$$\psi_{100} = \frac{1}{\sqrt{\pi}\, a_o^{3/2}} e^{-r/a_o}.$$

To carry out this three-dimensional calculation we require the transformation equations between Cartesian and spherical coordinates: $(x, y, z) = r(\sin\theta \cos\phi, \sin\theta \sin\phi, \cos\theta)$.

For the x-contribution,

$$\langle\psi_{210}|x|\psi_{100}\rangle = \frac{1}{4\sqrt{2}\,\pi a_o^4} \int_0^\infty \int_0^\pi \int_0^{2\pi} r e^{-3r/2a_o} \cos\theta\, (r\sin\theta\cos\phi)\, r^2 \sin\theta\, d\phi\, d\theta\, dr$$

$$= \frac{1}{4\sqrt{2}\,\pi a_o^4} \left\{ \int_0^\infty r^4 e^{-3r/2a_o}\, dr \right\} \left\{ \int_0^\pi \cos\theta \sin^2\theta\, d\theta \right\} \left\{ \int_0^{2\pi} \cos\phi\, d\phi \right\}.$$

These integrals are of the sort encountered in Chapter 7. The integral over ϕ vanishes, rendering $\langle\psi_{210}|x|\psi_{100}\rangle = 0$. The y-contribution involves an integral of $\sin\phi$ between zero and 2π and is likewise zero.

For the z-contribution, we have

$$\langle\psi_{210}|z|\psi_{100}\rangle = \frac{1}{4\sqrt{2}\,\pi a_o^4} \left\{ \int_0^\infty r^4 e^{-3r/2a_o}\, dr \right\} \left\{ \int_0^\pi \cos^2\theta \sin\theta\, d\theta \right\} \left\{ \int_0^{2\pi} d\phi \right\}$$

$$= \frac{1}{4\sqrt{2}\,\pi a_o^4} \left(\frac{256}{81} a_o^5 \right) \left(\frac{2}{3} \right) (2\pi) = \left(\frac{256}{243\sqrt{2}} \right) a_o.$$

From the usual expression for the Bohr energy levels, $E_{210} - E_{100} = 3m_e e^4/32\,\epsilon_o^2 h^2$. Inserting the expression for the Bohr radius gives

$$A_{210,100} = \frac{48}{19683} \frac{\pi m_e e^{10}}{\epsilon_o^5 c^3 h^6}.$$

Substituting the appropriate numerical values yields a transition rate of 6.27×10^8 per second. The experimental value of this quantity is somewhat less, 4.70×10^8 per second [1]. The difference is attributable to the fact that Equation (1) is an approximation; transition rates are also influenced by spin, relativistic, and magnetic effects.

In practice, transition rates are deduced by measuring the energy associated with them: knowing the stationary energy states for some system and hence $E_n - E_m$ (from solving the time-independent Schrödinger equation), a measured rate of energy emission can be transformed to a transition rate.

■ 11.2   Transition Rules

Depending on the properties of the wavefunctions involved, it is clear that the integral in Equation (1) will vanish in some cases. In this event the corresponding transition is said to be **forbidden**. For any quantum system it is possible to derive a set of **transition rules** or **selection rules** that indicate in what way the quantum number(s) of the system must change during a transition in order that it not be forbidden.

A convenient example is provided by harmonic-oscillator transitions. The integral appearing in Example 11.1 was of the form

$$\int_{-\infty}^{\infty} \xi e^{-\xi^2} H_n(\xi) H_m(\xi) \, d\xi = \sqrt{\pi} \, [2^{n-1} n! \, \delta_m^{n-1} + 2^n (n + 1)! \, \delta_m^{n+1}].$$

Since this integral is nonzero only when $m = n \pm 1$, it follows that the quantum harmonic-oscillator is restricted to transitions in which n increases or decreases by 1; that is, the system can transit only to "immediately adjacent" states. The transition rule for this case is then written as $\Delta n = \pm 1$. (If a "downward" transition is possible, so is its "upward" counterpart.) In the case of the infinite one-dimensional well (treated in Problem 11-2), the alternating parity of the wavefunctions restricts permissible transitions to those that involve a change of parity. For the hydrogen atom, the properties of the spherical harmonics are such that only transitions with $\Delta \ell = \pm 1$ and $\Delta m = \pm 1$ or 0 are permissible; there is no restriction on any change (or not) of the principal quantum number n. A change of value in ℓ, incidentally, implies a change in the system's angular momentum. If **L** is to be conserved, where, then, does angular momentum come from or disappear to? The answer is that photons possess intrinsic angular momentum of amount $\hbar$: by absorbing or giving up a photon, an electron can make its transition while conserving **L**.

The transition frequencies computed via Equation (1) of the preceding section correspond to what are known as **electric-dipole transitions**. Other transition mechanisms (quadrupole, octopole, and so forth) between states are possible but are usually much less frequent than their dipole counterparts. However, it is possible for transitions forbidden to dipole radiation to be permissible by other mechanisms.

Equation (1), when evaluated for different combinations of m and n, yields predictions of the **relative intensities** of spectral lines simply by taking appropriate ratios of the results. In the case of multidimensional systems, predictions can also be made as to the angular distribution and polarization of the emitted radiation. Predictions along these lines are in accord with the observed characteristics of atomic and molecular spectra. This success of wave mechanics represented a significant improvement in our understanding of spectra that was not contained in the older Bohr theory.

■ 11.3 The Sudden Approximation

Imagine a quantum harmonic-oscillator in some state—say, ψ_n. As a result of some process (perhaps a chemical reaction), the force constant k of the system is suddenly reduced to one-half of its original value. What is the probability of finding the "new" system in the "corresponding" state ψ_n or in some other state, ψ_m? ("Corresponding" here is meant in the sense of numbering the energy levels of both systems integrally, increasing from lowest energy to highest.) Questions of this sort can be examined with the so-called sudden approximation.

The mathematical statement of this approximation is that if the system was in state n before the change, then the probability of finding it to be in state j after the change is given by

$$P_{n \to j} = \left| \int \psi_j^{new}(x)\, \psi_n^{old}(x)\, dx \right|^2. \tag{1}$$

The ψ's are presumed to be normalized and to apply over the same domain. In a three-dimensional problem, dx is replaced by the volume element dV appropriate to the coordinate system in use.

We can give a semi-intuitive justification of Equation (1). Short of performing some sort of experiment, we have no idea in which of a number of possible states ψ_j the altered system will find itself after the change. However, we can imagine expressing the new wavefunction as a linear sum over all of the old system wavefunctions, as was done in Section 9.2. Intuitively, the greater the coefficient multiplying any "former" state ψ_n, the greater will be the probability of finding the system in the "new" nth state as well. By a development similar to that presented in Section 9.2, it is possible to show that the probability of the new system being in state j is given by the square of the absolute value of the expansion coefficient a_j in Equation (9.2.5). If the ψ's are normalized, the sum over Equation (1) for all possible values of j is unity, in analogy to Equation (9.2.9).

EXAMPLE 11.3

The force constant of a harmonic oscillator in the ground state suddenly decreases to one-half of its original value. What is the probability of the system remaining in the ground (lowest energy) state?

We have

$$\psi_0^{old}(x) = \frac{\sqrt{\alpha}}{\pi^{1/4}} e^{-\alpha^2 x^2/2}, \quad \alpha^4 = mk/\hbar^2.$$

Halving the force constant causes α^4 to decrease by a factor of 2:

$$\alpha_{new}^4 = \alpha_{old}^4/2.$$

Setting $\alpha = \alpha_{old}$, we have

$$\psi_0^{new}(x) = \frac{\sqrt{\alpha}}{\pi^{1/4} 2^{1/8}} e^{-\alpha^2 x^2/2\sqrt{2}}.$$

Equation (1) then gives

$$\sqrt{P} = \int_{-\infty}^{\infty} \psi_0^{new}(x) \, \psi_0^{old}(x) \, dx = \frac{\alpha}{\sqrt{\pi} \, 2^{1/8}} \int_{-\infty}^{\infty} \exp\left[-\left(\frac{1}{2} + \frac{1}{2\sqrt{2}}\right)\alpha^2 x^2\right] dx$$

$$= \frac{2\alpha}{\sqrt{\pi} \, 2^{1/8}} \int_0^{\infty} \exp(-a^2 x^2) \, dx,$$

where

$$a^2 = \frac{(1 + \sqrt{2})}{2\sqrt{2}} \alpha^2.$$

This integral evaluates to $\sqrt{\pi}/2a$, hence

$$P = \frac{4\alpha^2}{\pi\, 2^{1/4}4a^2}\frac{\pi}{} = \frac{\alpha^2}{2^{1/4}(1+\sqrt{2})\alpha^2}\frac{2\sqrt{2}}{} = \frac{2^{5/4}}{(1+\sqrt{2})} = 0.985.$$

The probability is overwhelming that the system will remain in the ground state. Note that all of the physical constants canceled out in this calculation: the result must be a pure number.

■ Summary

The *transition frequency* A_{mn} (transitions/sec) between states m and n for a transiting particle of charge q is given by

$$A_{mn} = \frac{16\pi^3 q^2}{3\epsilon_o c^3 h^4}(E_m - E_n)^3 |\langle \psi_n^* | x | \psi_m \rangle|^2, \quad (m > n).$$

Transition is said to be forbidden between states n and m if A_{mn} is zero.

The *sudden approximation* gives a means of computing the probability $P\,(n \rightarrow j)$ that a system initially in state n will be in state j after a sudden change in the parameters of the system:

$$P_{n \rightarrow j} = \left| \int \psi_j^{new}(x)\, \psi_n^{old}(x)\, dx \right|^2.$$

■ Problems

11-1(E) Verify that the units of Equation (11.1.1) are reciprocal seconds.

11-2(I) Determine the transition frequency for a particle of mass m and charge q between any two states n and j $(n > j)$ of the infinite one-dimensional rectangular potential well.

11-3(E) Verify by direct calculation that transition between the (3, 2, 0) and (1, 0, 0) states of hydrogen is forbidden.

11-4(I) A hydrogen-like atom with a nuclear charge of $+Ze$ is initially in the (1, 0, 0) state. As a result of an inverse β-decay, $Z \rightarrow Z - 1$. Determine the probability that the new species remains in the (1, 0, 0) state. Evaluate your answer numerically for $Z = 2$.

11-5(I) A particle of mass m is in state $\psi_n(x)$ of an infinite rectangular well of width L ($0 \le x < L$). The right wall of the well suddenly expands to $x = KL$ ($K > 1$; the well now occupies $0 \le x \le KL$). Determine the probability that the particle will be in any state ψ_k after the expansion. (Take the original wavefunction to be zero between $x = L$ and $x = KL$.) Following the expansion, what state is the particle most likely to be in?

A | Miscellaneous Derivations

The proof of the uncertainty principle given here is adopted from Section 12 of Leonard Schiff, *Quantum Mechanics*: 3rd edition, McGraw-Hill, New York, 1968. This proof assumes one-dimensional wavefunctions, utilizes the time-dependent Schrödinger equation of Chapter 2, assumes that wavefunctions vanish asymptotically (strictly, $\psi \to 0$ at the limits of its domain), and requires an integral identity from functional analysis.

We begin by reiterating the definitions of Δx and Δp from Section 4.3:

$$\Delta x = \sqrt{\langle x^2 \rangle - \langle x \rangle^2} \tag{1}$$

and

$$\Delta p = \sqrt{\langle p^2 \rangle - \langle p \rangle^2} = \sqrt{\langle p^2 \rangle}. \tag{2}$$

In writing Δp, we have made use of the proof in Section 4.2 that $\langle p \rangle = 0$ for any well-behaved wavefunction. Actually, it is easier to work with the *squares* of these quantities,

$$\Delta x^2 = \langle x^2 \rangle - \langle x \rangle^2 \tag{3}$$

and

$$\Delta p^2 = \langle p^2 \rangle. \tag{4}$$

We begin with the Δx part of the uncertainty principle. It is helpful to introduce a new operator α defined by

$$\alpha = x - \langle x \rangle. \tag{5}$$

Now consider the integral

$$X = \int (\alpha\psi)(\alpha*\psi*)\,dx, \tag{6}$$

where an asterisk denotes complex conjugation and where the limits of integration are those of the domain of ψ. Invoking the definition of α gives

$$X = \int (x\psi - \langle x\rangle\psi)(x*\psi* - \langle x\rangle\psi*)\,dx$$

$$= \int xx*\psi\psi*\,dx - \langle x\rangle\int x\psi\psi*\,dx - \langle x\rangle\int x*\psi\psi*\,dx + \langle x\rangle^2\int \psi\psi*\,dx.$$

Since $x* = x$, the first integral here is just $\langle x^2\rangle$ and the middle two integrals are both equal to $\langle x\rangle$. If ψ is normalized, the last integral will be equal to unity. Hence

$$X = \langle x^2\rangle - 2\langle x\rangle^2 + \langle x\rangle^2 = \langle x^2\rangle - \langle x\rangle^2 = \Delta x^2. \tag{7}$$

We will return to this result later.

Now we consider Δp^2. In analogy to Equation (6), consider the quantity

$$P = \int (p\psi)(p*\psi*)\,dx = \int \left(-i\hbar\frac{d\psi}{dx}\right)\left(+i\hbar\frac{d\psi*}{dx}\right)dx = \hbar^2\int (\psi)'(\psi*)'\,dx, \tag{8}$$

where p is the momentum operator and a prime denotes differentiation with respect to x. Now consider the second derivative

$$\frac{d^2}{dx^2}(\psi*\psi) = 2(\psi')(\psi*)' + (\psi*)''(\psi) + (\psi*)(\psi''). \tag{9}$$

But for a factor of 2, the first term on the right side of Equation (9) is the integrand appearing in Equation (8). Hence we can write Equation (8) as

$$P = \frac{\hbar^2}{2}\int (\psi*\psi)''\,dx - \frac{\hbar^2}{2}\int (\psi*)''(\psi)\,dx - \frac{\hbar^2}{2}\int (\psi*)(\psi'')\,dx. \tag{10}$$

The first integral in Equation (10) vanishes as follows:

$$\int (\psi*\psi)''\,dx = \int \frac{d}{dx}\left[\frac{d}{dx}(\psi*\psi)\right]dx = \int d\left[\frac{d}{dx}(\psi*\psi)\right]$$

$$= [(\psi*)'(\psi) + (\psi*)(\psi')]_{\text{limits}} = 0.$$

What remains of Equation (10) is then

$$P = -\frac{\hbar^2}{2}\int(\psi^*)''(\psi)\,dx - \frac{\hbar^2}{2}\int(\psi^*)(\psi'')\,dx. \qquad (11)$$

Now, Δp^2 is given by Equation (4) as

$$\Delta p^2 = \int(\psi^*)(p^2\psi)\,dx = -\hbar^2\int(\psi^*)(\psi'')\,dx. \qquad (12)$$

Compare Equations (11) and (12). The second integral in (11) is identical to (12) but for a factor of 2. Also, the first integral in (11) is just the complex conjugate of the second one. If we make the assumption (the proof follows) that conjugation leaves Equation (12) unchanged; that is, that we can write

$$\Delta p^2 = -\hbar^2\int(\psi^*)''(\psi)\,dx, \qquad (13)$$

then Equation (11) reduces to

$$P \equiv \int(p\psi)(p^*\psi^*)\,dx \equiv \Delta p^2. \qquad (14)$$

From Equations (6), (7), and (14) we now have

$$\Delta x^2\,\Delta p^2 = XP = \left\{\int(\alpha\psi)(\alpha^*\psi^*)\,dx\right\}\left\{\int(p\psi)(p^*\psi^*)\,dx\right\}. \qquad (15)$$

The reason for going through this manipulation is that Equation (15) is of the form of a theorem from functional analysis known as Schwarz's inequality. This theorem states that for two functions $f(x)$ and $g(x)$, both possibly complex and both running over the same domain,

$$\left\{\int f^*(x)f(x)\,dx\right\}\left\{\int g^*(x)g(x)\,dx\right\} \geq \left|\left\{\int f^*(x)g(x)\,dx\right\}\right|^2, \qquad (16)$$

where the limits of integration are those of the domain of $f(x)$ and $g(x)$. (A proof of this inequality can be found in any good text on mathematical physics.) Applying this to Equation (15) gives

$$\Delta x^2\,\Delta p^2 \geq \left|\int(\alpha^*\psi^*)(p\psi)\,dx\right|^2. \qquad (17)$$

Since α is a real operator, we can write $\alpha^* = \alpha$. Evaluating the integral gives

$$\int (\alpha^* \psi^*)(p\psi)\,dx = \int [(x\psi^*) - \langle x \rangle \psi^*](p\psi)\,dx$$

$$= \left\{ \int \psi^* x (p\psi)\,dx - \langle x \rangle \int \psi^* (p\psi)\,dx \right\} \tag{18}$$

$$= \{\langle xp \rangle - \langle x \rangle \langle p \rangle\}.$$

Since $\langle p \rangle = 0$, the second term within the curly brackets vanishes. Now consider the integral for $\langle xp \rangle$ in more detail:

$$\langle xp \rangle = \int \psi^* x (p\psi)\,dx = -\iota\hbar \int \psi^* x \left(\frac{d\psi}{dx} \right) dx = -\iota\hbar \int \psi^* x\,d\psi.$$

Integrating this by parts gives

$$\langle xp \rangle = -\iota\hbar \left\{ [\psi^* x \psi]_{\text{limits}} - \int \psi\, d(\psi^* x) \right\}.$$

If ψ vanishes at its limits, then the first term within the curly brackets will be zero. Expanding out the integral gives

$$\langle xp \rangle = \iota\hbar \left\{ \int \psi \psi^* dx + \int \psi x\, d\psi^* \right\}. \tag{19}$$

The first integral on the right side of Equation (19) will be equal to unity if ψ is normalized. In the second integral, convert $d\psi^*$ back to a derivative: $d\psi^* = (d\psi^*/dx)dx$, and then put the derivative in terms of the momentum operator: $d\psi^* = -(1/\iota\hbar)(p\psi^*)dx$. This gives

$$\langle xp \rangle = \iota\hbar \left\{ 1 - \frac{1}{\iota\hbar} \int \psi x (p\psi^*)\,dx \right\} = \iota\hbar - \langle xp \rangle,$$

where we have invoked the assumption that the order of ψ and ψ^* in an expectation-value integral is irrelevant. Hence we have

$$\langle xp \rangle = \frac{\iota\hbar}{2}. \tag{20}$$

Equations (17), (18), and (20) consequently reduce to

$$\Delta x \Delta p \geq \frac{\hbar}{2},$$

the formal statement of the uncertainty principle.

One step remains to complete this proof: that it is indeed legitimate to write (Equations 12 and 13)

$$\int (\psi^*)''(\psi)\, dx = \int (\psi^*)(\psi'')\, dx. \tag{21}$$

A proof of this begins with the normalization condition, which we write in Dirac notation:

$$\langle \psi^* | \psi \rangle = 1. \tag{22}$$

Now, even if ψ should be time-dependent, this condition must always be satisfied; that is, the time-derivative of Equation (22) must vanish:

$$\frac{\partial}{\partial t}\langle \psi^* | \psi \rangle = \left\langle \frac{\partial \psi^*}{\partial t} \middle| \psi \right\rangle + \left\langle \psi^* \middle| \frac{\partial \psi}{\partial t} \right\rangle = 0. \tag{23}$$

To deal with the time derivatives, invoke the time-dependent Schrödinger equation and its complex conjugate (Equation 2.3.10)

$$\left(\frac{\partial \psi}{\partial t}\right) = \frac{1}{\iota \hbar}\left[-\frac{\hbar^2}{2m}\frac{\partial^2 \psi}{\partial x^2} + V\psi \right] \tag{24}$$

and

$$\left(\frac{\partial \psi^*}{\partial t}\right) = -\frac{1}{\iota \hbar}\left[-\frac{\hbar^2}{2m}\frac{\partial^2 \psi^*}{\partial x^2} + V\psi^* \right], \tag{25}$$

where V is the potential function. Substituting these into Equation (23), canceling a factor of $(\iota \hbar)$, and expanding out the Dirac brackets gives

$$\frac{\partial}{\partial t}\langle \psi^* | \psi \rangle = \frac{\hbar^2}{2m}\langle (\psi^*)'' | \psi \rangle - \langle V\psi^* | \psi \rangle - \frac{\hbar^2}{2m}\langle \psi^* | \psi'' \rangle + \langle \psi^* | V\psi \rangle = 0. \tag{26}$$

Since the potential V is purely multiplicative, the two terms involving V cancel each other. What remains of Equation (26) then gives

$$\langle(\psi^*)''|\psi\rangle = \langle\psi^*|\psi''\rangle, \tag{27}$$

exactly as presumed in Equation (21).

■ A.2   Explicit Series Form for Associated Legendre Functions

From Chapter 6, the azimuthal solutions for the angular part of Schrödinger's equation for a central potential are

$$\Theta_{\ell,m}(\theta) = \sqrt{\frac{2\ell+1}{2}\frac{(\ell-m)!}{(\ell+m)!}}P_{\ell,m}(\cos\theta) \quad (|m| \le \ell), \tag{1}$$

where $P_{\ell,m}(\cos\theta)$ denotes an associated Legendre function,

$$P_{\ell,m}(x) = \frac{1}{2^\ell\ell!}(1-x^2)^{m/2}\frac{d^{\ell+m}}{dx^{\ell+m}}(x^2-1)^\ell; \tag{2}$$

we have $x = \cos\theta$. This expression is valid for m positive, negative, or zero.

For computational purposes it can be convenient to express $\Theta(\theta)$ directly as a series in terms of, say, $\cos\theta$. This can be achieved as follows.

The binomial theorem states that the sum of any two quantities raised to a power can be expressed as

$$(a+b)^p = \sum_{k=0}^{p}\binom{p}{k}a^{p-k}b^k, \tag{3}$$

where the binomial coefficients $\binom{p}{k}$ are given by

$$\binom{p}{k} = \frac{p!}{k!(p-k)!}. \tag{4}$$

Applying this to $(x^2-1)^\ell$ gives

$$(x^2-1)^\ell = \sum_{k=0}^{\ell}(-1)^k\binom{\ell}{k}(x^{2\ell-2k}). \tag{5}$$

This expression is a polynomial in powers of x ranging from 0 to 2ℓ in steps of two, which, according to Equation (2), we need to differentiate $(\ell + m)$ times with respect to x. That is, we desire

$$\frac{d^{\ell+m}}{dx^{\ell+m}}(x^2 - 1)^\ell = \sum_{k=0}^{\ell}(-1)^k\binom{\ell}{k}\frac{d^{\ell+m}}{dx^{\ell+m}}(x^{2\ell-2k}). \tag{6}$$

Since m runs from $-\ell$ to $+\ell$, the order of the derivative may be any integer from 0 to 2ℓ; consequently, any number of terms in the series—from all of them down to only the highest-order one—may potentially survive the differentiation. Only those whose power $2(\ell - k)$ exceeds the highest order of the derivative, $(\ell + m)$, will survive the differentiation. Hence, we need only differentiate so long as $2(\ell - k) \geq (\ell + m)$; that is, as long as $k \leq (\ell - m)/2$. Since the derivative of a power can in general be written as

$$\frac{d^J}{dx^J}(x^N) = \left[\prod_{i=0}^{J-1}(N - i)\right]x^{N-J}, \tag{7}$$

we find, with $N = 2\ell - 2k$ and $J = \ell + m$,

$$\frac{d^{\ell+m}}{dx^{\ell+m}}(x^2-1)^\ell = \sum_{k=0}^{\left[\frac{\ell-m}{2}\right]}\left[(-1)^k\binom{\ell}{k}\prod_{i=0}^{\ell+m-1}(2\ell-2k-i)\right]x^{\ell-m-2k}, \tag{8}$$

where $\left[\dfrac{\ell - m}{2}\right]$ designates the greatest integer less than or equal to $(\ell - m)/2$.

The term within the large square bracket can be simplified. The product is first compacted by writing it in a binomial-coefficient form:

$$\prod_{i=0}^{\ell+m-1}(2\ell - 2k - i) = [2\ell - 2k][2\ell - 2k - 1][2\ell - 2k - 2]\ldots[2\ell - 2k - (\ell + m - 1)]$$

$$= \frac{(2\ell - 2k)!}{[2\ell - 2k - (\ell + m - 1) - 1]!} = \frac{(2\ell - 2k)!}{[2\ell - 2k - (\ell + m)]!}. \tag{9}$$

Now, the definition of the binomial coefficients can be rearranged to give

$$\binom{p}{k} = \frac{p!}{k!(p - k)!} \quad \Rightarrow \quad \frac{p!}{(p - k)!} = k!\binom{p}{k}, \tag{10}$$

which, when applied to Equation (9), yields

$$\prod_{i=o}^{\ell+m-1} (2\ell - 2k - i) = \frac{(2\ell - 2k)!}{[2\ell - 2k - (\ell + m)]!} = (\ell + m)! \binom{2\ell - 2k}{\ell + m}, \quad (11)$$

leading to

$$\frac{d^{\ell+m}}{dx^{\ell+m}}(x^2 - 1)^\ell = \sum_{k=0}^{\left[\frac{\ell-m}{2}\right]}\left[(-1)^k \binom{\ell}{k}(\ell+m)! \binom{2\ell-2k}{\ell+m} x^{\ell-m-2k}\right]. \quad (12)$$

Combining this result with the definition of $\Theta(\theta)$ gives

$$\Theta_{\ell,m}(\theta) = \sqrt{\frac{2\ell + 1}{2}\frac{(\ell - m)!}{(\ell + m)!}} P_{\ell,m}(\cos\theta)$$

$$= \frac{1}{2^\ell\ell!}(1 - x^2)^{m/2}\sqrt{\frac{2\ell + 1}{2}\frac{(\ell - m)!}{(\ell + m)!}}\frac{d^{\ell+m}}{dx^{\ell+m}}(x^2 - 1)^\ell \quad (13)$$

$$= \frac{1}{2^\ell\ell!}(1-x^2)^{m/2}\sqrt{\frac{2\ell+1}{2}\frac{(\ell-m)!}{(\ell+m)!}}\sum_{k=0}^{\left[\frac{\ell-m}{2}\right]}\left[(-1)^k\binom{\ell}{k}(\ell+m)!\binom{2\ell-2k}{\ell+m}x^{\ell-m-2k}\right],$$

or, with $x \equiv \cos\theta$,

$$\Theta(\theta) = \frac{1}{2^\ell\ell!}\sqrt{\frac{2\ell+1}{2}(\ell+m)!(\ell-m)!}(\sin^m\theta)\sum_{k=0}^{\left[\frac{\ell-m}{2}\right]}\left[(-1)^k\binom{\ell}{k}\binom{2\ell-2k}{\ell+m}(\cos^{\ell-m-2k}\theta)\right], \quad (14)$$

the desired explicit form of $\Theta(\theta)$.

■ A.3   Proof That $Y_{\ell,-m} = (-1)^m Y^*_{\ell,m}$

This proof is adapted from the one given in M. E. Rose, *Elementary Theory of Angular Momentum*: John Wiley & Sons, Inc., New York, 1957, Appendix III.

To prove this relationship, it is easiest to begin with the associated Legendre functions $P_{\ell,m}$ of Section 6.5:

$$\Theta_{\ell,m}(\theta) = \sqrt{\frac{2\ell + 1}{2}\frac{(\ell - m)!}{(\ell + m)!}}P_{\ell,m}(\cos\theta) \quad (|m| \le \ell), \quad (1)$$

where

$$P_{\ell,m}(x) = \frac{1}{2^\ell \ell!}(1 - x^2)^{m/2}\frac{d^{\ell+m}}{dx^{\ell+m}}(x^2 - 1)^\ell. \tag{2}$$

If we replace m by $-m$, Equation (2) becomes

$$P_{\ell,-m} = \frac{1}{2^\ell \ell!}(1 - x^2)^{-m/2}\frac{d^{\ell-m}}{dx^{\ell-m}}(x^2 - 1)^\ell, \tag{3}$$

where we have suppressed the x-dependence of $P_{\ell,m}$ for brevity.

Two results from calculus are central to this proof. The first is that the jth derivative of the nth power of x can be written as

$$\frac{d^j}{dx^j}(x^n) = \left[\prod_{i=0}^{j-1}(n - i)\right]x^{n-j} = \frac{n!}{(n-j)!}x^{n-j}. \tag{4}$$

The second is a similar result, a way of writing the jth derivative of a product of two functions of x, $A(x)$, and $B(x)$:

$$\frac{d^j}{dx^j}(AB) = \sum_{n=0}^{j}\binom{j}{n}\left(\frac{d^{j-n}A}{dx^{j-n}}\right)\left(\frac{d^n B}{dx^n}\right), \tag{5}$$

where $\binom{j}{n}$ denotes a binomial coefficient as in Appendix A.2. This result is known as Leibniz's rule for differentiating a product.

Now, write Equation (3) as

$$P_{\ell,-m} = \frac{1}{2^\ell \ell!}(1 - x^2)^{-m/2}\frac{d^{\ell-m}}{dx^{\ell-m}}[(x + 1)^\ell(x - 1)^\ell],$$

and apply Leibniz's rule, taking $A = (x + 1)^\ell$ and $B = (x - 1)^\ell$. The result is

$$P_{\ell,-m} = \frac{1}{2^\ell \ell!}(1 - x^2)^{-m/2}\sum_{n=0}^{\ell-m}\frac{(\ell - m)!}{n!(\ell - m - n)!}\left[\frac{d^{\ell-m-n}(x + 1)^\ell}{dx^{\ell-m-n}}\right]\left[\frac{d^n(x - 1)^\ell}{dx^n}\right]. \tag{6}$$

Apply Equation (4) to each of the derivatives appearing in Equation (6). This yields

$$P_{\ell,-m} = \frac{(1 - x^2)^{-m/2}(\ell - m)!}{2^{\ell}\ell!} \sum_{n=0}^{\ell-m} \frac{\ell!\,\ell!}{n!\,(\ell - m - n)!\,(m + n)!\,(\ell - n)!}(x + 1)^{m+n}(x - 1)^{\ell-n}.$$

(7)

Now we make a nonobvious manipulation of the product $(x + 1)^{m+n}(x - 1)^{\ell-n}$. First, break up the first term into $(x + 1)^m(x + 1)^n$. Then, multiply by a factor of $(x - 1)^m$ while dividing by the same factor. That is, write

$$(x + 1)^{m+n}(x - 1)^{\ell-n} = (x + 1)^m(x + 1)^n(x - 1)^{\ell-n}\left[\frac{(x - 1)^m}{(x - 1)^m}\right]$$

$$= (x^2 - 1)^m(x + 1)^n(x - 1)^{\ell-n-m}.$$

The factor of $(x^2 - 1)^m$ is now extracted from within the sum in Equation (7) and combined with that of $(1 - x^2)^{-m/2}$ appearing outside the sum, to give

$$P_{\ell,-m} = \frac{(-1)^m(1 - x^2)^{m/2}(\ell - m)!}{2^{\ell}\ell!} \sum_{n=0}^{\ell-m} \frac{\ell!\,\ell!}{n!\,(\ell - m - n)!\,(m + n)!\,(\ell - n)!}(x + 1)^n(x - 1)^{\ell-n-m}. \quad (8)$$

The reason for this manipulation is that by concocting a factor of $(1 - x^2)^{m/2}$ out front, we make the prefactor in Equation (8) look like that appearing in the expression for $P_{\ell,m}$, Equation (2).

Now, both multiply and divide Equation (8) by a factor of $(\ell + m)!$, placing the multiplicative factor inside the sum:

$$P_{\ell,-m} = \frac{(-1)^m(1 - x^2)^{m/2}(\ell - m)!}{2^{\ell}\ell!\,(\ell + m)!} \sum_{n=0}^{\ell-m} \frac{(\ell + m)!\,\ell!\,\ell!}{n!\,(\ell - m - n)!\,(m + n)!\,(\ell - n)!}(x + 1)^n(x - 1)^{\ell-n-m}. \quad (9)$$

Now we examine the sum appearing in Equation (9) in more detail, writing it as

$$\sum_{n=0}^{\ell-m} \frac{(\ell + m)!}{(m + n)!\,(\ell - n)!}\left[\frac{\ell!\,(x + 1)^n}{n!}\right]\left[\frac{\ell!\,(x - 1)^{\ell-n-m}}{(\ell - m - n)!}\right]. \quad (10)$$

Look back to Equation (4). With it, we can write the square-bracketed terms in Equation (10) as

$$\frac{\ell!\,(x + 1)^n}{n!} = \frac{d^{\ell-n}(x + 1)^{\ell}}{dx^{\ell-n}}$$

and

$$\frac{\ell! (x - 1)^{\ell - n - m}}{(\ell - m - n)!} = \frac{d^{m+n}(x - 1)^{\ell}}{dx^{m+n}}.$$

That is, the sum can be written as

$$\sum_{n=0}^{\ell - m} \frac{(\ell + m)!}{(m + n)!(\ell - n)!} \left[\frac{d^{\ell - n}(x + 1)^{\ell}}{dx^{\ell - n}} \right] \left[\frac{d^{m+n}(x - 1)^{\ell}}{dx^{m+n}} \right]. \tag{11}$$

In Equation (11), we now make a change in the index of summation to a new index "s" defined as $s = n + m$. This takes the lower and upper limits of summation to $s = m$ and $s = \ell$, respectively:

$$\sum_{s=m}^{\ell} \frac{(\ell + m)!}{s!(\ell + m - s)!} \left[\frac{d^{\ell + m - s}(x + 1)^{\ell}}{dx^{\ell + m - s}} \right] \left[\frac{d^s(x - 1)^{\ell}}{dx^s} \right]. \tag{12}$$

Now look carefully at the derivatives appearing in Equation (12). As the index s advances from $s = m$ up to $s = \ell$, the order of the derivative in the first square bracket *decreases* from ℓ down to m while at the same time the order in the second square bracket *increases* from m up to ℓ. If either term were to be differentiated more than ℓ times, the result would be zero. (Why?) Consequently, for the first square bracket, if the index s were to start at a lower value than m, all derivatives of $(x + 1)^{\ell}$ would be zero until s reached m. Similarly, if the upper index of s were increased beyond ℓ, all derivates of $(x - 1)^{\ell}$ would be zero for $s > \ell$. Hence we can safely both reduce the lower limit of s to zero (say) while increasing its upper limit to $\ell + m$ (say) without introducing any more terms in the sum than already appear:

$$\sum_{s=0}^{\ell + m} \frac{(\ell + m)!}{s!(\ell + m - s)!} \left[\frac{d^{\ell + m - s}(x + 1)^{\ell}}{dx^{\ell + m - s}} \right] \left[\frac{d^s(x - 1)^{\ell}}{dx^s} \right]. \tag{13}$$

The value of this curious manipulation will become clear momentarily.

Now, circuitous as it may seem, apply Leibniz's rule, Equation (5), to the product $(x + 1)^{\ell}(x - 1)^{\ell}$:

$$\frac{d^{\ell + m}}{dx^{\ell + m}}[(x + 1)^{\ell}(x - 1)^{\ell}] = \sum_{s=0}^{\ell + m} \binom{\ell + m}{s} \left[\frac{d^{\ell + m - s}(x + 1)^{\ell}}{dx^{\ell + m - s}} \right] \left[\frac{d^s(x - 1)^{\ell}}{dx^s} \right].$$

The sum here is precisely that appearing in Equation (13); this is why the limits on the index s were modified between Equations (12) and (13). Hence we can write Equation (13) as

$$\sum_{s=0}^{\ell+m} \frac{(\ell+m)!}{s!(\ell+m-s)!}\left[\frac{d^{\ell+m-s}(x+1)^{\ell}}{dx^{\ell+m-s}}\right]\left[\frac{d^{s}(x-1)^{\ell}}{dx^{s}}\right] = \frac{d^{\ell+m}}{dx^{\ell+m}}[(x+1)^{\ell}(x-1)^{\ell}].$$

Back-substituting this result into Equation (9) and writing $(x+1)^{\ell}(x-1)^{\ell} = (x^2-1)^{\ell}$ gives

$$P_{\ell,-m} = \frac{(-1)^m(1-x^2)^{m/2}(\ell-m)!}{2^{\ell}\ell!(\ell+m)!}\frac{d^{\ell+m}}{dx^{\ell+m}}(x^2-1)^{\ell} = (-1)^m\frac{(\ell-m)!}{(\ell+m)!}P_{\ell,m}.$$

$$(14)$$

From Equation (1), replacing m with $-m$,

$$\Theta_{\ell,-m}(\theta) = \sqrt{\frac{2\ell+1}{2}\frac{(\ell+m)!}{(\ell-m)!}}P_{\ell,-m},$$

or, with Equation (14),

$$\Theta_{\ell,-m}(\theta) = (-1)^m\sqrt{\frac{2\ell+1}{2}\frac{(\ell+m)!}{(\ell-m)!}}\left(\frac{(\ell-m)!}{(\ell+m)!}\right)P_{\ell,m} = (-1)^m\sqrt{\frac{2\ell+1}{2}\frac{(\ell-m)!}{(\ell+m)!}}P_{\ell,m}.$$

Comparing this result to Equation (1) shows that we have

$$\Theta_{\ell,-m}(\theta) = (-1)^m\Theta_{\ell,m}(\theta).$$

Now, the overall spherical harmonic is defined by

$$Y_{\ell,m}(\theta,\phi) = \Theta_{\ell,m}(\theta)\Phi_m(\phi).$$

Since the azimuthal part of the solution satisfies (Section 6.5)

$$\Phi_{-m}(\phi) = \Phi_m^*(\phi),$$

then

$$Y_{\ell,-m} = (-1)^m Y_{\ell,m}^*,$$

as claimed.

■ A.4   Radial Nodes in Hydrogen Wavefunctions

From Equation (7.4.44), the radial hydrogen wavefunctions are

$$R_{n\ell}(r) = \frac{1}{r}(r/a_o)^{\ell+1}\exp(-r/na_o) \sum_{k=0}^{n-\ell-1} b_k (r/a_o)^k = \left(\sum_{k=0}^{n-\ell-1} \frac{b_k}{a_o^{k+\ell+1}} r^{k+\ell} \right) \exp(-r/na_o).$$

When computing radial probability distributions $P(r)$, we have

$$P(r) = 4\pi r^2 R_{n\ell}^2(r) = 4\pi r^2 \left(\sum_{k=0}^{n-\ell-1} \frac{b_k}{a_o^{k+\ell+1}} r^{k+\ell} \right)^2 \exp(-2r/na_o).$$

The factor of r^2 outside the large bracket can be carried inside bracket if we write it simply as r, since the large bracket is itself squared. Combining this factor of r with the factor of $r^{k+\ell}$ within the sum gives

$$P(r) = 4\pi \left(\sum_{k=0}^{n-\ell-1} \frac{b_k}{a_o^{k+\ell+1}} r^{k+\ell+1} \right)^2 \exp(-2r/na_o). \tag{1}$$

Label the sum in Equation (1) as $\Re(r)$; this represents a polynomial in r whose lowest and highest orders are, respectively, $(\ell+1)$ (when $k=0$) and n (when $k = n - \ell - 1$). That is,

$$\Re(r) = \left(\sum_{k=0}^{n-\ell-1} \frac{b_k}{a_o^{k+\ell+1}} r^{k+\ell+1} \right) = \left(\frac{b_0}{a_o^{\ell+1}} r^{\ell+1} + \frac{b_1}{a_o^{\ell+2}} r^{\ell+2} + \frac{b_2}{a_o^{\ell+3}} r^{\ell+3} + \cdots + \frac{b_{n-\ell-1}}{a_o^n} r^n \right).$$

or

$$\Re(r) = r^{\ell+1} \left(\frac{b_0}{a_o^{\ell+1}} + \frac{b_1}{a_o^{\ell+2}} r + \frac{b_2}{a_o^{\ell+3}} r^2 + \cdots + \frac{b_{n-\ell-1}}{a_o^n} r^{n-\ell-1} \right).$$

Fundamentally, $\Re(r)$ is a polynomial of order $(n - \ell - 1)$. Since any polynomial of order p has p zeros, we see that $P(r)$ must have $(n - \ell - 1)$ nodes, as asserted in Chapter 7.

The proof that $r_{mp} = n^2 a_o$ when $\ell = n - 1$ proceeds similarly. In this case the upper limit of k in Equation (1) becomes zero, and we have

$$P(r) = 4\pi \left(\sum_{k=0}^{0} \frac{b_k}{a_o^{k+n}} r^{k+n} \right)^2 \exp(-2r/na_o) = 4\pi \left(\frac{b_0}{a_o^n} \right)^2 r^{2n} \exp(-2r/na_o).$$

Differentiating gives

$$\frac{dP(r)}{dr} = 4\pi \left(\frac{b_0}{a_o^n} \right)^2 \left\{ 2n r^{2n-1} - \frac{2}{na_o} r^{2n} \right\} \exp(-2r/na_o).$$

Setting the derivative to zero to maximize $P(r)$ gives $r_{mp} = n^2 a_o$, as claimed.

B

Answers to Selected Problems

1-1 1.28 Å, 1.14 Å, 1.14 Å, 1.56 Å, 1.24 Å

1-2 $P(E)/P(2E) \sim 15{,}800$

1-3 $T = 300$: 5.48×10^{14} m^{-3}; $T = 2.7$: 400 m^{-3}

1-4 21.59 kW

1-5 $v_n = e^2/2\epsilon_o hn \approx c/(137n)$. Relativistic effects negligible.

1-6 54.4 eV, 489 eV, 115 keV

1-7 $F_C = (\pi m_e^2 e^6/4\epsilon_o^3 h^4 n^4) = (8.233 \times 10^{-8}/n^4)$ Newtons

1-8 $d\lambda = -12.9$ Å

1-9 $DR = \dfrac{\pi m_e e^{10}}{12\epsilon_o^5 h^6 c^3}\left[\dfrac{(n-1)^2}{n^6(2n-1)}\right]$; 8.97×10^{-9} sec

1-10 $a_o = h^2/4\pi^2 Gm_S m_E^2 = 2.32 \times 10^{-138}$ m; $n_{\text{Earth}} \sim 2.54 \times 10^{74}$; undetectable

1-12 $(\lambda_h - \lambda_d)_{3 \to 2} \sim 1.78$ Å

1-14 For transitions down to orbit n: $\lambda_{\text{lowest}} = R_H^{-1}(n^2)$;
$$\lambda_{\text{highest}} = R_H^{-1}\left[\dfrac{n^2(n+1)^2}{2n+1}\right]$$

1-16 $E_n = n^2 h^2/4\pi^2 mL^2$, $n = 1, 2, 3, \ldots$

1-17 $\lambda_{n+1 \to n} = 16\pi^2 c M R^2/5h(2n+1)$; $\lambda_{3 \to 2} \sim 478{,}000$ Å; $n_{\text{optical}} \sim 240$

1-18 0.39 Å. Use QM.

1-19 $\lambda \sim 5.87 \times 10^{-15}$ m; closest approach $\sim 3.79 \times 10^{-14}$ m; marginally justified

1-20 $\lambda = \dfrac{h}{\sqrt{3mkT}}; \sim 1.46\ \text{Å}$

1-22 $E_{\text{photon}}/E_{\text{recoil}} = 2mc\lambda/h \sim 7.6 \times 10^8$

2-3 One possibility is $-\dfrac{\hbar^2}{2m}\left(\dfrac{d\psi}{dx}\right)^2 + V\psi^2 = E\psi^2.$

2-4 $D = A,\ C = kA,\ B = -(A/L^2)(1 + kL)$

Normalization:

$$\frac{A^2}{2k} + \frac{1}{5}B^2L^5 + \frac{1}{2}(BC)L^4 + \frac{1}{3}(2BD + C^2)L^3 + (CD)L^2 + D^2L = 1$$

2-5 $A = 2k^{3/2}$

2-6 $V(x) = E + \hbar^2 k^2/2m - \hbar^2 k/mx$

2-7 $V(x) = E + \dfrac{\hbar^2}{2m}(4k^2x^2 - 2k)$

3-3 $v = nh/2mL,\ v > c$ for $n \sim 82$

3-4 Reject the proposal.

3-5 0.0271

3-9 Four

3-11 $E_1 = 1.187\ \text{eV},\ E_2 = 4.667\ \text{eV}$

3-12 $P_{\text{out}}^{\text{odd}} = \dfrac{\xi}{(\xi - \eta\cot\xi + \eta\xi\csc^2\xi)}$

3-13 $\xi_{\text{true}} = 0.9149;\ \xi_{\text{approx}} = 1.0398$

3-14 0.0110, 0.0479, 0.1298, 0.4133

3-17 $T \sim 1.89 \times 10^{-70}$

3-18 $P_{\text{original}}/P_{\text{wider}} = 25.5$

3-20 $\ln P \approx -\dfrac{4(A/\alpha)\sqrt{2mA}}{\hbar} \displaystyle\int_0^{\text{Cos}^{-1}(\beta)} \sqrt{\cos y - \beta(\cos y)}\, dy;\ \sin y = \alpha x/A$

3-21 $\ln P \approx -\dfrac{4A\sqrt{2mV_0}}{3\hbar}(1 - E/V_0)^{3/2};\ P \sim 2.0 \times 10^{-4}$

3-22 $\ln P \sim -0.3768 \dfrac{\sqrt{m V_0} L}{\hbar}$; $P \sim 0.0473$

3-23 $T \sim 10^{-10^{36}}$

3-24 1.11×10^{52} per second.

3-25 Yes

3-26 Greater

3-28 $L = 2.045$ Å, $E_2 = 32$ eV

4-1 $1.678\ m, 2.816\ m^2, 2.825\ m^2, 0.095\ m$

4-3 $\sqrt{2\alpha}, 1/2\alpha, \iota\hbar\alpha$

4-4 3.17×10^{-8} sec

4-5 $\Delta p \geq 1.76 \times 10^{-40}\ kg\,(m/s)$; $\Delta v = 80\ sec^{-1}$

4-7 $A^2 = \dfrac{2a^3}{\pi}$; $V(x) = E + \dfrac{\hbar^2 (x^2 - a^2)}{m (a^2 + x^2)^2}$; $\Delta x \Delta p = \hbar$

4-8 $\Delta x \Delta p = \sqrt{5}\hbar/2\sqrt{3} \sim 0.645\hbar$

4-9

$$\Delta x \Delta p = \left[\Gamma^{-3/2}\!\left(\frac{n+1}{q}\right)\sqrt{(1 + nq - q)\Gamma\!\left(\frac{n-1}{q}\right)\left\{\Gamma\!\left(\frac{n+1}{q}\right)\Gamma\!\left(\frac{n+3}{q}\right) - \Gamma^2\!\left(\frac{n+2}{q}\right)\right\}} \right]\frac{\hbar}{2}$$

If $q > 0$, the only restriction is $n > 1$.

4-10 $E_1 \geq 1.191\,\alpha^{2/3}\,(\hbar^2/2m)^{1/3}$

4-11 $\Delta m \geq 9.54 \times 10^{-55}$ kg

4-16 $E > 9534$ MeV

4-17 $E \sim 4 \times 10^{18}$ GeV

4-18 $<E> = (61/12)\,E_1$

4-19 $\langle \psi^* | \psi \rangle = 1$

4-21 $\beta^3 = 12mk/\hbar^2$; not valid

5-6 $P_{out} \sim 0.1116$

5-7 $k = 514\ N/m$

5-9 Defining $\xi = \alpha x$ and $\lambda = \epsilon E$ with $\alpha = (km/\hbar^2)^{1/3}$ and $\epsilon = (m/k^2\hbar^2)^{1/3}$ reduces Schrödinger's equation to the dimensionless form $-(1/2)(d^2\psi/d\xi^2) + \xi\psi = \lambda\psi$. The asymptotic solution is of the form $\psi \propto \exp(-\beta\xi^n)$ with $n = 3/2$ and $\beta = 2\sqrt{2}/3$. No closed-from analytic solution is possible.

5-12 $\alpha = K_\alpha m^{1/(p+2)} A^{1/(p+2)} \hbar^{-2/(p+2)}$; $\epsilon = K_\epsilon m^{p/(p+2)} A^{-2/(p+2)} \hbar^{-2p/(p+2)}$. Fails for $p = -2$. Taking $K_\alpha = 2^{1/(p+2)}$ and $K_\epsilon = 2^{p/(p+2)}$ reduces Schrödinger's equation to $d^2\psi/d\xi^2 + (\lambda - |\xi|^p)\psi = 0$.

5-19 $e^2/\epsilon_o m_e c^3 \sim 1.18 \times 10^{-22}$ sec

6-1 Illustrative values: $E_{111} = 64.7$ eV; $E_{113} = 148.1$ eV; $E_{323} = 499.1$ eV

6-2 7.179×10^{22}; 1.077×10^{20}

6-3 (b) and (e) are separable

6-4 About 40 million

6-9 $L^2 = -\hbar^2\left\{(y^2 + z^2)\dfrac{\partial^2}{\partial x^2} + (x^2 + z^2)\dfrac{\partial^2}{\partial y^2} + (x^2 + y^2)\dfrac{\partial^2}{\partial z^2}\right.$

$$\left. -2x\dfrac{\partial}{\partial x} - 2y\dfrac{\partial}{\partial y} - 2z\dfrac{\partial}{\partial z} - 2xy\dfrac{\partial^2}{\partial x\,\partial y} - 2zx\dfrac{\partial^2}{\partial x\,\partial z} - 2yz\dfrac{\partial^2}{\partial y\,\partial z}\right\}$$

$$L^2 = -\hbar^2\left\{z^2\dfrac{\partial^2}{\partial\rho^2} + \rho^2\dfrac{\partial^2}{\partial z^2} + \dfrac{(z^2 + \rho^2)}{\rho^2}\dfrac{\partial^2}{\partial\phi^2} - 2z\dfrac{\partial}{\partial z} + \dfrac{(z^2 - \rho^2)}{\rho}\dfrac{\partial}{\partial\rho} - 2\rho z\dfrac{\partial^2}{\partial z\,\partial\rho}\right\}$$

7-2 $\langle r^2\rangle = \dfrac{a^2}{3}\left[1 - \dfrac{3}{2\pi^2 n^2}\right]$

7-3 $P_{out} = \dfrac{\xi}{(\xi - \eta\cot\xi + \eta\xi\csc^2\xi)}$; 0.1807

7-4 $\Delta r\,\Delta p = 1.670\hbar$

7-5 $V_0 = 36.6$ MeV

7-7 $V_0 > 940$ MeV

7-9 5.764×10^{-14} m

7-10 $b_0 = \sqrt{32/2187\,a_o}$

7-11 $\langle r\rangle = 5a_o$, $\langle 1/r\rangle = 1/4a_o$, $P(3.9a_o, 4.1a_o) = 0.039$

7-13 $r(50\%) = 1.337a_o$

7-16 $\Delta r \Delta p = \sqrt{3}\hbar$

7-20 Hydrogen $\sim 1.56 \times 10^{-14}$; uranium $\sim 2.88 \times 10^{-6}$

7-24 0.2354 eV

8-4 337.5 T/m

8-5 1.1×10^{-6} eV

8-6 1.564 Å

8-7 4.8768 mass units

8-8 F, B, B, F, B, F

9-1 $\phi(x) = x^2 = -\dfrac{2L^2}{\pi^3} \sum_{n=1}^{\infty} \dfrac{[(-1)^n(n^2\pi^2 - 2) + 2]}{n^3} \sin\left(\dfrac{n\pi x}{L}\right)$

9-2 $\phi(x) = e^{ax} = 2\pi \sum_{n=1}^{\infty} \left(\dfrac{n}{a^2 L^2 + n^2\pi^2}\right)[1 - (-1)^n e^{aL}] \sin\left(\dfrac{n\pi x}{L}\right)$

9-3 $E_n \approx (3\alpha h n/8\sqrt{2m})^{2/3}$

9-4 $n \gg 2\pi$

9-5 $n \gg 2.42$

9-6 $n \sim 2\alpha(0.5991)\sqrt{2mE}/h \quad n \sim 2.03$

9-7 $\dfrac{2\sqrt{2mV_0}}{\alpha} \displaystyle\int_{0}^{\ln(1+\beta)} \sqrt{1 + \beta - e^y}\,dy \sim nh; \ E = \beta V_0$ and

$y = \alpha x; \alpha \sim 0.01639 \ \text{Å}^{-1}$

9-9 $E \sim \dfrac{n^2 h^2}{8mL^2} + \alpha L^2\left(\dfrac{1}{3} - \dfrac{1}{2\pi^2 n^2}\right)$

9-10 $E \sim \dfrac{n^2 h^2}{8mL^2} - \dfrac{V_0}{2}$

$\psi^n \sim \psi_n^0 + \dfrac{8\sqrt{2}mL^{3/2}V_0}{\pi h^2} \sum_{k \neq n} \sin\left(\dfrac{k\pi x}{L}\right)\left\{\dfrac{\sin[(k-n)\pi/2]}{(k+n)(k-n)^2} - \dfrac{\sin[(k+n)\pi/2]}{(k+n)^2(k-n)}\right\}$

9-11 $E \sim E_n^0 + \beta a^2 \left(\dfrac{1}{3} - \dfrac{1}{2\pi^2 n^2} \right)$

$\psi \sim \psi_n^0(x) - \dfrac{64\beta\, ma^{7/2}}{\sqrt{2}\pi^{5/2}\hbar^2} \sum_{k \neq n} \dfrac{(-1)^{k-n}nk}{(k+n)^3(k-n)^3} \dfrac{\sin(k\pi r/a)}{r}$

9-12 $E \sim E_n^0 + \dfrac{\pi Aa^2}{4} \left(\dfrac{1}{3} - \dfrac{1}{2n^2\pi^2} \right)$

9-13 $E \sim \hbar\omega/2 + 3\beta/4\alpha^4$

$\psi \sim A_0 e^{-\xi^2/2} \left\{ 1 - \dfrac{\beta}{a^4\hbar\omega} \left[\dfrac{3}{8} H_2(\xi) + \dfrac{1}{64} H_4(\xi) \right] \right\}$

9-14

$(E_1/4 - E + 5a_o\lambda)^3 [(E_1 - E + 3a_o\lambda/2)(E_1/4 - E + 6a_o\lambda) - (64\lambda a_o/81\sqrt{2})^2] = 0.$

9-15 $\beta < \pi m_e^2 e^6 / 120\epsilon_o^3 \hbar^4 = 1.713 \text{ eV/Å}$

9-16 $\Delta\lambda \sim 0.06 \text{ Å}.$

9-17 $\lambda = 1.519 \times 10^{-6} \text{ m}$

9-18 $E = 3\epsilon\beta - \left[\dfrac{2^{5/2} A\Gamma(7/4)}{\sqrt{\pi}} \right] \dfrac{\beta^{3/2}}{(\alpha + 2\beta)^{7/4}}$

$\beta \sim 1.312 \text{ Å}^{-2}; E \sim -18.32 \text{ eV}$

9-19 $E = \epsilon\beta - \dfrac{A\sqrt{2\beta}}{\sqrt{\alpha + 2\beta}} \quad (\epsilon = \hbar^2/2m)$

$\beta \sim 0.428542 \text{ Å}^{-2}; E \sim -2.193 \text{ eV}$

9-20 For $\alpha = 0.5$, $\beta \sim 0.87$, $E \leq 0.2930 E_1$

9-21 $E \leq - m_e e^4 / 32\pi^2 \epsilon_o^2 \hbar^2$ (the hydrogen ground-state energy)

9-22 $\lambda_{min}^4 = 35\hbar^2/2mk < E_{min} > = \sqrt{5/14}\hbar\omega$

9-23 $\beta_{min} = \left[\dfrac{n\alpha(n+2)!}{2^{n+2}(\hbar^2/2m)} \right]^{1/(n+2)}$

$E \leq \dfrac{1}{4} \left(\dfrac{\hbar^2}{2m} \right)^{n/(n+2)} \left(1 + \dfrac{2}{n} \right) \{\alpha n(n+2)!\}^{2/(n+2)}$

9-24 $\beta_{min} = \dfrac{8\pi m_e^2 e^4}{9\epsilon_o^2 h^4}, E \leq - \dfrac{m_e e^4}{12\pi^3 \epsilon_o^2 \hbar^2}$

10-1 $E_3 \sim 8.6217$ eV

10-2 $E_1 \sim 14.654$ eV; $E_2 \sim 40.443$ eV

10-3 $E_1 \sim -3.800$ eV

10-4 $\ell = 0$: $E_1 \sim 13.094$, $E_2 \sim 30.553$ eV; $\ell = 1$: $E_1 \sim 21.823$, $E_2 \sim 39.282$ eV

   $W \sim -0.962$ at $n \sim 0.85$ for $K = 2$

10-6 $E_1 \sim -18.58$ eV; only one solution

10-9 ~ 3.65, 6.38, 8.62 eV for $\ell = 0$; identical to the linear case

10-10 $\ell = 0$: $E \sim 9.378$, 13.635, 17.774 eV; $\ell = 1$: $E \sim 11.646$, 15.763, 19.881 eV

10-11 $\ell = 0$: $E \sim -79.041$, -51.192, -25.488 eV; $\ell = 1$: $E \sim -65.991$, -38.346,
   -14.004 eV

10-12 $m = 0$: $(0.2354, 1.1760, 2.8683)_{\text{analytic}}$, $(0.2354, 1.1757, 2.8674)_{\text{numerical}}$

   $m = 1$: $(0.5744, 1.8903, 3.9585)_{\text{analytic}}$, $(0.5744, 1.8899, 3.9577)_{\text{numerical}}$

   $m = 2$: $(1.0199, 2.7145, 5.1594)_{\text{analytic}}$, $(1.0199, 2.7143, 5.1588)_{\text{numerical}}$

10-13 $m = (0, 1, 2)$: $(2.7594, 5.5193, 8.2805)$

10-14 Two bound states: -51.057 eV and -5.898 eV

11-2 $A_{nj} = \left(\dfrac{2q^2 h^2}{3 \pi \epsilon_o c^3 m^3 L^4} \right) \dfrac{(nj)^2}{(j + n)|j - n|}$, $(j - n)\, odd$

11-4 $P = \dfrac{64[Z(Z - 1)]^3}{(2Z - 1)^6}$, $P \sim 0.7023$ for $Z = 2$

11-5

$$\sqrt{P_{j \to n}} = \begin{cases} \dfrac{1}{\pi \sqrt{K}} \left\{ \dfrac{\sin[(j - n/K)\pi]}{(j - n/K)} - \dfrac{\sin[(j + n/K)\pi]}{(j + n/K)} \right\} & (n \neq jK) \\[4mm] \dfrac{2}{\sqrt{K}} \left\{ \dfrac{1}{2} - \dfrac{K \sin(2n\pi/K)}{4n\pi} \right\} & (n = jK). \end{cases}$$

C | Integrals and Trigonometric Identities

The gamma function, $\Gamma(n)$, appearing in **(38)**, can be expressed in terms of the factorial function via $\Gamma(n + 1) = n!$, and can be extended to nonintegral values of the argument. Note that $\Gamma(1/2) = \sqrt{\pi}$. Integral **(29)** is a generalization of **(26)–(28)**; similarly integrals **(37)** and **(38)** for **(30)–(36)**.

(1) $\displaystyle \int \frac{dx}{a^2 + x^2} = \frac{1}{a} \tan^{-1}\left(\frac{x}{a}\right)$

(2) $\displaystyle \int \frac{dx}{(a^2 + x^2)^n} = \frac{1}{2a^2(n - 1)}\left[\frac{x}{(a^2 + x^2)^{n-1}} + (2n - 3)\int \frac{dx}{(a^2 + x^2)^{n-1}}\right]$

(3) $\displaystyle \int \frac{x^2 dx}{(a^2 + x^2)} = x - a^2 \int \frac{dx}{a^2 + x^2}$

(4) $\displaystyle \int \frac{x^2 dx}{(a^2 + x^2)^{n+1}} = -\frac{x}{2n(a^2 + x^2)^n} + \frac{1}{2n}\int \frac{dx}{(a^2 + x^2)^n}$

(5) $\displaystyle \int \sqrt{a + bx}\, dx = \frac{2}{3b}\sqrt{(a + bx)^3}$

(6) $\displaystyle \int \sqrt{x^2 \pm a^2}\, dx = \frac{1}{2}\left[x\sqrt{x^2 \pm a^2} \pm a^2 \ln\left(x + \sqrt{x^2 \pm a^2}\right)\right]$

(7) $\displaystyle \int \sqrt{a^2 - x^2}\, dx = \frac{1}{2}\left[x\sqrt{a^2 - x^2} + a^2 \sin^{-1}\left(\frac{x}{|a|}\right)\right]$

(8) $\displaystyle \int \sin^2(ax)\, dx = \frac{x}{2} - \frac{1}{4a}\sin(2ax)$

(9) $\displaystyle\int \cos^2(ax)\,dx = \frac{x}{2} + \frac{1}{4a}\sin(2ax)$

(10)

$$\int \sin(mx)\,\sin(nx)\,dx = \frac{\sin[(m-n)x]}{2(m-n)} - \frac{\sin[(m+n)x]}{2(m+n)} \quad (m^2 \neq n^2)$$

(11)

$$\int \cos(mx)\,\cos(nx)\,dx = \frac{\sin[(m-n)x]}{2(m-n)} + \frac{\sin[(m+n)x]}{2(m+n)} \quad (m^2 \neq n^2)$$

(12)

$$\int \sin(mx)\,\cos(nx)\,dx = -\frac{\cos[(m-n)x]}{2(m-n)} - \frac{\cos[(m+n)x]}{2(m+n)} \quad (m^2 \neq n^2)$$

(13) $\displaystyle\int \sin(ax)\,\cos(ax)\,dx = \frac{1}{2a}\sin^2(ax)$

(14) $\displaystyle\int \sin(ax)\,\cos^m(ax)\,dx = -\frac{\cos^{m+1}(ax)}{(m+1)a}$

(15) $\displaystyle\int \sin^m(ax)\,\cos(ax)\,dx = \frac{\sin^{m+1}(ax)}{(m+1)a}$

(16) $\displaystyle\int x\,\sin(ax)\,dx = \frac{1}{a^2}\sin(ax) - \frac{x}{a}\cos(ax)$

(17) $\displaystyle\int x\,\cos(ax)\,dx = \frac{1}{a^2}\cos(ax) + \frac{x}{a}\sin(ax)$

(18) $\displaystyle\int x^2\,\sin(ax)\,dx = \frac{2x}{a^2}\sin(ax) - \frac{a^2x^2 - 2}{a^3}\cos(ax)$

(19) $\displaystyle\int x^2\,\cos(ax)\,dx = \frac{2x\cos(ax)}{a^2} + \frac{a^2x^2 - 2}{a^3}\sin(ax)$

(20) $\displaystyle\int x\,\sin^2(ax)\,dx = \frac{x^2}{4} - \frac{x\sin(2ax)}{4a} - \frac{\cos(2ax)}{8a^2}$

(21) $\displaystyle\int x\,\cos^2(ax)\,dx = \frac{x^2}{4} + \frac{x\sin(2ax)}{4a} + \frac{\cos(2ax)}{8a^2}$

(22) $\int x^2 \sin^2(ax)\,dx = \dfrac{x^3}{6} - \left(\dfrac{x^2}{4a} - \dfrac{1}{8a^3}\right)\sin(2ax) - \dfrac{x\cos(2ax)}{4a^2}$

(23) $\int x^2 \cos^2(ax)\,dx = \dfrac{x^3}{6} + \left(\dfrac{x^2}{4a} - \dfrac{1}{8a^3}\right)\sin(2ax) + \dfrac{x\cos(2ax)}{4a^2}$

(24) $\int xe^{ax}\,dx = \dfrac{e^{ax}}{a^2}(ax - 1)$

(25) $\int x^m e^{ax}\,dx = \dfrac{x^m e^{ax}}{a} - \dfrac{m}{a}\int x^{m-1} e^{ax}\,dx$

(26) $\displaystyle\int_0^\infty xe^{-ax}\,dx = \dfrac{1}{a^2}$

(27) $\displaystyle\int_0^\infty x^2 e^{-ax}\,dx = \dfrac{2}{a^3}$

(28) $\displaystyle\int_0^\infty x^3 e^{-ax}\,dx = \dfrac{6}{a^4}$

(29) $\displaystyle\int_0^\infty x^n e^{-ax}\,dx = \dfrac{\Gamma(n+1)}{a^{n+1}}\quad(a>0;\ n>-1)$

(30) $\displaystyle\int_0^\infty e^{-ax^2}\,dx = \dfrac{\sqrt{\pi}}{2\sqrt{a}}$

(31) $\displaystyle\int_0^\infty xe^{-ax^2}\,dx = \dfrac{1}{2a}$

(32) $\displaystyle\int_0^\infty x^2 e^{-ax^2}\,dx = \dfrac{\sqrt{\pi}}{4a^{3/2}}$

(33) $\displaystyle\int_0^\infty x^3 e^{-ax^2}\,dx = \dfrac{1}{2a^2}$

(34) $\displaystyle\int_0^\infty x^4 e^{-ax^2}dx = \frac{3\sqrt{\pi}}{8a^{5/2}}$

(35) $\displaystyle\int_0^\infty x^5 e^{-ax^2}dx = \frac{1}{a^3}$

(36) $\displaystyle\int_0^\infty x^{2n} e^{-ax^2}dx = \frac{1\cdot 3\cdot 5\cdot\,\cdots\,(2n-1)}{2^{n+1}a^n}\sqrt{\frac{\pi}{a}}$

(37) $\displaystyle\int_0^\infty x^{2n+1} e^{-ax^2}dx = \frac{n!}{2a^{n+1}}\quad (a>0)$

(38) $\displaystyle\int_0^\infty x^n e^{-ax^p}dx = \frac{\Gamma(k)}{pa^k}\quad [n>-1, p>0, a>0, k=(n+1)/p]$

(39) $\sin\alpha\,\sin\beta = \dfrac{1}{2}\cos(\alpha-\beta) - \dfrac{1}{2}\cos(\alpha+\beta)$

(40) $\cos\alpha\,\cos\beta = \dfrac{1}{2}\cos(\alpha-\beta) + \dfrac{1}{2}\cos(\alpha+\beta)$

(41) $\sin\alpha\,\cos\beta = \dfrac{1}{2}\sin(\alpha+\beta) + \dfrac{1}{2}\sin(\alpha-\beta)$

(42) $\cos\alpha\,\sin\beta = \dfrac{1}{2}\sin(\alpha+\beta) - \dfrac{1}{2}\sin(\alpha-\beta)$

(43) $\cos(n\pi) = (-1)^n$

(44) $\sin(n\pi) = 0$

(45) $\sin(n\pi/2) = 1,\ n = 1, 5, 9, \ldots$

(46) $\sin(n\pi/2) = -1,\ n = 3, 7, 11, \ldots$

(47) $\cos(n\pi/2) = 1,\ n = 0, 4, 8, \ldots$

(48) $\cos(n\pi/2) = -1,\ n = 2, 6, 10, \ldots$

(49) $\cos(n\pi/2) = 0,\ n = 1, 3, 5, \ldots$

Physical Constants

The National Institute of Standards and Technology (NIST) maintains an extensive listing of physical constants at physics.nist.gov/constants. The following values are taken from that site, truncated to four decimal places.

Quantity	Symbol	Value	Unit
Speed of light in vacuum	c	2.9979×10^8	$m\ s^{-1}$
Planck's constant	h	6.6261×10^{-34}	$J - s = kg\ m^2\ s^{-1}$
Planck's constant	$\hbar$	1.0546×10^{-34}	$J - s = kg\ m^2\ s^{-1}$
Gravitational constant	G	6.6742×10^{-11}	$m^3\ kg^{-1}\ s^{-2}$
Elementary charge	e	1.6022×10^{-19}	C
Electron mass	m_e	9.1094×10^{-31}	kg
Proton mass	m_p	1.6726×10^{-27}	kg
Neutron mass	m_n	1.6749×10^{-27}	kg
Atomic mass unit	AMU or u	1.6605×10^{-27}	kg
Bohr radius	a_o	5.2918×10^{-11}	m
Rydberg constant	R_∞	1.0974×10^7	m^{-1}
Avogadro's number	N_A	6.0221×10^{23}	mol^{-1}
Boltzmann's constant	k	1.3807×10^{-23}	J/K
Permeability constant	μ_o	$4\pi \times 10^{-7}$	$Tm/amp = kg\ m/C^2$
Permitivity constant	ϵ_o	8.8542×10^{-12}	$C^2\ N^{-1}\ m^{-2} = C^2\ s^2\ kg^{-1}\ m^{-3}$

Notes and References

Chapter 1

1. Stoney GJ, *Philosophical Magazine* 1881;11:381.

2. Thomson JJ, *Philosophical Magazine* 1897;44:293.

3. Pais A, *Inward Bound.* New York: Oxford University Press, 1986.

4. Herzberg G. Atomic Spectra and Atomic Structure. New York: Dover Publications, 1945.

5. Balmer JJ, *Annalen der Physik* 1885;261:80.

6. Planck M, *Annalen der Physik* 1900;306:69.

7. Einstein A, *Annalen der Physik* 1905;322:132.

8. Rutherford E, *Philosophical Magazine* 1911;21:669.

9. Bohr N, *Philosophical Magazine* 1913;26:1, 476, and 857.

10. Paschen F, *Annalen der Physik* 1908;332:537.

11. Lyman T, *Physical Review* 1914;3:504.

12. Brackett F, *Nature* 1922;109:209.

13. Pfund HA, *Journal of the Optical Society of America* 1924;9:193.

14. Moseley H, *Philosophical Magazine* 1913;26:1024 and 1914;27:703.

15. Hertz G, *Zeitschreift fur Physik* 1924;22:18.

16. French AP and Kennedy PJ, *Niels Bohr: A Centenary Volume.* Cambridge: Harvard University Press, 1985.

17. A relativistic treatment is given in Section 2-3 of French & Taylor.

18. Davisson C, Germer LH, *Physical Review* 1927;30:707.

19. Thomson GP, *Proceedings of the Royal Society* 1928;A117:600.

20. Jonsson C, *Zeitschreift fur Physik* 1961;161:454. A translation appears by Brandt D and Hirschi S, *American Journal of Physics* 1974;42:5. See also Tonomura A, et al., *American Journal of Physics* 1989;57:117.

21. Feynman RP, Leighton RB, and Sands M, *The Feynman Lectures on Physics.* Reading, MA: Addison-Wesley, 1963–1965.

Chapter 2

1. This derivation of the classical wave equation follows that given by Gauthier N, *American Journal of Physics* 1987;55:477.

2. Schrödinger E, *Annalen der Physik* 1926;384:361, 1926:384:489, 1926;385:437, and 1926;386:109.

3. Born M, *Zeitschrift fur Physik* 1926;37:863 and 1926;38:803.

Chapter 3

1. Aronstein DL, Stroud CL, *American Journal of Physics* 2000;68:943; Sprung DWL, Wu H, and Martorell J, *European Journal of Physics* 1992;13:21.

2. Eisberg R, and Resnick R, *Quantum Physics of Atoms, Molecules, Solids, Nuclei and Particles.* New York: John Wiley and Sons, 1974, Section 5-7.

3. Gamow G, *Zeitschrift fur Physik* 1928;51:204.

4. Geiger H, and Nutall JM, *Philosophical Magazine* 1911;22:613 and 1912;23:439.

5. See, for example, Heyde K., *Basic Ideas and Concepts in Nuclear Physics*, 3rd ed. Bristol, UK: Institute of Physics Publishing, 2004, Figure 4.9.

6. Ramsauer CW, *Annals of Physics* 1921;64:513; Townsend JS, *Philosophical Magazine* 1922;43:593.

Chapter 4

1. Gasiorowicz S, *Quantum Physics.* New York: John Wiley and Sons, 1974, Appendix B.

2. Pais A, *Inward Bound.* New York: Oxford University Press, 1986, p. 262.

3. Ehrenfest P, *Zeitschrift fur Physik* 1927;45:455.

4. Pais, p. 258.

Chapter 5

1. Morse P, *Physical Review* 1929;34:57. See also Section 35d of Pauling and Wilson.

Chapter 6

1. Eisenhart LP, *Physical Review* 1934;45:427.

2. Beard DB, and Beard, GB, *Quantum Mechanics with Applications.* Boston: Allyn and Bacon, 1970. See Chapter 1.

3. Leung PT, *American Journal of Physics* 1986;54:1148.

4. Equation (6) is by no means an obvious substitution and deserves some comment. Readers familiar with advanced techniques of solving differential equations will recognize this substitution as one that renders the Θ-equation in the form of a hypergeometric equation, a standard form for a second-order differential equation.

5. Liboff RL, *Introductory Quantum Mechanics*, 2nd ed, Reading, MA: Addison-Wesley, 1992, p. 147.

Chapter 7

1. Schrödinger E, *Annalen der Physik* 1926;384:361.

2. Shankar, R., *Principles of Quantum Mechanics*, 2nd ed, New York: Kluwer Academic/Plenum Publishers, 1994, Sections 12.6 and 13.1.

3. White HE, *Physical Review* 1931;37:1416.

Chapter 8

1. Stern W, Gerlach O, *Zeitschrift fur Physik* 1921;8:110. This historically important experiment was undertaken at the suggestion of Niels Bohr and preceded the development of wave mechanics.

2. See, for example, Landau LD, Lifshitz EM., *Quantum Mechanics (Non-relativistic Theory)*, Oxford: Pergamon Press, 1977, 3rd revised ed, p. 461.

3. Phipps TE, Taylor JB, *Physical Review* 1927;29:309.

4. Uhlenbeck GE, Goudsmit SA, *Naturwissenschaften* 1925;13:953 and *Nature* 1926;117:264.

5. Very readable treatments can be found in Section 28 of Pauling and Wilson, and Section 13.9 of French and Taylor.

6. Dirac, PAM, *Proceedings of the Royal Society* 1928;A117:610.

Chapter 9

1. Wentzel G, *Zeitschrift fur Physik* 1926;38:518; also Kramers HA, *Zeitschrift fur Physik* 1926;39:828 and Brillouin L, *Journal de Physique et radium* 1926;7:353. This method is also sometimes known as the JWKB method in honor of Harold Jeffreys, who established the basic mathematical approach in *Proceedings of the London Mathematical Society* 1923;23:428.

2. Reed BC, *American Journal of Physics* 1990;58:407.

Chapter 10

1. Abramowitz M, Stegun, IA, *Handbook of Mathematical Functions.* New York, Dover Publications Inc., 1965, Table 10.13, p. 478.

2. Flügge S, *Practical Quantum Mechanics*, Berlin, Springer-Verlag, 1974, pp. 94–100.

Chapter 11

1. *A Physicist's Desk Reference: The Second Edition of Physics Vade Mecum.* New York: American Institute of Physics, Anderson, HL, ed. Table 5.07.B.1, p. 99.

Index

A

Absorption spectrum, 5, *5*
ACPs. *See* Attractive central potentials
AFM. *See* Atomic force microscopy
Airy function, 303
Alpha decay, *98*
  as barrier penetration effect, 97–102
  Gamow factor for, 100
Ångstrom, 3
  atomic-scale problems characterized by
    lengths on order of, 352
Angular frequency, of a classical mass/spring
    system, 162
Angular momentum, *See also* Quantization of
    angular momentum
  Bohr quantization condition on, 26
  diatomic molecules and, 287–291
  lesser, and more eccentric planetary orbits,
    25, 258
  operator for magnitude of z-component of,
    208
  operators, 192, 203–209
  quantization of, 27, 214, 218
  raising and lowering operators and, 275–281
Angular momentum quantum number, state of
    electrons specified by, 297
Angular nodes, *260, 261, 262t*
Angular wavefunctions, 210
  spherical harmonics and, 211–221
Antisymmetric form, of Ψ, 294–297
Approximation, sudden, 374–376
Approximation methods, 299–342
  perturbation theory, 299, 309–316
    nondegenerate first-order, 314–316

variational method, 299, 327–335
  improved, 336–340
  WKB method, 299–305
Arbitrarily shaped barriers, penetration of,
    94–97
Arithmetic average, 118
Associated Laguerre polynomial, 250
Associated Legendre functions, 221, 261, 384
  explicit series form for, 384–386
Asymptotic solution, 164
Atomic beam, 283
Atomic force microscopy, 84
Atomic mass unit, 405t
Atomic units, 352–353
  Shrödinger's equation in, 354
Atoms
  Bohr's theory of, 14–21
Attractive central potentials, 332–335
Averages, expectation values and, 118–121
Avogadro's number (N_A), 405t

B

Balmer, Johann, 6
Barrier penetration, 76
B_e
  values and bond lengths, 290
BEC. *See* Bose-Einstein condensate
Bell Telephone Laboratories, 24
Bequerel, Henri, 97
Bessel's equation, 273
Binding energy, 269
Binning, Gerd, 83
Binning, for hypothetical distribution of heights,
    118–119, *119*
Binomial theorem, 384

"Blackbody" cavities, 8
Blackbody radiation formula, 12
Blackbody radiation theory, 4, 22, 146, 197
Bohr, Niels, 14–17
Bohr magneton, 284
Bohr model, 14–17
    hydrogen-atom bound-state energies
        predicted by Schrödinger's equation and,
        249
Bohr radius, 16, 405t
Bold type, operation notation and, 118
Boltzmann's constant, 10, 405t
Bond length, 290, 291
Born, Max, 49, 50, 51, 137
Bose, Satyendra, 296
Bose-Einstein condensate, 296–297
Bosons, 295, 296
Boundary conditions, 43
    imposition of, on solutions of Schrödinger's
        equation, 54, 67
    interpretation of psi (ψ): probabilities and,
        49–54
Bound energy state(s), 15, 61, 71
    car in, *62*
    number of, in finite potential well, 81–83
Bright-line (emission) spectrum, *5*

C

Car
    on a roller-coaster track, 60–62
Carbon-60 "buckyball" molecules, observed
        wave properties of, 24, 33
Cartesian coordinates
    operators for $x, y,$ and z components of
        angular momentum in, 226
    separation of variables in, 192–201
    spherical coordinates and, 201–202
Cartesian unit vectors, expression of, in terms of
        spherical unit vectors, 202
CCD chips, 59
    finite potential wells and application to,
        82–83
Center of mass (CM), Schrödinger's equation
        for any two-body system and, 240–243
Central potentials, 209–211, 231–267

Coulomb potential as example of, 192
Central radial node, 261, 262t
"Centrifugal" term, 266
Characteristic tunneling length, 76
Circular orbits, Newtonian dynamics of, 15
Classical approximation, 302, 303
Classical harmonic oscillator, quantum simple
        harmonic oscillator *vs.*, 176–179, *178*
Classical mechanics
    behavior of quantum system in accord with,
        135
    momentum given by time derivative in, 126
Classical probability density, 177
Classical turning points, 61, 85
Classical wave equation, 36–41
Coefficients, recursion relation and, 168
Collins, G. P., 297
Commutation relations, 276
Commutators, 276, 277
    angular momentum raising and lowering
        operators and, 278
    uncertainty relations and, 131–134
Complementary variables, 131
Complex conjugate of a quantity, 49–50
Compton, Arthur H., 13
Condon, Edward, 97, 99, 102
Condon-Shortley phase, 222
Conjugate variables, 131
Continuous spectra, 8
Continuum of energy levels, 20
Coulomb potential, 240–251, *304*
    dimensionless radial equation for, 245, 265
    effective potential curves for, *265*
CRC Handbook of Chemistry and Physics, 290
Crommie, M. F., 84
Cyclical permutation of coordinates, 204
Cyclic coordinate, 213

D

Dalton, John, 2
Daughter nucleus, 97, 99
Davisson, Clinton, 24
de Broglie, Louis, 23, 24
de Broglie matter-wave, particle and, *25*

de Broglie's hypothesis, sketching wavefunctions and, 85

de Broglie's quantization condition, *27*

de Broglie wavelengths, 23–27, *24*, 28, 127
  particle of mass m characterized by, 299

Degeneracy, 66
  explanation of, 197
  partially lifted, 326

Delta-function, 54

Derivations, miscellaneous
  explicit series form for associated Legendre functions, 384–386
  Heisenberg's uncertainty principle, 379–384
  proof that $Y_{l,-m}=(-1)^m Y_{l,m}^*$, 386–390
  radial nodes in hydrogen wavefunctions, 391

Deuteron, 269

Diatomic-bond potentials, 171

Diatomic molecules
  angular momentum and, 287–291
  model of, *288*

Differential equations
  numerical solutions of, 351–356
    cautionary note about, 364–365
  partial, 193
  series solution of, 166

Dimensional analysis
  lesson in, 160–163
  Planck time and, 163

Dirac, P. A. M., 179

Dirac notation (Dirac braket notation), 124, 125, 140, 383
  mathematical expression of orthogonality in, 139

Divergence theorem, 125

Dot product, of orthogonal unit vectors, 208

Doubly degenerate systems, 66

Dummy indexes, 167, 168

Dummy wavefunctions, 205, 276

Dynamical variables, 115

E

Effective potential, 264–266

Ehrenfest's theorem, 113, 134–137
  proof of, 137

Eigenfunctions, 67, 114

Eigenstates of a system, numerical approach and, 351

Eigenvalue equations, 43
  general form of, 114
  operator notation and, 113

Eigenvalue functions, for K = 10 finite well, *81*

Eigenvalues, 114
  expectation values and, 121
  simultaneous, measuring for two operators, 131

Einstein, Albert, 200
  photoelectric effect and, 12, 13
  theory of relativity, 3

Einstein coefficient of spontaneous emission, 370

Eisberg, R., 86

Eisenhart, L. P., 197

Electric-dipole transitions, 374

Electron capture, 272

Electron mass, 405*t*

Electron momentum spectroscopy, 266

Electrons, 4, 282, 283
  coining of term for, 2
  de Broglie wavelength and speed of, 26
  fermions and, 296
  modern values for mass and charge of, 3, 405
  orbital angular momentum of, 20
  orbital motion of, around proton, 283
  quantum numbers specifying state of, 297
  states of, 286*t*
  trapped in one-dimensional "box" made of electrodes and grids in evacuated tube, *64*
  wave nature of, 24–27

Electron spin, Stern-Gerlach experiment as evidence for, 282–287

Electron spin quantum number, 285

Elementary charge, 405*t*

Ellipsoid, 198–199

Energy degeneracy, 191, 195

Energy eigenvalues, infinite rectangular well, 65–67
  determining for perturbed potential, 312
  for a finite spherical well, illustration of solution for, *238*

finite rectangular well, 75, 78
finite spherical well, 237–238
harmonic oscillator, 170
hydrogen atom, 20, 249
infinite spherical well, 235
three-dimensional box, 195
WKB approximation for particle of mass m
    moving in one-dimensional linear
    potential, 302
WKB method and approximating of, 299–305
Energy-level diagrams, 20, 60
Energy-momentum-rest mass relation
    (Einstein), 200
Equilibrium rotation constant B_e, 290
Error functions, 174, 175
Even parity, 75, 76, 88
Even-parity solutions, finite rectangular well
    and, 79–81
Expectation values, 113, 118–126
    calculating, general rule for, 120–121
    calculating time-dependence of average
        position of particle and, 143
    Ehrenfest's theorem and, 134–137
"Experimental studies of Bose-Einstein
    condensation" (Ketterle), 297

F

Faraday, Michael, 1, 2
Femtometer, 99
Fermi, Enrico, 99, 295
Fermions, 295, 296
Feynman, R. P., 26
Field gradient, 285
Finite depth, particle trapped in potential well
    of, 70
Finite potential well, number of bound states in,
    81–84
Finite rectangular well, 70–78
    energy levels for a particle of mass m moving
        in, 75
    even-parity solutions and, 79–81
Finite spherical well, 236–239
First-order perturbation theory, time-
    independent, nondegenerate, 314
Forbidden transitions, 373

Force, as negative gradient of a potential, 135
Fourier analysis, 127
Fourier series, 308
Fourier transforms, 39
Franck, James, 22
Fraunhofer, Joseph, 4
Freidrich, B., 219
Frequencies, number of photon states lying
    within narrow band of, 197
Functions
    any ($f(x)$ of x), operator for, $117t$
    orthogonal set of, 138
    orthonormal set of, 139

G

Gamma function, 401
Gamow, George, 97, 99, 102
Gamow factor, for alpha-decay, 100
"Gaseous Bose-Einstein condensate finally
    observed" (Collins), 297
Gauss's theorem, 125
Gauss unit, 284
Geiger, Hans, 14, 97
Geiger-Nutall law, 97, 101
    alpha-decay as barrier penetration effect and
        explanation of, 102
General barrier penetration, *94*
Gerlach, O., 219
Germer, Lester, 24
Goudsmit, S. A., 285
Gradient operators, 204
    expressions for, in spherical coordinates, 203
Gravitational constant, $405t$
Green's second identity, 137
Green's theorem, 125
Ground state, 20, 67
    force constant of harmonic oscillator and
        probability of system remaining in,
        375–376
    least-bound, of attractive central potentials,
        334–335
Ground-state energy, 65
    attractive central potentials and upper limits
        for, *335*
    obtaining estimate of, 327

uncertainty-based arguments for, 129
Ground-state harmonic oscillator
  determining root-mean-square position for, and comparing to classical turning point, 175
  normalized wavefunction of, 173
Gurney, Ronald, 97, 99, 102

H

Half-life, alpha-decay, 97
Hamiltonian operator, 114, 118, 133, 134, 140, 146, 147, 152, 185, 226
  perturbed/unperturbed, 311
  in spherical coordinates, 207
  variational method and, 327
Harmonic-oscillator potentials, 129, 150, 159, 288, 363
  asymptotic solution for, 164–165
  Hamiltonian operator for, 181
  operator-based alternate solution to, 179–186
Harmonic oscillator, 159–187, 216, 217, 245
  classical *vs.* quantum simple, 176–179
  ground-state, normalized wavefunction for, 173
  probability of system remaining in ground state and force constant of, 375–376
  Schrödinger's equation solved for, 165–171
Harmonic oscillator raising and lowering operators, 179–186, 279
Harmonic-oscillator transitions, 373
Harmonic-oscillator wavefunctions, 172
  hermite polynomials and, 172–173
Harmonic potential, *160*
Heights, hypothetical distribution of, 118–119
Heisenberg, Werner, 45, 132
  website on life and work of, 131
Heisenberg's Uncertainty Principle. *See* Uncertainty Principle (Heisenberg)
Helium
  Bose-Einstein condensate and, 296, 297
  "closed" electron shells possessed by, 297
  nucleus, 97
Hermite polynomials, 172*t*, 177, 178, 371
  harmonic oscillator wavefunctions and, 172–175

perturbed ground-state wavefunctions and, 322
recursion relationships satisfied by, 184
Hershbach, D., 219
Hertz, Gustav, 22
High-energy scattering, 105
Hydrogen
  Balmer's formula for wavelengths of spectral lines for, 6
  Bohr model for, 14–17
  Bohr radius and Rydberg energy for, 244
  cumulative probability density for (1,0,0) state of, 257, *257*
  effective radius of lone proton in, 17
  emission spectrum of, *7*
  energy level diagram for, *21*
  energy levels, 324–326
  (1,0,0) state of, 254–256
  other states of, 258–259, 261–262, 264
  radial probability distribution for ground state of, *255*
  radial probability distribution for (2,0,0) state of, 257, *258*
  Rydberg constant for, 8, 18
  solving Schrödinger's equation for, 240–252
  transition frequency from (2,1,0) to (1,0,0) state of, 372–373
  (2,0,0) and other states of, 257–264
Hydrogen-atom bound-state energies, Schrödinger's equation and prediction of, 249
Hydrogen-atom wavefunctions, 253*t*
  solution for radial part of, 244–250
Hydrogen chloride, value of B_e for, 291
Hydrogenic electron/proton system, solving radial equation of, 243
Hydrogenic potential, 240
Hydrogenic systems, Bohr radius and, 250
Hydrogen radial probabilities, for $n = 2$ and $n = 3$, 258, *259*
Hydrogen radial wavefunctions, 250*t*
Hydrogen states, grayscale representations of, up to $n = 5$, 262, *263–264*

Hydrogen transition wavelengths, 19t
Hydrogen wavefunctions, radial nodes in, 391

I

Index of summation, series solution and, 167
Indistinguishability, 293
Induced emission and absorption, 370
Infiinte rectangular well wavefunctions, normalized, 66
Infinite potential box, 193–195
Infinite potential well, 62–69
    perturbed and unperturbed $n = 1$ states of, 316–320
Infinite rectangular well wavefunctions, superposition state constructed from sum of, 143–146
Infinite spherical well, 234–236
Infinite square well, 62–69
Infrared spectroscopy, rotational characteristics of molecules analyzed with, 289
Inner product, 125
Integrals, 401–404
"Internal" energy levels, Schrödinger's equation for any two-body system and, 240
Ions, 2
Iron atoms, quantum corral of, on a copper surface, 84

J

Joint probability wavefunction, 241, 292
Jonsson, Claus, 24

K

Ketterle, W., 297
Kinetic-energy operator, 115, 117, 117t
Kirchhoff, Gustav, 4
Kirchhoff's laws
    Bohr's model and, 21
    of spectroscopy, 4–5, 5
Kronecker delta, 139, 322, 371
    symbol for, 139
Kummer-Laplace equation, 269

L

Ladder operators, 182
Laguerre polynomial, 250
Laplacian operator, 147, 242, 292
    expressions for, in spherical coordinates, 203, 207
Lavoisier, Antoine, 2
Least-bound ground state, of attractive central potentials, 334–335
Lectures on Physics (Feynman), 26
Left-propagating matter-wave, 48
Leibniz's rule for differentiating a product, 387, 389
Lennard-Jones 6-12 potential, 368
Lifetime, of state m for transitions to state n, 370
Light, speed of, in vacuum, 405t
Light-quanta, 12
Linearity, 40–41
Linear momentum operator, 116, 117t, 118, 203–204
Linear potential, *302*
    computed wavefunction for, 358–361
    ground-state energy of, variational method, 330
    improved variational method, 338–340
    numerical integration for electron moving in, 356–361
Linear restoring force, 159
Lorentz, Hendrik, 346
Low-energy scattering, 105
Lowering operators, 179–186
    angular momentum, 209, 278–281
L-S coupling, 286

M

MacLaurin series, 166
Magnetic dipole moment for atomic systems, Bohr magneton and, 284
Magnetic flux density, 284
Magnetic quantum numbers, 210, 212, 232, 240, 276
    state of electrons specified by, 297
"Man behind Bose statistics, The" (Wali), 296
Marsden, Ernest, 14

Matter-waves (de Broglie), 23–27
Maxwell, J. C., 10
Maxwell's equations, 6, 200
Mermin, N. D., 26
Merzbacher, E., 76
Microwave spectroscopy
    rotational characteristics of molecules
        analyzed with, 289
Millikan, Robert, 3
Molecular spectra, harmonic oscillator potential
    and understanding of, 170
Molecules
    rotational characteristics of, 289
    structure and spectra of, 171
Momentum operator, 117
Morse potential, 171
Moseley, Henry, 22
Moving probability distributions, superposition
    theorem and, 141–146
Multidimensional problems, degeneracy and,
    197
Multielectron atomic wavefunctions, symmetry
    properties of, 286
Multiparticle systems, 291–297
    separation-of-variables issues in, 240–243

N

National Institute of Standards and Technology,
    physical constants listing by, 405t
Neon, "closed" electron shells possessed by, 297
Neutron mass, 405t
Neutrons as fermions, 296
NIST. *See* National Institute of Standards and
    Technology
Noble-gas atoms, scattering and, 106
Nodes, 68
Nondegenerate first-order perturbation theory,
    314–316
Normalization, 51
Normal state, 68
Nuclear model of atom, 14
Nuclei, as spherical potential wells, 233
Numerical integration, 353–365
Nutall, John, 97

O

Odd-indexed coefficients, recursion relation
    and, 168
Odd parity, 75, 76, 88
One-body system, reduction of two-body system
    to, 240
One-dimensional finite well, spherical analog
    of, 236
One-dimensional potential wells, scattering by,
    103–106
Operator algebra, ordinary algebra *vs.*, 117
Operator notation
    Schrödinger's equation expressed in, 114
Operators, 113
    angular momentum, 203–209
    commutators of, 131
    complex, 281
    defined, 114
    gradient, 203, 204
    Hamiltonian, 114, 118, 133, 134, 140, 146,
        147, 152, 181, 185, 207, 310, 311, 327,
        328, 329, 336
    kinetic-energy, 115, 117, 117t, 146–152
    ladder, 182
    Laplacian, 147, 203, 242, 292
    linear momentum, 115–117, 125, 126, 203,
        204
    lowering, 179–186, 209, 275–281
    measuring simultaneous eigenvalues for, 131
    order of, 117–118
    position, 115, 117
    potential-energy, 115, 117t, 146–152
    properties of, 114–118
    raising, 179–186, 209, 275–281
    raising and lowering, angular momentum and,
        275–281
    total energy, 114, 115
    useful, 117t
    vector, 118
"Op" notation, 115, 118, 204, 275
Orbital angular momentum, 206–207
Orbital angular momentum quantum number,
    218, 232
Order of operations, commutators and, 133

Orthogonality theorem, 137–141, 143, 154, 185, 305, 314, 315
  perturbation theory and, 310
Orthogonal set of functions, 138
Orthogonal unit vectors, dot product of, 208
Orthonormal set of functions, 139
Oscillators, Planck's energy-frequency relation for, 45
Overlap integral, 125

P
Pais, Abraham, 4, 50
Parent nucleus, 97, 101
Parity, alternating, 75, 87
Partial differential equations, 37, 193
  reduction of, to ordinary differential equations, 195
Partially lifted degeneracy, 326
Particles
  constructing time-dependent wave packet and, 141–146
  identical and indistinguishable, 293
  noninteracting, 292–293
  spin of, 295
  wave nature of, 24–27, 36
Paschen, Freidrich, 20
Pauli Exclusion Principle, 286, 297
Penetration probability, 95
Permeability constant, 405t
Permitivity constant, 405t
Perturbation theory, 137, 299, 309–316
  intended use for, 326
  interpreting results of, 324
  nondegenerate first-order, 314–326
  time-dependent, 369
Perturbed harmonic-oscillator potential, 320–324
Perturbed infinite rectangular well, *309*, 316–320
Phi (Φ) Equation, solution of, 212–215
Photoelectric effect, Einstein's work on, 12, 13
Photons, 12
Physical constants, 405
Pixels (CCD chip), 83
Planck, Max, 10–13, 16, 199

blackbody radiation formula, 12
  energy-frequency relation for oscillators, 11
Planck mass, 157
Planck's constant, 12, 20, 200, 405t
Planck time, 163
"Plum pudding" model, 6, 14
PN molecule, spectrum of, *7*
Polar diagrams, of absolute squares of spherical harmonics, *224*
Pöschl-Teller potential, 361–365
Position, expectation value of, 120
Position operator, 115, 117t
Positronium, 244
Potential barriers, 88–94
  thick barrier approximation, 92–93
  thin barrier approximation, 93–94
Potential diagrams, 61
Potential energy function, 60
Potential-energy operator, 115, 117t
Potential functions, 41–44, 52–54
Potential wells, *See* Wells, potential
Predictions
  expectation values and, 113
Principal quantum number, 16, 65, 251
  state of electrons specified by, 297
Probabilities, interpretation of psi (ψ): boundary conditions and, 49–55
Probability density, 51, 177, 254
Probability distributions, 51, 67, 68
  finite square well wavefunctions, 77
  hydrogen atom, 253–254
  infinite square well wavefunctions, *67*
  time-dependent wave packet, 141–146
Proton mass, 405t
Protons, 4
  fermions and, 296
  orbital motion of electron around, 283
psi (ψ)
  asymptotic form of, 86, 245–246
  probabilities and boundary conditions, 49–54
  time-independent wave pattern designated by, 43

Q

Qualitative sketches of wavefunctions, 85–88
Quantization (early history), 2, 12
Quantization of angular momentum, 20, 191, 219
  solutions of SE for potentials such as Coulomb potential and, 192
  Stern-Gerlach experiment and, 282–287
Quantum corral, 84
Quantum field theory, 4
Quantum mechanics
  birth of, 10
  birth of term, 50n2
  counterintuitiveness of, 1
  foundations of, 1–27
  momentum given by spatial derivative, 126
  wave-particle duality in, 23–26
Quantum Mechanics (Schiff), 379
Quantum numbers, 67
  state of electrons specified by, 297
"Quantum of time," Planck time and, 163
Quantum simple harmonic oscillator, classical harmonic oscillator *vs.*, 176–179
Quantum states, number of, lying between given energies, 199
Quantum tunneling, 59, 76, 88–93
Quarks, 4

R

Radial equation, 232, 233, 244
  effective potential form, 264–265
  finite spherical well, 236–239
  of hydrogenic electron/proton system, solving, 243–250
  infinite spherical well, 234
Radial nodes, 260, 261, 262t
  in hydrogen wavefunctions, 391
Radial potential, Coulomb potential as example of, 192
Radial probability distribution
  for ground state of hydrogen, 255
  for (2,0,0) state of hydrogen, 257, 258
Radial wavefunction, 210
Radioactivity, 97
"Raisin bread" model, 6

Raising operators (harmonic oscillator), 179–186
  angular momentum, 275–281
Ramsauer-Townsend scattering, 106
Rectangular barrier penetration, 89
Rectangular-well wavefunctions, approximating straight line as sum of, 308
Recursion relations, 168, 170, 217, 218, 247, 248, 252
  hermite polynomials, 173
Reduced electron mass, 244
Reduced mass, 241, 290
Reduced variables, 245
Relative coordinate of two masses, Schrödinger's equation for two-body problem and, 241–243
Resnick, R., 86
Resonance condition, 105
Right-propagating matter-wave, 48
Ritz combination principle, 32
Rohrer, Heinrich, 83
Roller-coaster track, car on, 60–62
Rose, M. E., 386
Rotational energies, 171, 288–290
Rubidium, gas-phase Bose-Einstein condensate, 297
Rutherford, Ernest, 14
Rutherford-Bohr atom, 2, 14–23
Rydberg, Johannes, 8
Rydberg constant, 8, 17, 18, 405t
Rydberg energy, 20

S

Scanning tunneling microscopy, 83–84
Scattering
  by one-dimensional potential wells, 103–106
  high-energy, 105
  low-energy, 105
  resonance, 105–106
Schiff, Leonard, 379
Schrödinger, Erwin, 42
  solution of wave equation for Coulomb potential by, 233
Schrödinger's equation, 35–56, 63, 70, 86–88, 159, 193, 209, 241–243, 310

angular momentum analysis of, for hydrogen atom, 203
approximate solutions of, 299–340
asymptotic solutions of, 245–246
in atomic units, 353
boundary conditions imposed on solutions of, 49–54
for central potential
    azimuthal solutions for angular part of, 215–222, 384
Coulomb potential and obtaining exact solution of, 240
in dimensionless form (harmonic oscillator), 161–162
energy degeneracy and multidimensional solutions of, 196–197
expressed in operator notation, 114
hydrogen-atom bound-state energies predicted by, 249
inside infinite potential box, 193
numerical solution of, 351–356
one-dimensional, 41–44
orthogonality theorem proof and, 137–139
perturbation theory and constructing approximate solution to, 309–316
philosophical remarks pertaining to, 266–267
separability of, 192–197
series solution and, 165–170, 216–218, 247–249
solutions of
    angular part of, for central potentials, 211–222
    for barriers, 88–95
    for Coulomb potential, 240–251
    for harmonic oscillator potential, 159–173
    for one-dimensional wells, 62–83
    for system of two (or more) particles moving in the same potential, 291–297
    for three-dimensional spherical wells, 234–239
superposition state and forming linear sum of solutions to, for some potential $V(x)$, 305–307
in three dimensions, 192–200
time-dependent, 45–49
time-independent, 41–44
Schwarz's inequality, 381
SE. *See* Schrödinger's equation
Second-order linear differential equations, 42
    with nonconstant coefficients, 245
Selection rules, 373
Semi-infinite potential step, 93
Separation constants, 195
Separation of variables, 192–197, 210, 212, 241
    in spherical coordinates: central potentials, 209–211
Series limit, 19, 20
Series of lines, 19
Series solution, 165–170, 216–218, 247–249
Shankar, R., 235
"Shooting" approach, 355
Sketching wavefunctions, 85–88
Sodium, absorption and emission spectra of, 7
Spatial derivative, for momentum, 126
Spectra, 4–13
    continuous, 8
    thermal radiation, 9
Spectral lines, "fine structure" of, 22
Spectrograph, 5
Spectroscopy, Kirchhoff's three laws of, 4–5, 5
Spherical Bessel and Neumann functions, 234
Spherical-coordinate radial unit vectors, 149, 202
Spherical coordinates, 201–203
    Laplacian operator in, 207
    operators for x, y, and z components of momentum in, 204
    separating the SE for central potentials in, 209–211
Spherical harmonics, 192, 220–225, 223t
    polar diagrams of, 224
Spherical unit vectors, Cartesian unit vectors expressed in terms of, 202
Spherical well
    finite, 236–239
    infinite, 234–236
Spin, 285, 295
"Spin-one" particles, 295
Spin-orbit coupling, 286
"Spin-1/2" particles, 295

Spin-state quantum number, state of electrons specified by, 297
Spontaneous emission, 370
Spreadsheets, numerical integration method and, 355
Squared angular momentum, 206–207, 231, 232, 276–277
Square integrability, 54
Stark, Johannes, 324
Stark effect, 286, 324
"Stern and Gerlach: How a bad cigar helped reorient atomic physics" (Freidrich and Hershbach), 219
Stern-Gerlach experiment, 282–285
  schematic illustration of, *285*
STM. *See* Scanning tunneling microscopy
Stoney, G. J., 2, 3
Strength parameter, 75
Strings, wave phenomena exhibited with, 36, 41
String theory(ies)
  current versions of, 157
  Planck time and, 163
Sub-barriers, 95
Sudden approximation, 374–376
"Sum of squares" form, harmonic-oscilllator Hamiltonian and, 185
Superfluids, 297
Superposition, 126
Superposition states, 121
  preparing/making measurements on quantum systems in, 145
  time-dependent, 141–146
Superposition theorem, 139–141, 305–309, 327
  moving probability distributions and, 141–146
  perturbation theory development and, 311
Symmetric form, of Ψ, 294–295
Symmetric potential, 88

T

Tangent functions, for K = 10 finite well, *81*
Tesla, 284
Thermal equilibrium, 9
Thermal radiation spectra, *9*
Theta (Θ) Equation, solution of, 215–219

Thick barrier approximation, 92–93
Thin barrier approximation, 93–94
Thomson, George P., 24
Thomson, J. J., 2, 3, 4, 8, 14
Thorium alpha-decays, *101*
Three-dimensional box potential, 192–196
Three-dimensional probability distribution plots
  flowchart for analysis of, *262*
  for hydrogen, 260
Three-dimensional Schrödinger equation, 43, 191–201
Time-dependent quantum theory, sampling of results from, 369–375
Time-dependent Schrödinger's equation, 45–49, 141
  proof of Heisenberg's Uncertainty Principle and, 379, 383
  time derivatives eliminated via, 135–136
Time-dependent wave packet, constructing, 141–146
Time derivative, for momentum, 126
Time-independent, nondegenerate first-order perturbation theory, 314–316
Time-independent Schrödinger's equation, 41–44
Total angular momentum, operator for magnitude of square of, 206–207
Total energy operator, 114, 115
Transition frequencies, 369–370
Transition rules, 373–374
Transmission coefficient T, 92
Trial wavefunctions, 329–330
Trigonometric identities, 404
Triply degenerate energy level, 196
Tunneling, 76, 88–92
Two-body system, reduction of, to equivalent one-body system, 240–243
Two-dimensional infinite-well wavefunction, *196*
"Two lectures on wave-particle duality" (Mermin), 26
Two-particle wavefunctions, for $n = 0$ and $n = 1$ harmonic-oscillator states, *295*, 296

U

Uhlenbeck, G. E., 285
Ultraviolet catastrophe, 10
Unbound energy state, car in, 61, 62
Uncertainty Principle (Heisenberg), 25,
       126–131, 357, 379–384
    formal statement of, 127
    order of operations and, 118
    practical aspect of, 129
    proof of, 379–384
    writing about, 132–133
    zero-point energy and, 171
Uncertainty relations
    angular momentum and, 208
    commutators and, 131–134
Uranium, decay of, into thorium-234, 97

V

Variational method, 327–330
    improving on, 336–338
Vector operators, 118
Vibrational energy levels, 171, 288, 289
Virial theorem, 15, 146–150
Vision, human, range of, 8, 20
VT. *See* Virial theorem

W

"Wag the tail", 355, 360, 363, 364
Wali, K., 296
Wave equations, space and time invariance in,
       40, 45
Wavefunctions, 37
    finite rectangular, 77
    finite spherical, 237
    harmonic oscillator, 172
    hydrogen, 253
    infinite rectangular, 66
    infinite spherical, 235
    $n = 9$, hypothetical, 87
    normalized, 51
    raising and lowering operators and, 179–186
    sketching, 85–88
    square-integrable, 51
    for two-dimensional infinite well, 196, *196*
Wavefunction symmetry/antisymmetry,
       chemical nature of elements and, 297
Wave-particle duality, 2, 23–27
Waves, traveling, 36, 49
Wells, potential
    finite rectangular, 70–84
    finite spherical, 236–239
    harmonic, 160
    infinite rectangular, 62–69
    infinite spherical, 234–236
Wentzel-Kramers-Brillouin method. *See* WKB
       method
WKB method, 299–305, 357
Wood-Saxon potential, 367

Z

Zeeman, Pieter, 346
Zeeman effect, 286, 346
Zero point energy, 171